PHYSIOGRAPHY.

PREFACE.

Nearly nine years ago, I was invited, by the Managers of the London Institution, to take part in a series of courses of Educational Lectures; which were intended to initiate young people in the elements of Physical Science.

My course was to be the first of the series; and I made use of the opportunity, thus afforded me, to put into practical shape the ideas, which I had long entertained and advocated, respecting the proper method of approaching the study of Nature.

It appeared to me to be plainly dictated by common sense, that the teacher, who wishes to lead his pupil to form a clear mental picture of the order which pervades the multiform and endlessly shifting phenomena of nature, should commence with the familiar facts of the scholar's daily experience; and that, from the firm ground of such experience, he should lead the beginner, step by step, to remoter objects and to the less readily comprehensible relations of things. In short, that the knowledge of the child should, of set purpose, be made to grow, in the same

manner as that of the human race has spontaneously
grown.

I conceived that a vast amount of knowledge respecting
natural phenomena and their interdependence, and even
some practical experience of scientific method, could be
conveyed, with all the precision of statement, which is what
distinguishes science from common information; and, yet,
without overstepping the comprehension of learners who
possessed no further share of preliminary educational dis-
cipline, than that which falls to the lot of the boys and girls
who pass through an ordinary primary school. And I
thought, that, if my plan could be properly carried out, it
would not only yield results of value in themselves, but
would facilitate the subsequent entrance of the learners into
the portals of the special sciences.

I undertook, therefore, to deliver twelve lectures, not on
any particular branch of natural knowledge, but on natural
phenomena in general; and I borrowed the title of "Physiography," which had already been long applied, in a different
sense, to a department of mineralogy, for my subject;
inasmuch as I wished to draw a clear line of demarcation,
both as to matter and method, between it and what is
commonly understood by "Physical Geography."

Many highly valuable compendia of Physical Geography,
for the use of scientific students of that subject, are extant;
but, in my judgment, most of the elementary works I have
seen, begin at the wrong end, and too often terminate in an
omnium gatherum of scraps of all sorts of undigested and
unconnected information; thereby entirely destroying the
educational value of that study which Kant justly termed
the "propædeutic of natural knowledge."

I do not think that a description of the earth, which commences, by telling a child that it is an oblate spheroid, moving round the sun in an elliptical orbit; and ends, without giving him the slightest hint towards understanding the ordnance map of his own county; or any suggestion as to the meaning of the phenomena offered by the brook which runs through his village, or the gravel pit whence the roads are mended; is calculated either to interest or to instruct. And the attempt to convey scientific conceptions, without the appeal to observation, which can alone give such conceptions firmness and reality, appears to me to be in direct antagonism to the fundamental principles of scientific education.

"Physiography" has very little to do with this sort of "Physical Geography." My hearers were not troubled with much about latitudes and longitudes; the heights of mountains, depths of seas; or the geographical distribution of kangaroos and *Compositæ*. Neglecting such pieces of information—of the importance of which, in their proper places, I entertain no doubt—I endeavoured to give them, in very broad, but, I hope, accurate, outlines, a view of the "place in nature" of a particular district of England, the basin of the Thames; and, to leave upon their minds the impression, that the muddy waters of our metropolitan river; the hills between which it flows; the breezes which blow over it; are not isolated phenomena, to be taken as understood because they are familiar. On the contrary, I endeavoured to show that the application of the plainest and simplest processes of reasoning to any one of these phenomena, suffices to show, lying behind it, a cause, which again suggests another; until, step by step, the conviction dawns upon the learner that, to attain to even an elementary conception of what goes on in his parish, he must know something about the universe ; that the pebble he kicks aside would not be what it is and where it is, unless a particular chapter of the earth's history, finished untold ages ago, had been exactly what it was.

It was necessary to illustrate my method by a concrete case ; and, as a Londoner addressing Londoners, I selected the Thames, and its basin, for my text. But any intelligent teacher will have no difficulty in making use of the river and river basin of the district, in which his own school is situated, for the same purpose.

The lectures on Physiography were delivered at the London Institution in 1869 ; and I repeated them, at South Kensington, in 1870. Verbatim reports were taken on the former occasion, as it was my intention to publish the course. But I am sorry to say that, in this, as in other cases, I have found a great gulf fixed between intention to publish and its realization.

Seeing a book through the press is a laborious and time-wasting affair ; greatly aggravated, in cases such as the present, by the necessity of superintending the execution of maps and figures. And, as I never could muster up the courage, or find the time, to undertake the business, the manuscript remained untouched until last year.

I then had the good fortune to be able to obtain the services of my friend Mr. Rudler, with whose extensive knowledge of various branches of physical science, I was well acquainted ; and, in whose conscientious accuracy, as an editor, I knew I could place implicit confidence.

In preparing the substance of the lectures for the press,

Mr. Rudler has entirely fulfilled my expectations, and has made many valuable suggestions and additions. I have entirely re-written such parts of the work as I thought I could improve; I have added to others; and I have carefully revised the proofs of every chapter.

I trust therefore that the book may be useful to both learners and teachers; but, I am most concerned, that the latter should find in it the ground-work of an introduction to the study of nature, on which their practical experience will enable them to erect a far better superstructure than that which I have been able to raise.

T. H. H.

LONDON,
  November, 1877.

PREFACE TO THE SECOND EDITION.

SEVERAL friends of mine have been good enough to read this work critically, and I have gladly availed myself of their suggestions to remove ambiguities of phraseology and errors of the press which had escaped my notice.

One of the most important errata to which my attention has been thus called, respects the occurrence of an eruption of Mount Ararat (p. 191), which, though mentioned on very good authority, turns out to have been no eruption at all.

The gravest mistake, however, is one which I have had the melancholy satisfaction of discovering for myself. At p. 84, the decimal points have got wrong in the course of the calculation of the weight of the air covering a square mile : whereby that weight is made to be ten times, and the weight of the contained carbonic acid gas a hundred times as great as it should be. Happily, when the amounts given are rectified, the quantity of carbonic acid in the air is still amply sufficient for the purposes of the argument.

T. H. H.

LONDON,
February, 1878.

CONTENTS.

CONTENTS.

CONTENTS.

CHAPTER XV.

CHAPTER XVI.

CHAPTER XVII.

CHAPTER XVIII.

CHAPTER XIX.

CHAPTER XX.

CHAPTER XXI.

LIST OF ILLUSTRATIONS.

COLOURED PLATES.

PHYSIOGRAPHY.

CHAPTER I.

THE THAMES.

No spot in the world is better known than London, and no spot in London better known than London Bridge. Let the reader suppose that he is standing upon this bridge, and, needless of the passing stream of traffic, looks down upon the river as it runs below. It matters little on which side of the bridge he may chance to stand ; whether he look up the river or down the river, above bridge or below bridge. In either case he will find himself in the presence of a noble stream measuring, when broadest, nearly a sixth of a mile from bank to bank. The quantity of water under London Bridge varies considerably, however, at different seasons, and even at different hours on the same day. When the water is highest, the greatest depth is about thirty feet and the width 800 feet ; when the water is lowest, the greatest depth is something like twelve feet and the width only 650 feet. This variation in the volume of water shows that the river is not at rest, and that its surface is, in fact, alternately rising and falling. Moreover, apart from the local agitation due to traffic, apart too from the surface ripples raised by the passing breeze, the whole body of water is in a constant state of motion. At one time in the day the water sweeps down below bridge in the direction of Greenwich and far onwards to the Nore; after this movement has been continued for some hours, it gradually slackens, and the water comes almost to a stand-still; then the motion begins afresh, but its direction is reversed, the water flowing this time towards Westminster and far away up the river; but, after a while, this motion slowly subsides, and is followed once more by renewed movement in a contrary direction.

Every one knows that this regular backward-and-forward movement of the great mass of water is due to tidal action. For about seven hours during *ebb tide*, the water of the Thames runs down towards the sea; and for about five hours during *flood tide* the movement takes place in the opposite direction, the water being then driven up the river. At the end of the ebb-tide the river is shallowest; at the end of the flood-tide it is deepest. The water at London Bridge is consequently twice in every four-and-twenty hours at its highest, and twice at its lowest level.

As we go up the river we find the effect of the tide gradually diminishing, until at length it ceases to be felt. In point of fact, the tidal wave has no influence beyond Teddington Weir, some nineteen miles above London Bridge. The very name *Teddington* is indeed said to be a corruption of "Tide-end-ton," the town where the tide ends. Up to Teddington, then, the Thames is a tidal river, moving alternately backwards and forwards at definite intervals. The tidal wave occupies about two hours in coming up from the Nore to London, a distance of about 40 miles; that is to say, it is high water at London Bridge two hours later than at the Nore. Then it takes two hours more for the wave to travel onwards from London

to Teddington, though the distance between these two points
is less than twenty miles. It is almost needless to add that
this tidal action is of vast service to the port of London,
since barges, lighters, and other boats are thus enabled at
certain periods of the day to float up or down the river with
little or no expenditure of power on the part of the boatmen.

Above Teddington Weir the motion of the river is
totally different from that which is observed at London
Bridge. There is no alternate backward-and-forward motion,
no regular rise and fall of the water, but the river flows
onwards in one constant direction, always running down
towards London. Careful observations at Teddington have
shown that, with the water at ordinary summer-level, about
380 million gallons[1] flow over the weir every four-and-twenty
hours. This vast volume of water is swept down past
London, and ultimately carried out to sea. As the ebb-
tide runs for about seven hours, whilst the flood lasts only
five, it is clear that much more water runs down than flows
up; and it is in this way that the vast volume of water
sent down from above Teddington drains away seawards.

In seeking the origin of the water thus brought down
by the Thames, it is necessary to trace the river to what
is commonly called its "source." On ascending, it is observed that the river grows smaller, the volume of water
becoming less and less. Thus at Teddington the Thames
is only 250 feet wide at high-water, whilst its width at
London Bridge is about 800 feet. Following the many
windings of the river past Windsor, Reading, and Oxford,
we observe the stream still growing more narrow and
more shallow, until at Lechlade, in Gloucestershire, 146
miles from London, the Thames ceases to be navigable.

---

[1] Many of the statistical data relating to the Thames have been
obligingly furnished by Mr. Leach, of the Thames Conservancy Board.

At Lechlade the quantity of water running down the river
has been roughly estimated at something like a hundred
million gallons per day, or only about one-fourth the
quantity flowing over Teddington Weir. The main stream
splits up at Lechlade into a number of smaller streams,
forming the "head-waters" of the river, and it is by no
means easy to say which of these streams should be
followed up in seeking the true source of the Thames.
Nor does it much matter, for the origin of any one of
them is much the same as the origin of any of the others.
It is usual, however, to single out one of these streams,
which takes its rise in a spring near Cirencester, about 170
miles from London Bridge, and is dignified with the name
of Thames Head.

Although the spring at Thames Head is thus popularly
called the "source" of the river, it should be remembered that the quantity of water delivered by this
spring is quite insignificant when compared with that
derived from the numerous streams which flow into the
Thames at various points along its course. Every
tributary helps to swell the bulk of the river by dis-
charging its water into the main stream ; yet it does not
follow that the river is necessarily increased in width by
the influx of this water, for it often happens that the
additional supply is carried off by increased rapidity of
flow. As the Thames rolls along, it receives a number
of these feeders, or *affluents*,[1] which empty themselves
into the river, some on one side and some on the other.

---

[1] *Affluent*, from the Latin *ad* and *fluo*, "to flow." The junction of an
affluent with the main stream is termed the *confluence*, or place where
they "flow together." Thus, the town of Coblentz takes its name from
the Latin form *Confluentes*, in allusion to its position at the junction of
the Moselle and the Rhine.

It is obviously convenient to have some ready means of distinguishing the two banks of a river. For this purpose, geographers have agreed to call that bank which lies upon your right side as you go down towards the sea the *right* bank, and to call the opposite side the *left* bank. All that you have to do then, in order to distinguish the two sides, is to stand so that your face is in the direction of the mouth of the river, and your back consequently towards its source, when the right bank will be upon your right hand and the left bank upon your left hand. At Gravesend, for example, the right bank is that which forms the Kentish shore, while the left bank is on the Essex side. With reference therefore to the rivers tributary to the Thames, it is said that the Churn, the Colne, the Leach, the Windrush, the Evenlode, the Cherwell, the Thame, the Coln, the Brent, and the Lea empty themselves into the Thames on the *left* bank; and the Rey, the Cole, the Ock, the Kennet, the Loddon, the Wey, the Mole, and the Darent, open into the river on its *right* bank. The relative positions of these affluents, and their relation to the Thames, may be seen in the map given in Plate I.

If a person in a balloon passed at a great height over any part of the earth's surface, and sketched in outline what he saw directly below, his sketch on a flat surface like this page would be called a *map*. When the portion of country thus delineated is but small, the sketch is generally termed a *plan*; and if the area depicted consist chiefly of water instead of land, it is called a *chart*. Hence we commonly speak of the plan of an estate, the map of a country, the chart of an ocean. A map of the Thames, then, is simply an outline-sketch of the river and neighbouring portion of the earth's surface, as would be seen from a balloon passing at a great height directly over the country. It is the

common practice to draw maps in such a position that the
north is towards the top, and the south towards the bottom ;
while the east lies on the right hand of the person who
looks at the map, and the west lies on his left hand. By
simply looking then at the map, forming Plate I., it is
seen at once that the Thames, though taking—like most
rivers—an irregular course, winding first in one direction
and then in another, nevertheless has, on the whole, a west-
and-east course ; it flows, in short, from the west towards
the east. At the same time it is seen that the left shore of
the river is its northern bank, and the right shore its southern
bank. It is clear, too, that the tributaries on the left or
north side flow generally from north to south, whilst those
on the right or south side run generally from south to
north.

These terms—north and south, east and west—are terms
which have a meaning quite independent of local circumstances, and indicate definite directions which can be
determined in any part of the world and at all times.
When, in the early part of this chapter, we used the local
expressions "up the river" and "down the river," "above
bridge" and "below bridge," it was assumed that the reader
was familiar with the Thames. But to a perfect stranger,
one who had never seen the river and knew nothing of
London Bridge, such a method of description would be
unintelligible. By employing, however, the terms north
and south, east and west, we are using expressions that
are familiar to all educated people, since they refer to
standards of direction universally recognised. It is desirable to explain how these cardinal points may be
determined.

Of the four points, the south is perhaps the most easily
found, at least on a sunshiny day. Every morning the sun

appears to rise slowly in the sky, and mounts to its greatest height at noon. At the instant of reaching its greatest height, or in other words at exact noon, the sun is precisely in the south. If, then, you place yourself in such a position as to have the sun shining full in your face at that particular time, you must be facing south; and you will consequently have your back to the north, your right hand towards the west, and your left towards the east.

As true noon does not always coincide with 12 o'clock, as indicated by an ordinary timekeeper, it is necessary to explain how it may be determined. Thrust a stick vertically into the ground, and observe, at different hours of the day, the length and direction of its shadow cast by the sun. When the sun is rising in the sky, the shadow is thrown towards the west; and when the sun is going down, it is thrown towards the east; at noon, however, it inclines neither to the east nor to the west, but falls exactly in a north-and-south line; and, moreover, the shadow is then *shorter* than at any other time. If, therefore, you observe when the shadow is shortest, that time will be exact noon. The line indicated by the shadow at noon is known as the *meridian line* or *mid-day line*. That end of the shadow-line which is towards the sun points to the south, and the opposite end to the north. If then a line be drawn anywhere at right angles across the shadow, the right-hand end of the cross-line, as you look to the south, points towards the west, and the left hand towards the east.

It is not easy, however, by merely looking at the shadow, to say when it is exactly reduced to its shortest length. It is well, therefore, to observe the shadow at some time in the forenoon and mark its length—say by sticking a peg in the ground, and then, in the afternoon, to observe the shadow again, when it has reached exactly the same length. The afternoon shadow will then be just as much on one side of the meridian line as the forenoon shadow was on the other side. The mid-day line, or line which runs due north and south, will therefore be exactly half-way between the two shadows.

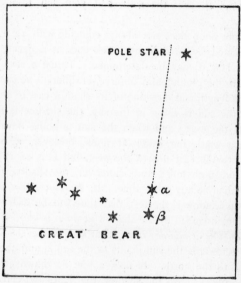

FIG. 1.—How to find the North point.

But it is by no means necessary to have daylight in order to discover the direction of the cardinal points. If you look up into the heavens on a clear starry night you will have no difficulty, in this part of the world, in finding that curious group of seven bright stars known as *Charles's*

Wain, forming part of the *Great Bear* (Fig. 1). A line drawn through two of these stars (β, α) will, if prolonged to about five times its length, pass very close to the famous *Pole-star*.[1] On a clear night, all the groups of stars appear to move slowly round a certain fixed point in the sky, which is the north pole of the heavens. That point of the earth immediately beneath the celestial north pole is the north pole of the earth. If the explorers in the *Alert* and *Discovery* could have reached the north pole, they would have found the pole star almost directly overhead. It must be remembered, however, that the pole-star is not exactly at the north pole of the heavens, although very near to it. By observing the position of the pole-star, the north can be determined on a clear night as readily as the south may be determined by the sun at noon.

If, however, the sky is beclouded so that the heavenly bodies are not visible, there is yet another easy means of finding the direction of the cardinal points. Let a thin bar of steel, or even a needle, be nicely balanced upon a pivot, or suspended by a thread, or floated upon a cork in water, so that it can turn freely in all directions horizontally; it will be found that the bar may be brought to rest in any desired position. If, however, the bar be rubbed with a magnet, a peculiar change is wrought in the steel, and it

---

[1] It is the practice of astronomers to distinguish the several stars of a particular group, or *constellation*, by means of Greek letters. Thus the two stars in the Great Bear, known as the *Pointers*, since a line joining them points towards the pole-star, are distinguished in Fig. 1 by the letters α and β. The first of these stars would be technically described as α *Ursæ Majoris*, or the *alpha* star of the Great Bear. This constellation contains several stars of which only seven conspicuous ones are represented in the figure. The pole-star, known also as *Polaris*, is the brightest of a group called the Little Bear, and is consequently described as α *Ursæ Minoris*.

then no longer exhibits this indifference to direction, but
when left free always takes up a definite position, one end
pointing in a northerly and the other in a southerly direction. This property is taken advantage of in constructing
the mariner's compass. About two hundred and twenty
years ago the compass pointed exactly north and south in
London ; but from the year 1660, or thereabouts, the end
which tends northwards, and is therefore commonly called
the *north pole* of the needle, began to turn a little to the
west ; this variation from true north continued until the

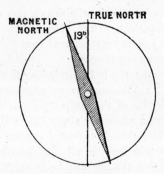

FIG. 2.—Magnetic Declination.

year 1818, when it reached its greatest divergence, and
since that time it has been steadily creeping back. The
divergence of the position of the magnetic needle from
the true north-and-south line is called its *declination*, or
by nautical men, its *variation*. In 1818 the declination
amounted to nearly 25°, and in the present year (1877) it
is 19° 3′ in London ; that is to say, the end or pole of
the needle which turns in a northerly direction, instead of
pointing due north, points 19° 3′ to the west of true

north. This declination is shown in Fig. 2. Knowing the amount of declination, it is easy to make the proper allowance and thus find the true points of the compass. By means of the compass the direction of the river in all its windings may be traced, and the course of the meandering stream laid down upon a map, as has been done, for example, in Plate I.

This map, however, does something more than show simply the *direction* of the Thames and its tributaries; it gives us, in addition, some notion of their *length*. A map, as we have seen, is a kind of picture, and the size of this picture must bear a certain relation to the size of the object represented. This relation or proportion is called the *scale* of the map. If a map is said to have a scale of one inch to the mile, it is simply meant that a mile measured along the ground is represented by an inch measured on the map; or a square mile of country is represented by a square inch on the map, and so on. Most of the wonderfully-accurate maps of the Ordnance Survey are constructed on this scale of one inch to the mile. In other words, in the map of a given district, the distance between any two points is $\frac{1}{63360}$th of the actual distance, since there are 63,360 inches in one statute mile. The fraction which denotes the ratio of the two distances is sometimes termed the *representative fraction*. A map of the Thames on the one-inch scale would extend to a length of about 120 inches, since the greatest width of the basin of the river from east to west is about 120 miles. Maps on a scale even much greater than this are occasionally constructed. The Ordnance Survey, for example, issues county maps on a scale of six inches to a mile, the representative fraction being here $\frac{1}{10560}$. But it is evident, from the size of a page of this book, that our map must be on a very much smaller scale; in fact,

a mile of ground is represented there by the fourteenth part
of an inch.

In most maps, except those on an extremely small scale,
an attempt is made to show something of the general
features of the ground, especially whether the country is
hilly or not. This is commonly effected by a system of
hill-shading, such as that represented in Fig. 3.[1] If the

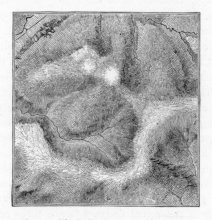

FIG. 3.—Hill-shading by means of hachures.

ground is steep, the lines, or *hachures*, are drawn thick and
close together, so that the hilly spots become dark ; if the
ground is tolerably level the lines are thinner and farther
apart, and the general appearance of the map is conse-

---

[1] This figure is copied from part of sheet 59 of the one-inch Ordnance
map of England and Wales, and shows the physical characters of a
district in North Wales. The portion of the map here copied is a
square measuring two inches along each side, so that the total area
represented in Fig. 3 amounts to four square miles.

quently lighter. Such a system of shading, however effec-
tive by its combination of light and shade, shows in most
cases merely that one part of the country is higher or
lower than another, without enabling us to judge how
much higher or how much lower. But in very accurate
maps, such as those employed for military purposes, a
definite scale of shade is often used. The same object
may, however, be attained by an entirely different system,
such as that used in the map of the Thames forming
Plate I.

It will be observed that, instead of hill-shading, a number
of curved lines have been traced over the map, giving it a
peculiar character. These curves are called *contour lines*,
and their meaning is extremely simple. Suppose the valley
of the Thames were flooded with water, and that this water
could be dammed in or prevented from escaping, by a
wall built across the mouth of the valley. If sufficient
water covered the ground to stand 100 feet above the
level of the sea, the surface of the water would form a
plane, and its margin would trace a line, winding round
every hill and up every valley, at a height of exactly 100 feet.
Such a line has been traced on our map, and being the first
of the series of curves, it is numbered 1. This is consequently the 100-*feet contour line.* The second line, No. 2,
is drawn at a height of 200 feet above the sea-level, and
therefore represents the margin of a body of water standing
in the Thames Valley 200 feet above the sea. In like
manner a succession of these contour-lines has been drawn,
each at a distance of 100 feet from the next one below, just
as though the flood had risen in the valley and stopped at
every 100 feet to leave its mark around its margin. It is
evident that a system of such lines conveys a far better
notion of the character of the ground than can be obtained

from ordinary hill-shading. Where the ground is very steep
the contour-lines run close together; where very flat they
stand far apart. The relation between the contour-lines and
the form of the ground is clearly shown in Fig. 4. In the
upper part of this figure, a hill is represented by contour-
lines; and supposing this hill were cut through, along the
line A B, it would give such an outline as that drawn in
the lower part of the figure, the corresponding points in
the plan and the section being connected by broken lines.

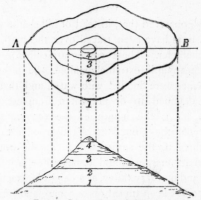

Fig. 4.—Contour-lines round a hill.

Inspection of the map in Plate I. shows, as might have
been expected, that the river there represented flows
from high ground to low ground. In fact, if the reader
were to travel up the Thames, by walking along its banks,
he would find himself continually going up-hill. Between
Thames Head and London Bridge, a distance of about
170 miles, as measured along the winding course of the
river, there is a difference of level of 370 feet. We
have seen that the head of the navigation is at Lechlade,
about 146 miles from London ; between Lechdale and

London the river has a total fall of about 250 feet; and as the descent is tolerably uniform, it may be taken at an average of 21 inches per mile. At Teddington, where the river ceases to be tidal, the ordinary summer-level of low water is 16½ feet above low-water level at London Bridge ; and the fall of the bed of the river below Teddington is nearly a foot in every mile. The rapidity with which a river flows will of course depend upon the amount of slope in its bed; where the fall is great the stream is rapid; where small the stream is slow. The bed of the Thames, fortunately, is tolerably uniform in its descent, so that the stream is free from rapids.

What has been said of the Thames is equally true of any one of its tributary streams : the source is always higher than the mouth. It is seen from the contour-lines on the map that, if we travel along any of the little rivers which open into the Thames upon its left bank, we go up-hill in passing from south to north ; if we travel along any of the streams on the opposite side of the river, we go up-hill in passing southwards. As a consequence of all this, it follows that the tract of country drained by the Thames and its tributaries must be bounded on at least three sides—the west, the north, and the south—by comparatively high ground. It thus forms a shallow depression, with an outlet to the east through which the river flows out to sea. Such a depression is known as a *river-basin*, and the country through which the Thames and its tributaries flow is consequently called the *Thames basin;* while the deepest part of the basin, that in which the main stream flows, is termed the *Thames Valley*. The basin of the Thames, depicted in Plate I., includes a very large tract, extending over 6,160 square miles ; the Thames, in fact, drains more than one-seventh of all England.

Fig. 5.—Section across the Thames basin, showing the form of the ground.   Vertical to horizontal scale as 12 to 1.

Perhaps the term "basin," just used, is one which is likely to mislead unless properly qualified. It is true that, if you go north from any part of the valley of the Thames, you find yourself sooner or later travelling up-hill, and therefore reach higher ground than that through which the river flows; if you travel southwards you do the same thing; while towards the west, the ascent is not less marked. The river then really does occupy a hollow, inclosed on three sides by high ground. But, it must be borne in mind, that this hollow is nothing like the deep hollow associated with our ordinary notion of a basin; it is, in fact, so slight a depression that it would perhaps be better to speak of the "dish" of the Thames rather than of its "basin." In Fig. 5 the undulating line indicates the general contour of the surface of the country along a north-and-south line drawn across the basin of the Thames, from the Chiltern hills on the north, to the North Downs on the south. The very gentle curvatures of this line show the extreme shallowness of the so-called basin; and also show the irregularities in the form of the ground. Although the opposite north and south hills may attain to a height of several hundred feet above the river, yet the distance between them is so great, amounting to some fifty or sixty miles, that the rise from the river to their summits would be almost inappreciable in a diagram brought within the limits of this page. Hence it is a common practice in constructing such diagrams to draw the heights to a scale many times greater than that used for the lengths. This has, in fact, been done in Fig. 5, where the vertical is as much as twelve times greater than the horizontal scale. Without such exaggeration, the surface of the country would appear in a small diagram to be almost flat; and even with it, the extreme shallowness of the Thames basin is strikingly apparent. There is clearly no harm in the practice of drawing diagrams on this principle, provided that the exaggeration of one dimension is always acknowledged by the draughtsman, and borne in mind by the reader. Great misconception, however, constantly arises from mistaking these intentionally distorted diagrams for true figures.

To the north-west of London, the margin of the Thames basin is formed, in part, by a line of low hills called the Chiltern Hills; and, on the south of London, there is another series known as the North Downs; while, if we go far enough to the west in the Thames basin, we come to a still higher country forming the Cotteswold Hills in Gloucestershire. Suppose the reader were to ascend one of these ranges of hills, say the Cotteswolds, on the west. As he went up he would meet with many little streams which are flowing down to feed the affluents of the Thames. But having reached the summit, and walked on in the same direction, he would soon begin to go down-hill, and then meet fresh streams running in an opposite direction to those he had left. These new streams cannot possibly flow into the Thames, for to do that the water would have to run up-hill. By following these streams, however, he would find that they ultimately flow into a river entirely distinct from the Thames; thus, on the other side of the Cotteswolds, the streams find their way, sooner or later, into the Severn. On

C

crossing these hills, then, we have passed from the basin of the Thames into that of the Severn. The high land which forms the divisional line between two contiguous river-basins is called the *water-parting*.

Instead of " water-parting," some writers employ the term *watershed*; but although the two words originally meant precisely the same thing, the latter has become rather ambiguous. " Watershed " is a word which has been borrowed from German geographers. The verb *scheiden* signifies " to separate," and *die Wasserscheide* is simply the " water-separation " or the " parting of the waters "—the old *Divortium· aquarum*. But many writers, looking at the common meaning of the English verb " to shed " have used the term " watershed" to denote the surface from which the waters are shed, or the slope along which they flow; hence it is not uncommon to hear such expressions as " the crest of the watershed." To avoid this double use of the word " watershed," the term " water-parting" has been introduced as the English equivalent of the German *Wasserscheide*, or the boundary-line between two adjacent river-systems. Such a line was called by Professor Phillips " the summit of drainage ;" and in the north of England, where it often separates one estate from another, it is known as " the heaven-water boundary." To avoid all ambiguity it is perhaps best to set aside the original meaning of " watershed," and employ the term to denote the slope along which the water-flows, while the expression " water-parting" is employed for the summit of this slope. Thus the ridge of a roof is the water-parting ; and the slates or tiles on each side, down which the water drains, will form the watershed. It must be remembered, however, that the water-parting is not necessarily the summit of a range of hills, like the ridge of a roof. Frequently, indeed, the ground is only relatively high; but the water easily finds the slope, however small, and runs down it, thus showing at once the direction of the water-parting.

A little consideration will show that water-partings may be drawn on a map of any country, so as to divide the entire region into a series of river-basins. Plate II. is a map of Great Britain and Ireland thus completely divided into river-basins, separated one from another by water-partings, which are indicated by dotted lines. All the rivers which empty themselves into the sea on the eastern side of Britain may, in this way, be separated from those which run into the western seas, and both systems may be separated from the southern rivers which open into the English Channel: the northern drainage is insignificant. We thus obtain the general water-parting of Great Britain, distinguished in the map by a line of red dots. This is a sinuous line running from near John-o'-Groat's House, through Scotland and the north of England, down the Peak of Derbyshire and through the Midland counties, till it gets as far south as Salisbury Plain. Such a line divides the western drainage of the country from its eastern drainage. At Salisbury Plain the line splits into two branches, one stretching to the east coast and terminating somewhere about Dover, the other striking to the west coast and terminating at the Land's End. To the south of this great east-and-west line, all the rivers flow into the English Channel. This three-branched line consequently represents the main water-parting of the country; it is in fact the general high-level line of Britain, though it has no direct relation to the mountain-systems of the country. The main water-partings of Ireland are also indicated on the map, the rivers being grouped in four great systems, which drain to the north, south, east, and west.

We shall restrict our attention, for the present, to one of these river-basins of England—the basin of the Thames—and endeavour to extract from its study as much instruction as possible. In several of the succeeding chapters we shall therefore inquire how this basin is fed with water, by what means it has received its present shape, and what has been its history in the past. Even the first question—how the basin is fed—suggests prolific material for study. It is true we have, in the present chapter, traced the Thames to its head-waters, but it must not for a moment be supposed that by doing this we have yet reached its real origin. The streams and springs from which a river is popularly said to take its rise are in truth only its proximate sources, and the ultimate source is to be sought elsewhere. In seeking that source, the inquiry may fitly be commenced by examining more closely into the nature and origin of springs.

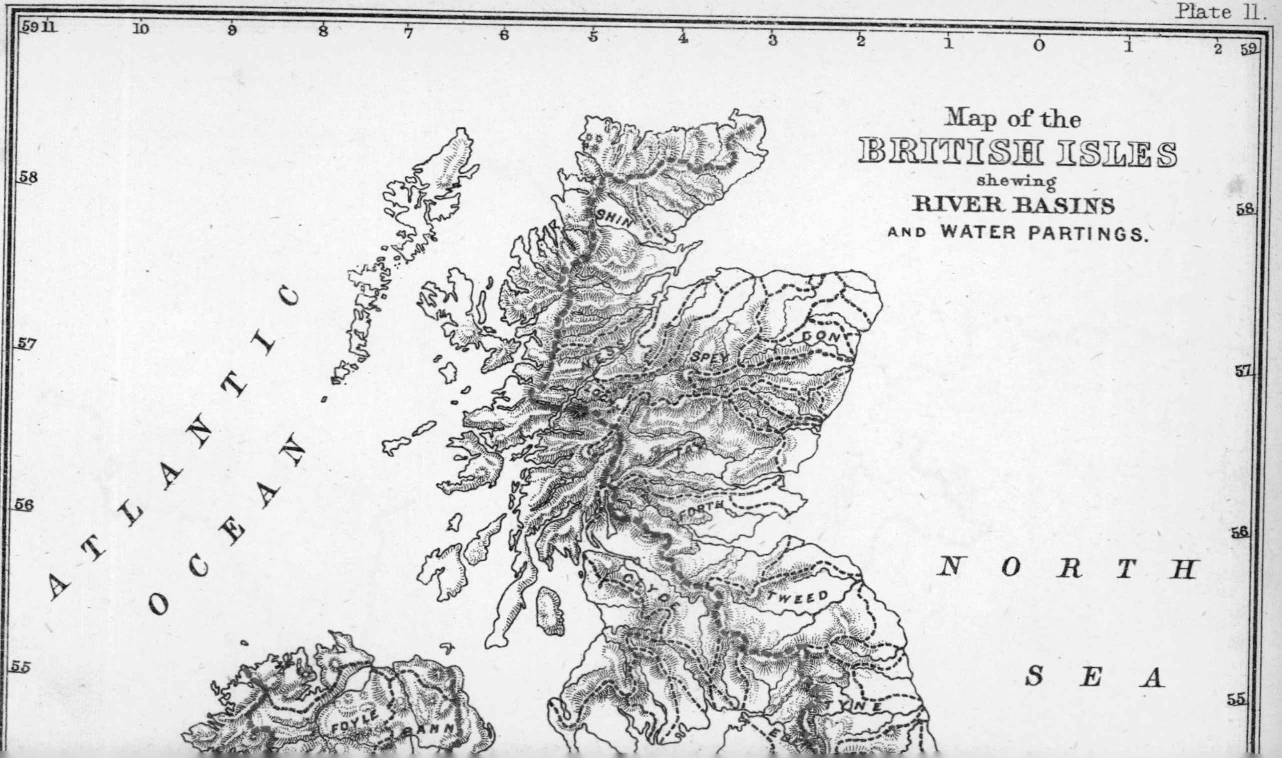

Plate II.

Map of the
BRITISH ISLES
shewing
RIVER BASINS
AND WATER PARTINGS.

NORTH

SEA

ATLANTIC

OCEAN

DON

SPEY

DOON

SHIN

TAY

TWEED

TYNE

ENGLISH CHANNEL

IRISH SEA

ST GEORGE'S CHANNEL

ENGLISH MILES

COOPER & HODSON, LITH. RED LION SQ. w.c.

CHAPTER II.

MARK what happens when a heavy shower of rain falls upon dry ground. If the ground be formed of hard and solid rock, such as granite, the rain, after wetting the surface, runs off in all directions; some finding its way to the nearest streamlet, whence it flows sooner or later into a river, and some finding lodgment in little hollows of the rock, where it collects in pools which are slowly dried up by wind and sunshine. But if the ground, instead of being hard like granite, is soft and porous like sand or chalk, the water will then sink into its substance, and may even pass out of sight before the surface of the thirsty soil is thoroughly wetted. Rocks which thus allow water to filter through them are said to be *permeable*, while those which refuse to allow the water to soak in are said to be *impermeable*: a bed of sand, for example, is permeable; a bed of clay impermeable.

It is by no means necesssary, however, that a rock, in order to be porous and permeable, should be either soft like chalk, or loose like sand. Take for instance a sandstone, or a hard limestone: these rocks are sufficiently coherent to form durable building stones, yet porous enough,

in most cases, to allow water to drain more or less freely
through them. The particles of which the rock is made up
are themselves impermeable, but they are so built together that
little spaces, or interstices, are generally left between the
individual particles, and the result is the formation of a
rock which, hard as it may be, presents a texture approximately like that of a sponge. The water trickles between
the particles of such a rock, and thus gradually soaks
through its mass. Close in grain as the rock may appear
to the eye, it is nevertheless capable, in most cases, of
absorbing water; and, hence, stone when freshly taken from
the quarry usually holds moisture, known to the workman
as "quarry water." Even when a rock offers too close a
texture to admit moisture freely, it commonly happens that
it is more or less fissured; and the water which falls upon
the rock then dribbles through the little cracks, and thus
gains ready access to subterranean channels, much in the
same way as it would if the rock were of open texture.

After a good deal of rain has fallen upon a porous rock,
its pores become choked with water, and the rock at last
gets saturated, like a piece of sugar which has been dipped
for a few moments into a cup of tea. If more rain now
fall upon the rock, it can no longer be sucked in and
retained, but will flow off the damp surface, just as it would
from the surface of an impermeable rock.

Suppose a layer of a porous substance to rest upon a bed
of comparatively impervious rock, and it is easy enough to
see what, under such circumstances, will become of the rain
which falls upon the surface. Let Fig. 6 illustrate such a
case. Here the dotted part of the figure A B C D, represents a permeable rock, say beds of sand, whilst the lower
shaded portion, C D E F, indicates an impermeable rock,
say a stiff clay. It is supposed, in a figure such as this, that

the rocks in question have been cut through so as to expose clean-cut surfaces, and hence such diagrams, which are constantly used in writings on the structure of the earth, are termed *sections*. Natural sections are frequently exposed in river-beds, sea-cliffs and inland valleys ; whilst artificial sections are seen in wells and shafts, in mines and quarries, and especially in railway-cuttings. A good general notion of the character of the rocks forming a given country may

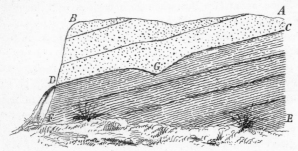

FIG. 6.—Formation of a spring.

often be gained, during a railway journey, by observing the cuttings along the line.[1]

[1] Some good geological sections may be seen in railway cuttings in the neighbourhood of London. Thus, in travelling by the North Western Railway to Watford, the passenger may observe the London clay ; and, further on, the Lower London Tertiaries overlying the chalk. On the Great Western Railway, the route to Maidenhead passes over the brick-earth and gravel which overlie the London Clay, and, at Windsor, the chalk is exposed, but not on the railway. To the south of London, some good sections may be seen in the cuttings on the North Kent Railway in the neighbourhood of Lewisham and Charlton, where the sandy deposits, known as the Thanet Sands, are exposed. A journey to Reigate, on the Brighton line, carries the passenger over the London clay, the chalk, and the beds below the chalk known as Greensand. For other sections see Whitaker's *Guide to the Geology of London*.

It is clear that when rain falls upon the surface A B, it will be readily absorbed, at least if the sandy rock be dry, and will gradually sink lower and lower until it reaches the bottom of the upper bed C D.   Here it comes in contact with the surface of the clay, and, as the clay refuses to absorb the water, its downward course is arrested.   Should the surface of the clay present irregularities, the water which has percolated through the sandy bed will lodge in the hollows, as at G.   But when such cavities have become filled, the water with which the rock is charged will flow over them, and continue to run down in whatever direction the rocks may chance to slope.

It rarely happens that the successive layers of rock, or as they are technically called *strata*,[1] exposed in any given section are perfectly horizontal, or spread out with flat surfaces, like the surface of a piece of still water.   Generally the beds slope or incline in a definite direction, and this slope is technically termed the *dip*.   If then we read in a scientific description of a given section that " the strata dip 30° S.W." it means simply that the layers of rock slant in a south-westerly direction, and make an angle of thirty degrees with a perfectly horizontal surface.   Thus, in the diagram the dip is shown by the general direction of the line CD, and its amount may be measured by the inclination of this line to the horizon ; that is, by the angle which the line CD makes with the top or the bottom edge of the page, when these edges are horizontal.   Now when the water, having percolated through the sandy rock A B C D, has reached the junction represented in section by C D, it flows down this plane in the direction of the dip, and escapes at

[1] *Stratum* (plural *strata*) from the Latin *stratum*, signifying that which is extended or spread out.

the first outlet, as at D. Such a flow of water thrown out
from a rock constitutes a *spring*.

Springs of this simple character, which issue at the
junction of permeable and impermeable strata, are extremely
common. If the reader who lives in London will take the
trouble to walk across Hampstead Heath soon after rain
has fallen, he can observe for himself exactly the condition
of things which has just been described. The highest
ground at Hampstead rises to about the height of St.
Paul's, or rather more than 400 feet above the sea-level,
and consists of loose sand which forms irregular ground
overgrown with ferns and gorse. This sand is similar to
the sand which is spread out in large mass over the widely-
separated district of Bagshot Heath in Surrey, whence it is
termed *Bagshot sand.* It is, however, only the highest
ground on Hampstead Heath that is formed of such sand,
which indeed does not attain, in this locality, more than
eighty feet in thickness. Beneath the sand is the same
stiff brown clay which underlies the whole metropolis, and is
consequently known as the *London clay.* Hampstead Heath
is therefore formed of London clay capped by Lower
Bagshot sand, as shown in Fig. 7. This is taken from a
section drawn by the Geological Survey, but in order to
bring the section within the width of the page, and yet preserve its characters, the vertical scale has been exaggerated.
On a natural scale the heights in the figure would require to
be reduced by one half, and the capping of sand would
consequently appear of insignificant thickness. Where one
kind of soil ends and the other kind begins, is pretty sharply
mapped out by the effect of rain. Any one who walks over
the Heath after a shower will not fail to observe that
the sandy soil remains almost perfectly dry, the rain having
been at once sucked in, while the clay, only a few yards off,

remains wet and sticky. The water absorbed by the sands
drains through them until it reaches the clay beneath, when
it either oozes out in an irregular sheet of water, or is discharged through definite channels as springs. The line
of springs consequently serves to mark the junction between
the two kinds of soil. As the surface of the clay receives
the drainage of the sands it is constantly kept wet, and
thus forms swampy ground, often marked by the growth of
rushes. It sometimes happens that the upper part of the
London clay is more or less sandy ; and, consequently, it is
not always easy to say precisely where the London clay
ends and the Bagshot sands begin. The springs are,

FIG. 7.—Section of Hampstead Heath. Vertical scale twice the horizontal scale.

however, thrown out as soon as the water reaches an
impervious bed.

The sands of the Bagshot series as exposed on Hampstead
Heath are commonly of yellow and brownish colours.
These colours are due to the presence of a peculiar compound of iron, oxygen,[1] and water, known to chemists
as *hydrous peroxide of iron* or *ferric hydrate.* As the rain-
water slowly filters through these ferruginous sands it dissolves more or less of this iron-compound, and carrying
it off in a soluble form, acquires medicinal properties. Thus
the spring in Well-walk at Hampstead is locally valued as a
tonic ; while its inky taste, and the foxy-red sediment

[1] For description of the gas called *oxygen*, see pp. 78, 79, 80.

which it deposits on standing, sufficiently attest the presence
of iron : it is in fact a *Chalybeate*[1] spring. This example
sufficiently illustrates the origin of *mineral springs.* The
saline and other substances which they contain, and on
which their peculiar properties depend, are generally
dissolved out of the rocks through which the water flows.
In the basin of the Thames, mineral springs are by no
means uncommon, some being chalybeate, others sul-
phureous, and others again saline. This is a subject,
however, which will be considered by and by.

What has been said, with respect to the structure of
the high ground at Hampstead, applies equally to
that at Highgate, and at Harrow. In each of these
localities, an isolated patch of Bagshot sand rests upon
London clay. And, coming down to the lower ground on
which the greater part of the metropolis is seated, a very
similar condition of things is met with ; that is to say, a
layer of highly pervious material is spread over a rock well
nigh impervious. The porous material, however, instead of
being Bagshot sand, is here a bed of gravel, varying from
ten to twenty feet in thickness, and resting upon the
London clay. When the rain has soaked into this gravel,
it is held up by the clay below, and is thus preserved in a
great underground reservoir, which offers a never-failing
source of supply to the shallow wells which were formerly
sunk in great numbers throughout London. Here and
there, a little valley cuts down through the gravel to the underlying clay ; and, the natural reservoir being thus tapped,
a spring of water flows out at the junction. Such is the
origin of the springs which gave names to Clerkenwell,

---

[1] *Chalybeate* from χάλυψ, *chalups*, steel or hardened iron, a Greek
word derived from the people called Chalybes, who dwelt on the
southern shore of the Black Sea, and were famous iron-workers.

Holywell, Bagnigge Wells, and other localities. Wells supplied from this gravel constituted for centuries the sole water-supply of the metropolis, and Professor Prestwich has well pointed out how "the early growth of London followed unerringly the direction of this bed of gravel." [1] As long as this was the case, settlement was quite impossible where the gravel was absent and the clay exposed. Indeed, it was not until an independent source of water was supplied by the great water-companies, that a population was established on the clay-districts of Camden Town, St. John's Wood, Notting Hill, &c.

Along the banks of the Thames and its tributary streams there is a bed of valley-gravel, at a lower level than that to which reference has just been made. This low-lying gravel also forms a source of water-supply to shallow wells, and has determined the site of many centres of population. Thus, Westminster, Battersea, Hammersmith, Brentford, Eton, Maidenhead, and many other towns up the Thames, were originally dependent upon this source for water.

From the cases hitherto considered, namely, those in which a porous rock rests upon one that is not sensibly porous, it is desirable to advance to the case in which the porous material is not only supported, but is also covered, by an impermeable stratum; the pervious substance being thus inclosed between two impervious beds, one forming its floor and the other its roof. Thus, the sandy stratum B, in Fig. 8, is supported by one bed of clay, C, and covered by another, A. As long as the strata remain in the horizontal position here represented, the rain which falls upon the surface of A is effectually prevented from reaching the porous material B, save only through any cracks which

---

[1] Anniversary Address to the Geological Society 1872, *Quart. Journ. Geol. Soc.* vol. xxviii. No. 110. p. liii.

may happen to run through the upper bed. Though the
material of B may be as porous as a sponge, not a drop of
water can reach it, as long as the waterproof roof remains
sound. But the case is extremely different when the beds
are inclined, as represented in Fig. 9. Here are three
beds, in the same order as those previously described, but
dipping at a slight angle. The porous bed B is exposed
at the surface, or as a geologist would say "crops out."

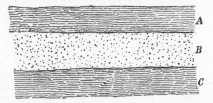

FIG. 8.—Horizontal permeable and impermeable strata.

Rain falling upon the ground A B C is thrown off by
the two clay beds A and C, but is absorbed by the outcrop, or exposed surface, of the sandy stratum B. This
absorbed water, whether directly falling upon B, or drained
off from A, runs down in the direction of the dip until

FIG. 9.—Inclined permeable and impermeable strata.

it reaches an outlet, whence it issues as a spring. If a
valley should cut through the beds, and have its bottom
below the water-level, springs will be thrown out along
the sides of the valley, as at D.

In following the course of a set of strata, it is no uncommon thing for the geologist to find that they come

abruptly to an end, that their continuity is suddenly broken,
and that one set of beds abuts upon another along a sharply-
defined plane.   The beds have, indeed, been fractured, and
have slid one over another.   Such a fracture, accompanied
by displacement of the strata, constitutes what geologists call
a *fault*.   Thus the set of beds represented in Fig. 10 have
been broken along a plane represented in section by the
line D E ; and, though once continuous, are now dislocated ;
the bed A having been thrown down to A′, the bed B
having slipped to the position B′, and the bed C to C′.
The drainage received by the surface of the porous stratum
B, will flow down until it reaches the fault, where it will be

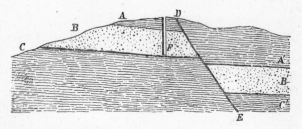

Fig. 10.—Effect of a fault on the position of a spring or well.

prevented from escaping by the clay wall of A′.   If therefore a bore-hole be put down to F, the water which has
percolated through the bed down to this point will be
forced upwards by the pressure of the water in the surrounding rock, and will therefore rise in the hole to nearly
the level which it occupies in the bed B.   Or, in the absence
of a bore-hole, the water will escape from the saturated
bed B, by oozing out at the surface,. near the junction of
the adjacent strata.   It is obvious, from this illustration,
that faults must be of great importance in determining the
position of springs and wells.

It frequently happens that the beds of rock, instead of having a uniform dip, slope first downwards and then upwards, so as to assume a basin-like form, such as that shown in Fig. 11. Here it is seen that the strata on opposite sides slope in opposite directions, as indicated by the arrows. Rain falling upon the exposed edges of the porous rock B B, will be readily absorbed, and will percolate through the pervious material until it reaches the bottom of the trough, where it will accumulate, and of course be accessible to the boring-rod. If, therefore, a bore-hole be put down through the impervious bed A, it will tap this reservoir of water, and the liquid will then rise to a height dependent on the level of the water in

FIG. 11.—Diagrammatic section across the London basin.

the bed B B. The laws which regulate the flow of water underground are precisely the same as those which regulate its flow above ground. The water pent up in the bed B B will therefore rush up the tube, and tend to find its own level.

This arrangement of strata in Fig. 11, may be taken to represent, roughly, the disposition of the rocks beneath London. The beds in that area have been thrown into a trough-like form, and have thus produced what is commonly known as the *London basin*.[1] Yet it must not for

[1] The London basin, or area around the metropolis, forms only a small portion of the Thames basin. The two are to be kept carefully distinct.

a moment be supposed that they lie in a deep hollow anything like that of an ordinary domestic basin, or even like that represented by the curves in the figure. It is true the rocks to the north and south of London slope gently inwards, and thus produce a depression, but it is a depression of the very shallowest kind. The inclination is indeed so gentle that it can scarcely be shown in a diagram brought within the compass of a page of this book. Hence most diagrammatic sections, as already explained (p. 17), in the description of the basin of Thames, are necessarily exaggerated, and false notions have thus got abroad as to the nature of the London basin. It is only when true sections are drawn, having the vertical heights represented on the same scale as that of the horizontal distances, that its extremely gentle concavity becomes apparent.

With this caution, we may proceed to examine more closely the section in Fig. 11. This may be taken to represent an exaggerated section across London, from north to south ; A representing the London clay, and B indicating the position of certain underlying rocks which geologists are in the habit of calling the *Lower London Tertiaries*. These lower strata are extremely variable, but in the neighbourhood of London they consist for the most part of sandy deposits, and are therefore highly permeable. Thin beds of clay, spread out at different levels in the sands, serve to retain the water ; and the supply, thus stored up, has been utilized by borings carried down through the overlying London clay. Such borings were frequently made in the early part of this century, and an abundant supply of water was obtained from depths varying from 80 to 140 feet. So numerous, however, were these wells, that a great drain was thrown upon the water-yielding power of the strata, and the supply ultimately became unequal to the demand. Of late years, therefore, most of the deep wells in London have been carried yet lower, passing in fact into the great mass of chalk which underlies the Lower Tertiaries in the position represented by C C in Fig. 11. The water is obtained partly from the saturated chalk and partly from fissures, the latter being in this case the more important source. As the position of these irregular cavities cannot be predicted, it is clearly impossible to foretell the depth at which stores of water will be found in the chalk.

When a deep boring is made through the London clay down to the Lower Tertiary sands, or still deeper, into the chalk, the water tends to rise in the tube, and may even reach the surface and overflow. If the point from which the water is tapped be in low ground, as would be the case with the boring D in the hollow of the London basin, it is necessarily at a much lower level than that of the outcrop of the beds along the margin of the trough, as at C C. The water is consequently forced up the tube by the pressure of the liquid with which the water-bearing bed is charged. When this pressure is sufficient to cause the water to flow over the surface of the bore-hole, it produces what is termed an "Artesian Well." This name, however, is now commonly extended to other wells in which the water, without overflowing, yet rises to a sufficient height to be economically employed. Artesian wells are of great antiquity in the East; in North-Western Europe they were first constructed in the province of Artois, in France, whence the name *Artesian*.

In the London basin there are numerous wells supplied on the Artesian principle. Thus the fountains in Trafalgar Square are fed with water from an Artesian well, which penetrates the chalk to a depth of about 390 feet beneath the surface. It would be curious to trace the history of a

D

drop of water brought up by these fountains. It may have fallen originally as rain upon the chalk hills around London, perhaps twenty miles off, and after slowly trickling through a long, dark underground course, where it was pent up under pressure, ultimately found relief in the bore-hole of the Artesian well.

London and Paris are situated under very similar geological conditions, and what is said with respect to the deep wells of one city applies with but little modification to those of the other. In the Paris basin, the Artesian system has been very largely carried out, and many of the borings have reached extraordinary depths. Thus at Grenelle, a suburb of the south-western part of Paris, there is a famous Artesian well, 1,798 feet deep, fed by the rains which fall on the permeable strata of Champagne at a distance of 100 miles from Paris. Several other borings have since been carried to much greater depths than that reached by the well at Grenelle.

Having explained the origin of ordinary springs and the nature of Artesian wells—which in truth are merely artificial springs—it is now time to return to the study of the Thames basin, the springs of which are the immediate source of all the fresh water in the river, except the small portion derived from the rain which falls directly into it.

The alternations of pervious and impervious strata which constitute that district, present all the necessary conditions for an abundant supply of springs yielding excellent water. "In the whole course of our experience," said the Rivers' Pollution Commissioners, in their sixth Report, "we have found no catchment-basin [1] so rich in

---

[1] The *catchment-basin* is a term applied to all that part of a river-basin from which rain is collected, and from which therefore the river is fed (p. 145).

springs of the finest drinking-water as that of the Thames."
The basin of the Thames, as we have seen above (p. 15),
has an area of more than 6,000 square miles, and rather
more than half of this area is formed of porous soil,
resting upon water-bearing strata, whilst the remainder
consists of clayey soil. The pervious ground, which absorbs the rain, is, for the most part, under cultivation ; the
impervious ground, which throws off the rain, is mostly
permanent meadow-land and pasture.

In describing the springs in the upper part of the Thames
basin, or those springs which rise above Oxford, we may
be guided by the careful observations which have been
made for many years by Mr. Bravender, of Cirencester.[1]
The source of the river Churn, or the extreme western
tributary of the Thames, is known as "The Seven Springs,"
and is situated about four miles from Cheltenham on the
road to Cirencester. It has been estimated that these
springs yield on an average about 150,000 gallons of water
daily. The Seven Springs are thrown out from clayey beds
which belong to the series of rocks known to geologists as
Lias ;[2] the water having been absorbed by the overlying
loose limestones which are technically called *Inferior Oolite,*
and which contain cavities that serve as excellent subterranean reservoirs for storage of water. The term "oolite,"
which has just been used, is applied by geologists to a large
series of rocks, which occupy a definite position in the scale of
strata and include many limestones which are composed of
peculiarly rounded grains, that give the rock somewhat the
appearance of the roe of a fish, whence the word *oolite* (ὠόν,

[1] See his evidence before the Royal Commissions on Water Supply
and Rivers' Pollution.

[2] The geological structure of the Thames basin is shown in Plate
V., and will be explained in detail in Chapter XVII.

an egg). The lower part of this oolitic series, which rests directly on the Lias, is termed, from its position, the *Inferior Oolite*. It is from some of the beds of this formation that the Seven Springs are fed. Rain falling on the rubbly lime-stones, the sandstones, and loose sands of the Inferior Oolite, percolates downwards, through numerous cracks and crannies, until it reaches the impermeable clays of the Lias, when it gushes forth wherever a channel offers itself. About one-third of all the rain that falls upon the inferior oolites is returned in the form of springs. So porous and open-jointed are some of the rocks of this series that, where they form the channel of the river, a considerable quantity of the water which flows over them is absorbed, and the volume of the stream may thus be diminished to a serious extent.

The Syreford Spring at the head of the river Colne— one of the streams in the upper basin of the Thames— has an origin similar to that of the Seven Springs. The Syreford source yields daily from three to four millions of gallons of water. This water has been absorbed by the Inferior Oolites and is thrown out by the underlying Lias clays.

Many of the springs in the head-waters of the Thames take their origin in the water-bearing limestone beds known as the *Great Oolite*—a set of rocks separated from the inferior oolite by the so-called *Fuller's earth*. This Fuller's earth forms a thick bed of clay, which retains the water that reaches it, in enormous quantity, by percolation through the porous limestones and sands of the great oolite series. Thus, the famous well at "Thames Head," the position of which is indicated on the map in Plate I., rises in this way from the surface of the Fuller's earth, and yields a vast volume of water which has been collected in the fissures of

the Great or Bath Oolite. Three million gallons of water are
every day pumped up by the engine from a depth of 35
feet into the summit-level of the Thames and Severn canal.
This artificial withdrawal of water to feed the canal has
lowered the level of the water-bed in the surrounding
country, so that the natural discharge at Thames Head is
now contracted and takes place lower down the valley.

About five miles south-east of the engine at Thames
Head is the Boxwell Spring, which discharges into the
Churn more than a million gallons daily. This large body
of water is drawn off from the surface of the Fuller's earth;
and many other springs, such as the Ewen Spring and the
Ampney Spring, have a like origin.

Other streams tributary to the Thames take their rise in
the springs of the porous sandy beds called *Upper Greensand*, which rest upon a stiff clay known as *Gault*. In
the lower part of the basin, or nearer to the mouth of
the river, the *Chalk* becomes the great reservoir; and it
often happens, that water which has drained through the
porous upper part of this formation, and made its way
through fissures, is held up by the lower part of the chalk,
which becomes stiff and retentive. The Kennet, which is
one of the main feeders of the Thames, receives its water
chiefly from the chalk downs near Hungerford and Marl-
borough; whilst the Coln collects a large body of water
from the Hertfordshire chalk. A great part of the New
River water too is drawn from the chalk. Finally, as a
source of water in the Thames basin, the *Bagshot Sands*,
already noticed, must not be neglected. Thus, the Loddon,
a tributary from the south, which falls into the Thames
about five miles below Reading, derives part of its water
from the Bagshot series.

As the Thames pursues its course, it receives supplies of

water not only from its tributary streams, but from springs
gushing up in the very bed of the river. These springs
are in some cases of enormous magnitude, especially
between Wallingford and Reading, and thus swell the
volume of the river to no inconsiderable extent.

Enough has been said, in this chapter, respecting the
nature and origin of springs, to show that all such sources
of water owe their origin, directly or indirectly, to the
rain which falls upon the collecting ground, and finds its
way through the pores and cracks of the rocks beneath.
Proximately, the source of the Thames and other rivers is to
be found in springs; but, ultimately, it must be traced to
rain. It is true the springs feed the river, but it is the rain
that feeds the springs. It will therefore be necessary, in the
next chapter, to study the formation of rain and kindred
phenomena.

CHAPTER III.

RAIN AND DEW.

IN travelling by steamer, it often happens that on going to that side of the boat towards which the wind is blowing the passenger suddenly finds himself in a shower of fine rain. This artificial shower is produced by the steam which issues from the waste-pipe being cooled down by contact with the surrounding cold air until it is condensed in the shape of drops of liquid. Every natural shower of rain is produced by a process of condensation similar to this, but carried on in the higher regions of the atmosphere.

It is instructive to observe the dense clouds of steam which roll forth from the spout of a kettle of boiling water, or from the escape-pipe of a steam-engine. In most cases, nothing can be seen close to the point from which the vapour issues, and it is only at some distance from this point that the white clouds first make their appearance. But, since that intervening space lies directly in the path of the issuing vapour, it is clear that it must be traversed by steam, though the eye fails to detect it. In fact, the steam, or watery vapour, when pure and uncondensed, is as transparent, as colourless, and as invisible as the air we breathe or the gas we burn. It is only when the vapour is partially condensed, and therefore ceases to be true vapour, that it appears in those cloud-like forms which are popularly called "steam." Could you look into the interior of a kettle or of a boiler from which clouds of so-called steam are issuing, you would see absolutely nothing in the space above the boiling water. It is only necessary to boil water in a glass vessel, such as a Florence flask, in order to observe that the steam remains invisible until exposed to some chilling influence, such as that of a body of cold air.

More or less of this watery vapour or steam, in its invisible condition, is constantly present in the surrounding atmosphere. It is drawn up into the air from every exposed piece of water, by means of solar heat, just as steam is generated from the water in the boiler by the aid of artificial heat. Whether it be evolved rapidly, with for- mation of bubbles, as in the ordinary process of boiling, or slowly and quietly, as in the course of evaporation, the product is the same—namely, invisible watery vapour. But let the air thus charged with moisture be sufficiently cooled, and its burden of vapour, previously unseen, makes its appearance as cloud, or mist, or fog. And, under certain atmospheric conditions, the condensation proceeds further, until the moisture ultimately falls to the earth in the shape of rain. Every one knows that if a cold object, such as a steel knife, be held in a cloud of steam, the surface rapidly becomes covered with drops of condensed water; and the drops of water in a shower of rain have been generated by a similar process of condensa- tion, carried on in nature.

In most cases, the atmospheric moisture passes through the condition of visible cloud, or mist, before finally con- densing as rain. Yet it sometimes happens that rain falls from a clear and cloudless sky. By local refrigeration, after sunset, the vapour, invisibly diffused through the atmosphere, is condensed, at once, into excessively fine drops of liquid water, forming the rain called *serein*. But such phenomena are rare ; and, as a rule, we may fairly expect the formation of rain to be preceded by that of cloud.

Many opinions have been advanced to explain the precise condition in which water exists in a cloud. At one time it was commonly supposed that a cloud is made up of a vast number of minute vesicles, or little watery bladders, which remain suspended in the air by reason of their small size and hollow structure. It appears probable, however, that the water is merely condensed in a very finely-divided state, its extremely minute particles remaining suspended in the surrounding moist air, as fine dust would do. Such particles have, indeed, been expressively called by Prof. Tyndall "water-dust." It is supposed that, in the upper regions of the atmosphere, the watery cloud-drops are frequently frozen into ice—a supposition strongly supported by the optical characters of certain clouds, which appear to be explicable only by the presence of a crystalline structure.

When a current of warm air, laden with moisture, rises from the surface of the earth, and reaches the higher and colder regions, the uppermost portion of the ascending current deposits its moisture in visible form, and thus produces a cloud, supported at the top of an invisible column. If the temperature fall, or the course of the current be arrested, the cloud descends, and regaining the lower and warmer regions, returns to its original state of invisible vapour, and thus becomes dissipated. Observe the clouds of steam which issue from the chimney of a locomotive engine, and you will see that as they float away in the air they gradually disappear. They are, in

fact, absorbed by the atmosphere; and the drier and
hotter the air happens to be, the more greedily does it
drink up this moisture.

Again, if a current of warm and moist air meet a colder
current, its temperature is reduced, and more or less of
its moisture is deposited. In this country, the south-west
winds, having swept over the warm waters of the Atlantic,
are charged with moisture, and ready to deposit a portion
of their freight whenever they are sufficiently chilled, as
they may be, for example, by meeting a cold east wind.
Hence south-west winds act as the chief rainbearers to
our islands.

So fantastic and varied are the forms presented by clouds
that they seem, at first sight, to defy scientific classification.
In 1802, however, Mr. Luke Howard, an eminent meteorologist, proposed, in an essay *On the Modifications of Clouds*,
a system of nomenclature and classification, which has
since been so commonly adopted that his terms are frequently
used, even in popular descriptions of scenery. Reference
to Plate III. will convey a better idea of the typical forms of
clouds than could be got from any long technical descriptions.[1]

Delicate white fleecy clouds may often be seen floating
in the upper regions of the atmosphere, where they are
arranged in groups running in more or less parallel directions.
Frequently a cloud of this class will present the appearance
of hair, or feather, with its fibres curled, and hence it has
received the name of *cirrus*.[2] The cirrus clouds are always
lofty, sometimes as much as ten miles above the surface of
the earth; and, being wafted along by currents in the upper
regions of the atmosphere, they may often be seen to move in

---

[1] These figures are partly taken from *Instructions in the Use of
Meteorological Instruments*, by R. H. Scott, M.A., F.R.S. 1875.
[2] *Cirrus*, a curl.

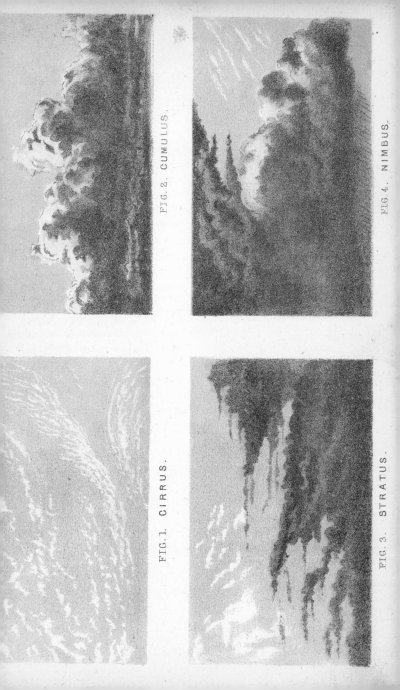

FIG. 2. CUMULUS.

FIG. 4. NIMBUS.

FIG. 1. CIRRUS.

FIG. 3. STRATUS.

a direction opposite to that of the wind which happens to be blowing over the surface. It is these clouds that are supposed to be made up of minute ice-particles (p. 41), since they produce, when they come between us and the sun or moon, those coloured circles which are known as halos.

Very different from the cirrus is the well-known *cumulus*,[1] a dense cloud which forms towering heaps of convex or concave form resting on a nearly horizontal base. Different again are the continuous sheets of cloud which are often to be seen extending widely in a horizontal direction, and are known consequently as the *stratus*.[2]

It often happens that the clouds under observation will not fall into any place in the foregoing classification. Instead of belonging definitely to any one class they may combine the characters of two or more groups, and in such cases expressive designations are framed by combining the preceding elementary terms. Thus, the beautiful effect of what is known popularly as the "mackerel sky" is due to numerous detached clouds of the composite forms termed *cirro-cumulus*. In like manner we may have a *cirro-stratus* and a *cumulo-stratus*, but such words sufficiently explain themselves. The dull rain-cloud, termed the *nimbus*,[3] is a composite form sometimes described as a *cumulo-cirro-stratus*. It is the dark grey cloud, or system of clouds, from which rain is actually falling. Before leaving the nomenclature of clouds, it may be useful to remark that the term *scud* is frequently applied to any loose detached clouds which drift rapidly before the wind.

In meteorological reports, it is convenient to express approximately the proportion of sky which, at any given time, is covered by cloud. This is effected by using an

[1] *Cumulus*, a heap. [2] *Stratus* or *stratum*, a bed.
[3] *Nimbus*, a rain-cloud.

arbitrary scale. Thus, a clear blue sky is represented by
a cipher, while a sky completely obscured is designated
by 10; the intermediate numbers from 0 to 10 being used
to express varying proportions of cloudiness.

It has been shown that, when watery vapour condenses in
the upper regions of the atmosphere, it gives rise to the
formation of clouds. But, if the condensation occurs near
to the surface of the earth, it produces those visible vapours
which are known as *mist* or *fog*. Beyond the difference in
the place of origin there is really little or no distinction
to be drawn between a fog and a cloud. A fog is a cloud
resting on the earth; a cloud is a fog floating high in
the air.

Whenever moist air near the surface of the earth has its
temperature sufficiently reduced, the moisture may be condensed as mist or fog. Thus fogs almost constantly hang
over the banks off the coast of Newfoundland, where they
are produced by the warm moist air of the Gulf Stream[1]
coming in contact with the cold air of the Labrador
current. In like manner, icebergs are often attended by
fogs, simply because the mass of ice cools the surrounding
air, and thus precipitates its moisture. Mountains, again,
are frequently enveloped in mist, since the warm air, on
being driven up the slope of the hill, becomes chilled to
the point at which its moisture is partially condensed. So
too the position of a river is often marked by mist; and
this whether the water be colder or warmer than the
overlying air: in the former case, the air is cooled down
by contact with the water, and its moisture discharged; in

[1] It will be explained in Chapter XI. that the Gulf Stream is a body
of warm water which flows from the Gulf of Mexico across the Atlantic
Ocean; the Labrador current is a body of cold water coming down
from the north along the coast of Labrador.

the latter case, the warm water yields more vapour than the air can retain at the given temperature. The British Isles, washed by warm water on their western shores, are peculiarly subject to fogs; and, of all places, large towns seated on rivers are the most affected, since the artificial heat, coupled with the moisture of the air over the river, produces conditions favourable to the formation of fogs whenever the air becomes sufficiently cooled. The proverbial London fog owes its density and darkness to the smoke, or particles of carbonaceous matter, disseminated through the atmosphere and mingled with the partially condensed water.

As long as water remains in the state of cloud, or fog, its particles are so minute that they hang suspended in the air, or mount upwards on the slightest current. But, when these droplets run together, they produce drops too heavy for suspension in the atmosphere, and are then precipitated to the earth as rain. The *rainfall*, or amount of rain which falls in any given locality, is a most important element in determining its climate.

What does a meteorologist mean when he says, in his technical language, that the annual rainfall in London is about 24 inches? By such a statement he means, simply, that if all the rain which falls on any level piece of ground in London during an average year could be collected—none being lost by drying up, none running off the soil, and none soaking into it—then, at the end of the year, it would form a layer covering that piece of ground to the uniform depth of two feet. The year's accumulation of rain would thus form a vast mass of water. Remembering that an inch of rain represents about 100 tons of water to the acre, it will be found that every acre of land in the metropolis receives during the year, when the year is neither very wet nor very dry, not less than 2,400 tons of rain.

In passing across England from east to west, it is found
that, as a rule, the rainfall increases. Thus, in the basin of
the Thames, the fall varies, from about 24 inches in the
eastern part, to between 30 and 40 inches among the western
hills, in which the river takes its rise. Looking at the entire
basin of the Thames, it may be said that the average rainfall
is about 26 inches. Now the area of the basin, as already
stated, comprises upwards of 6,000 square miles. Suppose
then that we measured out a square space a mile in length
on each side, and built upon this base a four-sided tower
two and a half miles in height, which we completely filled
with fresh-water; this enormous column would represent the
quantity of water which falls upon the surface of the
Thames basin in the course of twelve months. And it
should be borne in mind that every drop of this water has,
at some time, existed in the atmosphere as invisible vapour.
In one sense, therefore, it may be truly said that the Thames
has its source in the air.

Passing beyond the western limits of the Thames basin,
it is found that the rainfall becomes heavier, until, in the
western promontory of Cornwall, it exceeds 40 inches. The
maximum, however, is attained among the mountains of
Wales and Cumberland; the wettest spot in England being
near Seathwaite in Cumberland, where the average rainfall
has been recorded as 165 inches.

A general view of the rainfall throughout England and
Wales is presented by the accompanying rain-map (Plate
IV.), which is reduced from the map published in the
sixth report of the Rivers Pollution Commission, for which
it was prepared by Mr. G. J. Symons. Such maps are
generally called *Hyetographical*[1] or *Hyetological* maps. In
the one given here, the differences of rainfall are indicated

[1] From ὑετός, *huetos*, rain.

by differences of tint, which are sufficiently explained by the accompanying index.

In examining the distribution of rain, it will be found to be regulated partly by the physical features of the country, and partly by the character of the prevailing winds. In the neighbourhood of mountains, the rainfall is increased, since, as has already been pointed out, a mass of moist air, when forced up the side of a mountain, is chilled in the ascent, and its moisture consequently discharged. Among our western counties, in the neighbourhood of hills, the rainfall rises to eighty, or even to a hundred, inches, and upwards ; while away from hills, though still in the west, it is only from thirty to forty-five inches. A table-land, or high plain surrounded by mountains, will generally receive but little rain, since the winds which reach it have been more or less drained of moisture in sweeping over the surrounding hills. For a like reason, but little rain is likely to fall on the lee side of a high hill, and many mountains, consequently, have a wet and a dry side ; the wet side being, of course, that towards which the predominant winds blow. As regards the influence of winds on rain, it is evident that, when air has blown over a large expanse of warm water, it must have become laden with moisture, which will be readily precipitated on exposure to refrigerating influences. Hence, as in Britain, so in the greater part of Europe, the southerly and westerly winds bring rain ; and most rain falls in the exposed westerly parts, such as the coasts of Portugal, Spain, France, Britain, and Norway. There are certain conditions, however, under which rain is brought to our islands by easterly rather than by westerly winds.

It is in those regions in which the sun's heat is intense, and powerful currents of highly-heated air, saturated with watery vapour, are raised into the atmosphere, that the heaviest rains occur. But the heavy tropical rains are usually confined to definite periods—the *rainy season*—and are not spread over the entire year, as in the temperate zone.

The Khasi Hills (which lie about 100 miles to the north-east of Calcutta) present the greatest rainfall in the world. Sir J. Hooker recorded upwards of 500 inches during a stay of nine months, and the total annual fall is about 524 inches. On the other hand, there are certain localities in which little or no rain falls : the chief of these rainless regions being Upper Egypt, the Sahara, the desert of Gobi in Central Asia, and the coast of Peru. As we recede from the hotter regions of the earth, either to the north or south, the rainfall, as a rule, diminishes, but the number of rainy days in the year increases ; so that, speaking roughly, it may be said that, where the rainy days are fewest, the amount of rain is greatest.

In temperate regions, the number of rainy days varies greatly in different localities, and in different seasons. But it is difficult to know exactly what is meant by so vague a phrase as a "rainy day." To secure uniformity among observers, Mr. Symons has therefore proposed that meteorologists shall regard as a "rainy day," every day on which the rainfall is not less than one-hundredth of an inch.

It is matter of common observation that the rainfall varies not only in different localities, but in the same locality at different times. One year may be much wetter than another. A remarkable instance of this was presented by the exceptional rainfall of 1872, a fall which, in most districts, was excessive, and in some was unprecedented. It is believed that no such fall has been recorded since observations were first instituted, now two centuries ago.

It is curious to compare the 1872 fall with that of the following year, which was remarkably dry. Thus, Mr. Symons has recorded the rainfall in Camden Square,

Plate IV.

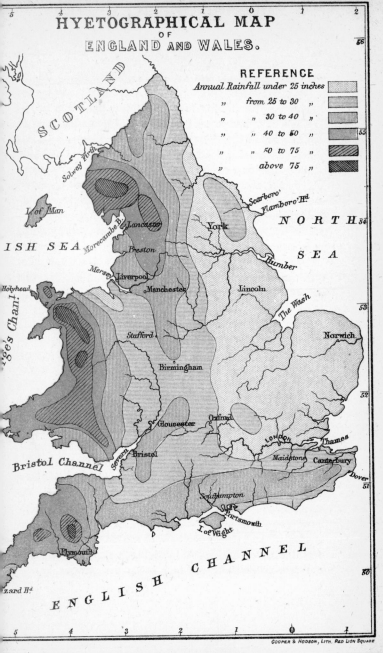

HYETOGRAPHICAL MAP
OF
ENGLAND AND WALES.

REFERENCE

Annual Rainfall under 25 inches
,, from 25 to 30 ,,
,, ,, 30 to 40 ,,
,, ,, 40 to 50 ,,
,, ,, 50 to 75 ,,
,, above 75 ,,

SCOTLAND

Solway Firth

I. of Man

IRISH SEA

Holyhead

St George's Chan.l

Morecambe B.

Lancaster

Preston

Mersey Liverpool

Manchester

Stafford

Birmingham

Gloucester

Severn Bristol

Bristol Channel

York

Humber

Lincoln

Scarboro'

Flamboro' H.d

NORTH

SEA

The Wash

Norwich

Oxford

LONDON Thames

Maidstone Canterbury

Dover

Southampton

Portsmouth

I. of Wight

Plymouth

Lizard H.d

ENGLISH CHANNEL

COOPER & HODSON, LITH. RED LION SQUARE.

London, as 33·86 inches in 1872, and only 22·67 inches in 1873. But striking as the difference is here, it is yet more marked in other localities. At Barnsley, for example, the fall in 1872 was 42·28 inches, and in 1873 only 15·9 inches; in other words, the rainfall in the dry year was but 38 per cent. of that of the preceding year.

It may be useful, before quitting the subject of rain, to explain how the rainfall at any given station may be determined. Although the operation is extremely simple, numerous kinds of rain-gauge have been devised. The accompanying figure (Fig. 12) represents a simple form recommended in the *Instructions in the use of Meteorological Instruments* (1875), compiled by Mr. R. H. Scott, director of the Meteorological Office. The instrument consists of little more than a
circular metallic funnel for catching the
rain, and a vessel for storing it. All
the rain which falls upon the open
mouth is collected, and, when collected,
is exposed to but little loss by evaporation. The area of the collecting vessel
varies in different forms of apparatus,
the Meteorological Office employing a
funnel eight inches in diameter. By
means of the high cylinder around the

FIG. 12.—Rain-gauge

top of the funnel, snow may be collected; but there are great difficulties in making accurate observations on the fall of snow. It is notable that different amounts of rain will be collected by gauges placed at different heights in the same locality; a gauge at a low level always reading higher than one above. In all cases the instrument must, of course, be placed in a freely-exposed situation. Every morning, at nine o'clock, the rain collected during the preceding twenty-four

E

hours is transferred from the collecting-can to the graduated
measure-glass, and its amount accurately recorded.

Of the rain which falls in any given district, such as the
basin of the Thames, part is lost by evaporation and passes
invisibly into the air; at the same time another part soaks
into the soil, and this also appears to be lost; whilst part
again flows off the surface of the ground to lower levels.
Rain is thus disposed of in a threefold way, but the relative
proportion between the three parts will vary considerably
in different localities, and at different times in the same
locality. It is dependent on climate and season, on the
character of the soil, and on the physical features of the
district. But whatever the proportion may be, the rain
which is absorbed by the ground and that which flows off
the surface will contribute sooner or later to the formation
of springs and streams.[1] And in this way the rains indirectly
nourish the rivers, since we have already seen that rivers
are mainly fed by springs and streams. The more rain which
falls upon the surface, the greater therefore will be the
yield of the river. "Rivers," said Captain Maury, "are the
rain-gauges of Nature."

Atmospheric moisture is frequently condensed in other
forms than that of rain. If a glass of water recently
drawn from a cold spring be brought into a warm room,

[1] From what has been said respecting the origin of springs, it is
obvious that, independently of the effects of evaporation, the quantity
of water which reaches a river may be less than that which falls in the
shape of rain upon its catchment basin; inasmuch as some may go
to feed the springs of other catchment basins. And, on the other
hand, the quantity of water conveyed by a river may be indefinitely
greater than that which falls upon its catchment basin, if the geological
structure of the basin is such as to lead the rain from beyond its limits
into the springs of the river.

it will be found that the outer surface of the glass gradually
loses its brightness; a dimness soon creeps over the surface
that was previously clean and bright, and, before long,
drops of water may be seen trickling down the sides of the
vessel. It is true that certain kinds of glass, such as some
of the old Venetian, constantly exude moisture, or "sweat,"
so that after the surface has been dried it soon becomes
moist again—an effect probably due to an excess of soda
in the glass. But the moisture which appears on ordinary
glass, under the circumstances indicated above, is clearly due
to an entirely different cause, since it is produced with
equal readiness on glass of any chemical constitution, or
indeed upon a vessel of polished metal. It is evident then
that the moisture is not derived from the substance of the
vessel itself; neither is it obtained by percolation through
the walls of the vessel, for the metal has no sensible pores.
The only remaining source of moisture is the surrounding
medium, or the atmosphere. That medium always contains
more or less watery vapour ready to be deposited upon any
object when sufficiently chilled, and the necessary refrigeration is brought about by the cold water in the glass or the
metal vessel. Moisture which is thus deposited upon any
cold surface, without production of mist, is termed *dew*.

The proportion of watery vapour that can be held in the
atmosphere depends principally on the temperature of the
air; the lower the temperature the less it retains. If charged
so highly with moisture that it can take up no more, the air
is then said to be *saturated*. When a body of moist air is
cooled, the point of saturation is gradually reached; and,
when saturated, any further cooling causes a deposition of
dew: hence the temperature at which this occurs is called
the *dew-point*. This point may be determined in a variety
of ways, but it is interesting to note that some of the instru-

ments used for this determination are based on the principle
to which reference has just been made. Thus, the instrument designed by the late Prof. Daniell, and represented in
Fig. 13, consists of a glass tube bent twice at right angles,
and terminated at each extremity by a bulb : one of these
bulbs, A, contains ether, while the other, B, is empty and
inclosed in muslin. If a few drops of ether be poured
upon this muslin, the ether-vapour within the tube is condensed, and the liquid in A rapidly evaporates ; but this

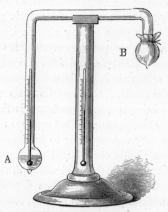

FIG. 13.—Daniell's hygrometer.

evaporation is attended with reduction of temperature, and
consequently the bulb A is rapidly cooled. When the
temperature of the surrounding air is sufficiently lowered,
the dew-point is reached, and a film of moisture is then
deposited on the outside of the bulb A. The temperature
at which this takes place is indicated approximately by the
thermometer inside the bulb, while the temperature of the
air outside is given by the thermometer placed on the

upright stand. In another form of the instrument, devised by M. Regnault, the moisture is precipitated upon the surface of a small vessel of polished silver. It will be seen, however, that both instruments are but refined modifications of our familiar experiment with the tumbler of cold water.

After sunset, on a clear night, the grass and other objects on the surface of the earth give off the heat which they have absorbed during the day, while the sun has been shining upon them, and their temperature is thus gradually lowered. The air in contact with these objects is also cooled; and, as it gets cool, it grows less able to retain its moisture, until at length the dew-point is reached, when drops of liquid are deposited on the blades of grass. Some bodies throw out, or *radiate*, their heat much more freely than others, and dew is therefore precipitated copiously upon such good radiators. Thus it may sometimes be seen in a garden that every blade of grass is bedecked with sparkling dew-drops, while the neighbouring gravel path remains almost dry. The grass has parted with its heat, and consequently become chilled, more readily than the gravel has cooled; and the dew is therefore distilled more abundantly upon the grass than upon the gravel.

Whatever prevents the radiation or giving-off of heat from terrestrial bodies tends to hinder the formation of dew. A cloud, for example, acts in this way, since it reflects, or throws back upon the earth, the heat which would otherwise be projected into space. Dew is therefore most copious on a cloudless night. A calm atmosphere also promotes the formation of dew, for it is obvious that agitation by currents of air must be unfavourable to local refrigeration; while it promotes the evaporation of any dew that may have been deposited.

It was not until the beginning of the present century that

so common a phenomenon as the formation of dew was thoroughly understood. Observations on the subject had indeed been made at a much earlier date, but it remained for Dr. W. C. Wells, an American settled in this country, to undertake a systematic inquiry into the conditions under which dew is deposited. After much patient investigation he published, in 1814, his famous essay entitled *The Theory of Dew*, and the simple explanation which he set forth in this essay has been corroborated by subsequent investigators.

Atmospheric moisture is precipitated not only as rain and dew—the particular forms which have been studied in this chapter—but also occasionally as snow and hoar-frost; the formation of these will form the subject of the next chapter.

CHAPTER IV.

THE CRYSTALLISATION OF WATER : SNOW AND ICE.

DURING the greater part of the year, in this country, the atmospheric moisture is condensed in a liquid state, partly as rain and partly as dew. But, when the temperature of the air falls below the freezing-point, the water, unable any longer to retain this liquid condition, is reduced to a solid form ; and the moisture is consequently precipitated as snow instead of rain, and as hoar-frost instead of dew. It is of much importance to have some knowledge of the manner in which this great change in the physical condition of water is brought about.

Daily observation shows that almost everything gets smaller as it is cooled. Reduction of temperature, as a rule, causes the particles of which a given body is composed to be brought more closely together, and the substance consequently shrinks in bulk. Suppose a quantity of air is confined in a vessel standing over water or quicksilver, and that it is found at a given temperature to occupy a certain bulk ; then, on lowering its temperature, the air will shrink in volume, or occupy less space, so that the water or quick-silver will tend to rise in the vessel, and thus fill the space which would otherwise be left by contraction of the air.

By careful observation it has been found that the shrinkage proceeds with great regularity as the air gets cooler, but there is no need to trouble ourselves, at present, with the law of contraction.

Now watery vapour, such as that present in the atmosphere, is a body which may be said roughly to have a constitution similar to that of the air with which it is associated. But when this vapour is cooled, a limit is soon reached, beyond which any further cooling brings about the condensation of the vapour as liquid water. In fact, watery vapour, or steam, differs from fluids like air chiefly in the readiness with which it can thus be condensed or liquefied.

Having in this way reduced the vapour to the condition of a liquid, it is important to observe the effect of still further lowering its temperature. As the water becomes cooled, the bulk of the liquid is diminished. With most liquids, this reduction of bulk continues until their parts lose that freedom of motion upon one another which is characteristic of a liquid, and the mobile liquid passes into a compact rigid solid. The solid thus obtained by the congelation of water is termed *ice*. It is important however to note that water and a few other liquids, instead of continuing steadily to contract when cooled, reach a limit at which contraction stops and is succeeded by expansion, so that the solid water actually occupies a good deal more space than did the liquid from which it was derived. When a water-pipe bursts during a frost, or a jug of water cracks as the liquid freezes, we are practically taught that water, during the process of solidification, undergoes a large increase of bulk.

By reason of this expansion, a piece of ice necessarily weighs much less than an equal bulk of water. If, for

instance, a given bulk of water, measured at that temperature at which its relative weight is greatest, be found to
weigh 1,000 pounds, an equal bulk of ice will weigh only
916 pounds. Hence ice floats readily on water, and floats
with only about one-tenth of its volume above the surface.
This may be seen by dropping a lump of ice into a tumbler
of water, and observing how much is exposed, and how
much buried in the water (Fig. 14.) Sea-water is denser,
or heavier bulk for bulk, than fresh water ; and therefore a
mass of ice floats higher in the ocean, about one-ninth of its
volume being then exposed. Hence, in those huge masses
of ice which are frequently seen floating in the sea and are

known as *icebergs*, the bulk of ice which
is submerged is about eight times as
great as that above water. But it must
be remembered that the proportion of
the submerged to the exposed part of
the total height of the berg will be
affected by the shape of the mass ; and
probably, in many cases, the shape of
the berg is such as to cause it to sink

FIG. 14.—Ice in water

to a very much smaller proportion of its total height beneath
the surface than that represented in Fig. 14.

It must not be supposed that the compact hard substance
which is produced by the freezing or consolidation of
water is a solid body without structure, like a piece of glass.
Look at a bedroom window on a frosty morning, and you
will probably find that some of the moisture present in the
room has condensed upon the glass and frozen into solid
ice ; but you will see at once that this ice, instead of
spreading itself uniformly over the surface, has shot out in
definite directions, producing beautiful branching forms, not
unlike the graceful fronds of a fern. The ice has, in fact,

assumed forms which are extremely definite in themselves, and are known as *crystals.*

In the rocks of Snowdon, and of many other parts of Britain, there may be found a beautifully transparent substance, of great hardness, which puts on very definite shapes. These shapes, as represented in Fig. 15, usually look like little six-sided towers, shooting in all directions from the rock, and terminated at one end, or sometimes at each end, by a short six-sided spire. The faces are as smooth and bright as though they had been just polished

Fig. 15.—Rock crystal.[1]

on the lapidary's wheel; whilst the edges are as sharp and straight as though cut by a skilful workman. The ancients, who were familiar with these clear and colourless solid bodies as they occur in the granitic rocks of the Alps, supposed that they were composed of ice; that they

[1] The lines on these crystals indicate shading, and not markings on the natural specimen. The prisms of rock-crystal are often marked by lines, but they run *across* the prisms, not longitudinally in the direction of the shading in the figure.

were, in fact, nothing but water which had been congealed
by so intense a cold that it was impossible to thaw it.
And the Greek word for *ice* (κρύσταλλος, *krustallos*), thus
suggested our term *crystal*. Even at the present day many
crystallised minerals are vulgarly called " congealed water."
The substance which has just been noted as having given rise
to the word " crystal " is known as *rock-crystal*, and must be
familiar to most readers, since it is used by the jeweller for
working into ornamental objects, and by the optician for the
manufacture of those spectacle lenses which are said to be
made of "pebbles." The term "crystal" is now applied
to all symmetrical solid shapes assumed spontaneously by
lifeless matter.

Rock-crystal is sometimes found in crystals of gigantic
size; at other times in excessively small specimens. This
seems to show that the same species or kind of matter may
assume forms unlimited in size. A few years ago some
enormous specimens of dark-coloured rock-crystal were
found in cavities of a rock above the Tiefen Glacier in
Switzerland ; one crystal, christened the " Grandfather,"
weighing as much as 276 lbs., and another, called the
" King," weighing 255 lbs. Yet this same substance may
be obtained in crystals so minute as to be seen only with
aid of a microscope. Such great variation of size in the
same kind of crystalline matter has no parallel among living
bodies. It is true that certain animals and plants, placed
under very favourable conditions, may increase beyond their
average size, but this increase is confined within compara-
'ively narrow limits. A crystal, however, has absolutely no
limit to its growth ; it increases in size by addition of matter
from the outside, and as long as new matter is thus presented
to it, so long will it continue to enlarge. A small crystal of
alum, for example, suspended in a saturated solution of the

same salt, gradually grows larger by deposition of new alum in a solid form from the surrounding medium. This method of growth is therefore entirely different from that by which the growth of a living body is effected. It is as though a man could actually grow bigger by putting on coat after coat, instead of growing by the ordinary process of nutrition from within.

Just as there is nothing distinctive about the size of an individual crystal, so there is nothing distinctive about the size of the several faces of the crystal. A six-sided spire or pyramid of rock-crystal may have one face very large, and the next face so small as to be little more than a mere line. Size of crystal and size of face thus count for nothing, but what does tell for something in studying crystals is the slope or inclination which one face has to another; in other words, the angle made by two neighbouring faces. A set of faces symmetrically related, such as the six faces of the prism of rock-crystal, is called technically a *form;* and the faces of any given form, however irregular in size and shape, are always inclined to one another at the same angle.

Although it is not every substance that can assume these regular forms, yet by far the larger number of bodies, including water, are capable of crystallization. When water solidifies, by reduction of temperature, the particles group themselves in definite directions, and thus produce regularly-shaped solids, closely related to those of the rock-crystal. In fact the forms of ice and the forms of rock-crystal are characterised by the same kind of symmetry; a symmetry which is such that each crystal may be divided into six similar parts. The best examples of this hexagonal sym metry in solid water is furnished by crystals of *snow.*

If the air during a snow-storm be still, each flake that falls will be found to exhibit a regular shape. A perfectly-formed snow-flake is, in fact, an exquisite little crystal; but it commonly happens that a flake is made up of several of these crystals grouped together. Some idea of the beauty and variety of snow-crystals may be formed by reference to Fig. 16, which represents a few of the shapes observed by

Fig. 16.—Snow-crystals

Captain Scoresby in the Arctic Regions. More than a thousand different kinds have been described; but various as these are, they are all characterized by the same kind of symmetry. Some of these snow-crystals are simply solid rods or flat scales, each with six sides; others are six-sided pyramids, but the most common form is that of little

six-pointed stars variously modified. Each star has an icy
centre as a nucleus, from which six little spicules or rods
of ice are shot forth at regular angles ; and from the sides
of these rays, secondary rays, or raylets, may be given off
at the same angle, thus producing complex stars of great
beauty, but, in spite of their complexity, always true to the
hexagonal symmetry of the system to which ice belongs.
Each part of the pattern is repeated round the centre six
times, as is generally the case with the beautifully-sym-
metrical shapes seen in a common kaleidoscope.

Although ice does not ordinarily exhibit well-defined
crystals, it is nevertheless built up of crystalline particles
interlaced together. Prof. Tyndall has shown us how to
reveal this beautiful architecture, by submitting a block
of ice to the action of a sunbeam, or even to a beam of
electric light. Part of the heat enters the solid, and produces internal liquefaction, which proceeds with great
regularity. Small shining points first appear in the ice,
and around each of these points, as a centre, six rays
shoot forth, producing figures such as those represented
in Fig. 17.[1] These beautiful forms, which commonly resemble blossoms with six petals or floral leaves, are not
solid crystals, like our crystals of snow, but are simply
hollow spaces of regular shape filled with water; they
may indeed be called "negative" or "inverse" crystals,
developed by the breaking-down or "decrystallisation"
of the ice. The ice is in fact *crystalline*, whilst the snow
is *crystallised*.

When there is much wind astir, the snow falls in
shapeless masses, or even in small hardened pellets. If
the snow-flakes become partially melted in their descent
by falling through a layer of warm moist air, they produce

[1] See Tyndall's *Heat as a Mode of Motion*, 5th ed. p. 11.

what is called *sleet*. The largest snow-flakes fall when the
temperature is near the freezing-point, and the smallest
when the temperature is very low. It need hardly be
said that snow is much lighter than rain ; it is usually
estimated at about one-tenth the weight of an equal bulk
of water, so that if a fall of snow lies on the ground to

FIG. 17.—Ice-flowers.

the depth of ten inches, it may be taken roughly to
represent one inch of rain : it is obvious, however, that
snow varies much in its state of compactness, and this
method is consequently, in many cases, far from accurate.
The loose texture of snow renders it an extremely
bad conductor of heat, and a fall of snow thus acts like
a mantle of fur thrown over the earth. The air entangled

in the snow not only confers upon it this valuable property, but it also gives the snow its opaque white appearance, so different from the transparency of common ice. The light, instead of penetrating the snow, is thrown back from the ice-walls of each little air-cell or cavity, and thus becomes scattered, the snow losing its transparency; just as the foam of the sea becomes opaque white, by the light being scattered from the particles of water into which a wave is broken.

When snow falls upon a mountain in winter, it may lie there unmelted until the warmth of summer returns to thaw it. But, if the mountain be very high, the summer-heat may never be strong enough to melt all the ice on its top, and the top will therefore be enveloped in perpetual snow. A line drawn at the level above which the snow never melts is called the *snow-line*. On the north side of the Himálaya Mountains this line is 16,600 feet high; that is to say, all the snow which falls below this height is melted in summer, but all above remains unmelted. In the Andes of Peru the limit of perpetual snow is about 15,500 feet; but in passing northwards or southwards from these hot regions, we expect to find the snow-line descending; in the Swiss Alps, for example, it comes down to about 8,500 feet above the sea. Still farther north it reaches yet lower, and, in the Arctic regions, descends to the very sea-level; the winter's accumulation of snow is never completely melted by the summer-sun, and the snow consequently lies on the ground all the year round.

Snow is not the only solid form in which atmospheric moisture is precipitated. Occasionally, during a storm, it takes the shape of *hail*, which consists of hard masses of ice varying in size from the smallest shot to pieces several inches in diameter. These hailstones are in some cases perfect spheres, as though the drops of rain had rapidly congealed while falling. When broken open, a hailstone occasionally exhibits crystals shooting out from the centre in all directions towards the surface; but it is more usual to find a number of layers of ice, some clear and some opaque, coating a white snowy central mass, around which they appear to have been frozen in definite succession. As a rule, hail falls in summer rather than in winter, and in the day rather than in the night. The origin of hail is still obscure, but it is probably formed by an intensely cold current of air passing into a region of warm moist air, and reducing the temperature of the whole below the freezing point.

There is yet another form of atmospheric precipitate that needs a passing notice. If the temperature after dew-fall should sink below the freezing-point, the moisture which would, under ordinary conditions be deposited as dew, takes a solid form, and is then known as *hoar-frost*. Blades of grass, and other objects cooled by freely throwing off their heat into space, thus become coated with delicate icy crystals instead of dew. The hoar frost is, in fact, nothing but dew which has been frozen as it was formed.

In one or other of the forms described in this and the preceding chapter, all atmospheric moisture must be precipitated. It is not however always easy, nor is it by any means necessary, to distinguish between these several forms, and they are therefore practically massed together under the general head of " rainfall." If then it is said that the basin of the Thames is fed by a rainfall of twenty-six inches, what is meant is that the total quantity of atmospheric moisture precipitated within this area—adding together the rain and the snow, the hail and the dew—amounts in the course of an average year to a depth of six-and-twenty inches spread uniformly over the surface of the basin.

F

CHAPTER V.

In whatever shape water may be thrown down upon the earth—whether as rain or dew, as snow or hail—it must, at one time, have existed in the state of invisible vapour diffused through the atmosphere, and not to be distinguished from the air itself. However dry the air may appear to be, it always contains more or less of this moisture. Though not recognized by the senses, its presence is readily revealed by the behaviour of certain substances which greedily absorb moisture, and are consequently said to be *hygroscopic*.[1] Oil of vitriol, or sulphuric acid, for example, is one of these hygroscopic substances. If a bottle of this corrosive liquid be left without its stopper, it will be found that, after a few hours' exposure, the bulk and weight of the liquid have sensibly increased; indeed a pound of oil of vitrol may in this way become two pounds in the course of a few days. This increase of weight is due to moisture absorbed from the surrounding air, and, after exposure, the acid is consequently found to be weaker. When the air is damp, the increase of weight is rapid; when dry, the increase is but slow. Yet the liquid can never be exposed, even to the driest air, without absorbing some amount of moisture, how-

---

[1] *Hygroscopic*, from ὑγρὸς, *hugros*, moist.

ever small. It is clear, therefore, that the atmosphere must always contain aqueous vapour. Nor is it necessary to seek far for its source.

The damp towel on which you have just wiped your wet hands does not stand long on the towel-horse before it becomes dry again ; the water left forgotten in the flower-vase a week ago has completely dried away. In such cases the water passes imperceptibly as vapour into the surrounding air by a process termed *evaporation*. It is a quiet process, very different from the noisy production of vapour during *ebullition*, or boiling ; yet the same in its ultimate result. The general process of converting a liquid into a vapour, by any means whatever, may be called *vaporisation ;* and two modifications of this general process may be distinguished—evaporation and ebullition. Whilst ebullition takes place only when the liquid undergoing vaporisation reaches a definite temperature, called its *boiling point*, evaporation is a permanent process going on at all times and in all places. Every piece of open water, from the narrowest stream to the broadest sea, is constantly giving off vapour in greater or less volume. More vapour will be drawn into the air on a hot than on a cold day ; yet, on the coldest day, the process of evaporation is simply slackened, not stopped. Even a piece of ice, exposed to air at the freezing-point, gradually diminishes in size, showing that vapour is given off from the frozen surface. A fall of snow may be evaporated, just as a shower of rain is dried up, but the process is immeasurably slower. It is therefore by no means difficult to account for the watery vapour in the atmosphere. And it should be remembered that, in addition to that which reaches the air by direct evaporation from river, lake, and ocean, there is a good deal of water thrown into the atmosphere as vapour by the agency of living beings, exhaled from

F 2

the leaves of plants and from the lungs and skin of animals.
Decay, and other chemical phenomena likewise contribute
their quota to the moisture of the atmosphere. Evaporation,
however, remains the principal source of watery vapour in
the air.

It need hardly be said that the rapidity of evaporation
may be materially affected in a variety of ways. If you
wish to dry a damp object quickly, you at once place it
before the fire. Temperature, then, clearly affects the rate
of evaporation; the higher the temperature the quicker the
process, other conditions remaining the same. Again, the
rate of evaporation is greatly affected by the hygrometric
state of the air; in other words by the proportion of
moisture already present in the atmosphere. If the air
were perfectly dry, evaporation would be extremely rapid,
and the vapour greedily licked up ; if, on the other hand, the
air were thoroughly saturated with moisture, evaporation
would be utterly impossible. As a matter of fact we rarely,
if ever, experience either one or the other of these extreme
conditions ; but, between these extremes, there are any
number of intermediate states. Every laundress knows that
there are " good drying days " and bad ones. When there
is but little moisture in the air the clothes dry quickly ;
when there is much moisture, they dry but slowly. Let it
not be supposed, however, that the proportion of moisture
in the air is easily estimated by our sensations. True, we
say that one day is dry, and another damp ; but, after all, it
is not so much the absolute quantity of moisture in the air
as its relative humidity that determines these sensations ;
that is to say, it is the ratio of the vapour actually present
to the amount which would saturate the air at the given
temperature. The hotter the air the greater its capacity for
moisture, and consequently the air may seem dry, though

containing absolutely a large quantity of vapour. On the other hand, if the temperature be low, a small quantity of vapour may render the air damp, since it approaches nearer to the point of saturation. Hence the paradox that, in summer, dry as the air may feel, it usually contains more moisture than in winter, when it is popularly said to be damper.

Another condition affecting evaporation is the rapidity with which the air is renewed in the neighbourhood of the water to be evaporated. A windy day soon dries a wet pavement, the currents of air promoting evaporation. The air immediately around the damp object takes up vapour and soon receives its full complement, so as to prevent further evaporation ; but, when the air is disturbed, the portions which have become charged with vapour are rapidly removed and fresh ones brought into their place, which in turn become laden with vapour and are carried away to make room for others. It need hardly be said, too, that the rapidity of evaporation depends on the extent of the exposed surface of liquid. Ink dries up quickly in a wide-mouthed inkstand, but the same quantity may be preserved much longer in a narrow bottle. In fact, the vapour is derived only from the exposed *surface* of the liquid, and herein lies one of the great differences between evaporation and ebullition : in the rapid process of boiling, bubbles of vapour are generated throughout the mass of liquid, while, in the slow process of evaporation, the vapour is derived from the surface only.

Meteorologists occasionally measure the rapidity of evaporation by means of instruments called *atmometers*.[1] It is more useful however to determine the proportion of moisture

---

[1] *Atmometer*, from ἀτμὸs, *atmos*, vapour ; whence also *atmosphere*, the sphere of vapour or air.

in the atmosphere, and this determination is effected by
instruments termed *hygrometers.* The simplest but least
trustworthy of such instruments depend for their action on
the fact that organic structures readily absorb moisture and
change their dimensions ; a hair, for instance, is longer when
wet than when dry. Taking advantage of this fact De
Saussure constructed the simple little
instrument represented in Fig. 18. It
consists of a human hair free from
grease, stretched by a small weight,
and furnished with an index, moving
over a graduated arc. As the hair is
affected by moisture the index moves
over the scale, but its indications are
not sufficiently exact to be of much
scientific value. The instrument,
though still used in certain parts of
Europe, simply indicates the presence
of moisture without accurately measuring its amount; it is, in truth, a *hygroscope* rather than a *hygrometer.*[1] Cruder
even than this hair hygroscope is the
well-known toy in the form of a little
house with two doors, having the figure

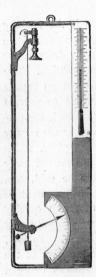

FIG. 18.—Hair hygrometer.

of a man at one door and of a woman
at the other. When the air is moist
and rain may be expected, the man comes out; when the
air is dry and the weather likely to be fine, the woman
makes her appearance. The movements of the figures

[1] Instruments having names terminated in *meter* (μέτρον, *metron,*
measure) are generally more exact in their indications than those terminated in *scope* (σκοπέω, *skopeo,* to view). Thus a *microscope* enables us
to see very minute objects, whilst a *micrometer* enables us to measure
them.

depend on the effect of moisture upon pieces of catgut or
of twisted string.

True hygrometers, or instruments for measuring humidity
with considerable precision, have been constructed by
Daniell, Regnault, and Mason, and are daily employed by
meteorologists. Some of these instruments effect their
purpose by indicating the dew-point directly, whilst others
depend for their indications on the rapidity of evaporation.
Daniell's hygrometer, a common in-
strument of the former class, is represented in Fig. 13, and described on p.
52. The form of hygrometer now
commonly used in this country is
known as Mason's *Dry-and-wet bulb
Thermometers*, a name sufficiently de-
scriptive of its construction. It consists,
in fact, of two thermometers, placed
side by side as represented in Fig. 19;
one of the instruments has its bulb
free, whilst the other is covered with
muslin, which is connected, by means
of a strand of cotton, with a small reservoir of water : the thread constantly
sucks up the liquid, just as the wick of
a candle draws up the melted wax or
tallow, and the bulb is, in this way,

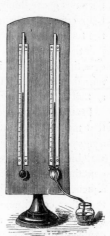

FIG. 19.— Dry and wet
bulb the. mometers.

constantly kept moist. Whenever a body passes from the
state of liquid to that of vapour heat is absorbed : hence
a little water dropped upon the hand gives rise to the sensation of cold as it evaporates; a sprinkling of *Eau de
Cologne*, or other liquid containing spirit of wine, produces
greater cold, since it is more volatile than water and dries
up much more rapidly; a little ether, again, being still

more volatile, reduces the temperature yet lower. The evaporation of the water from the wet bulb therefore lowers its temperature, and the more rapid the evaporation the greater will be this difference of temperature between the wet and the dry bulbs. If the air were saturated with moisture there could be no evaporation, and consequently the two thermometers would stand exactly alike. When, on the other hand, the air is very dry, evaporation becomes exceedingly rapid, and the temperature of the wet bulb consequently falls very low. From a comparison of the temperatures shown by the two thermometers, the dew-point, the relative humidity of the atmosphere, and the quantity of vapour in a given volume of air, can be determined by simple methods of calculation. Such an instrument as that just described is sometimes called a *Psychrometer*.[1]

From what has been advanced in this chapter, it is evident that more or less watery vapour is always to be found in the atmosphere; its presence is constant, but its proportion variable. It may perhaps be said that the air of England contains on an average something like $1\frac{1}{2}$ per cent. of aqueous vapour. This vapour is intimately associated with the other constituents of the atmosphere, all being gaseous bodies existing in a state of mechanical mixture. The composition of the atmosphere, however, is so important a subject that its full discussion must be reserved for the next chapter.

When the temperature of the air is sufficiently reduced in any given locality, the watery vapour which it contains condenses as a liquid, while the other constituents retain their gaseous state. The liquid drops of water thus condensed as rain are said to be *distilled*. In fact, the process carried on in nature is precisely similar in principle to the

[1] *Psychrometer*, from ψυχρὸς, *psuchros*, cold.

artificial process of distillation. If it is required to distil a liquid, the liquid is evaporated in a boiler, and the vapour conducted to the condenser, where it becomes sufficiently cooled to be deposited in drops. The natural process is effected, not by boiling the water over a fire, but by the heat of the sun, which quietly steals vapour from every exposed piece of water, and the vapour thus raised into the atmosphere is ultimately condensed as drops of rain. In artificial distillation, any solid matter which happens to be dissolved in the original liquid will be left behind in the boiler, and the liquid consequently distils over in a state of purity, excepting so far as it may be contaminated by the presence of volatile matters. Just such a purification of water is effected by the natural process of distillation. The sea, which covers so large a proportion of the earth's surface, offers a vast exposure of salt water to the heat of the sun ; yet the salt is left entirely behind and nothing but pure water evaporated. Fresh water is thus being constantly distilled from the briny ocean.

Thus, in seeking for the sources of the Thames, we are led from the springs of the earth to the rain of the heavens ; and from this to the watery vapour which forms part of the atmosphere ; and thence to the great caldron, the ocean, whence the heat of the sun distils that vapour. The great stream of fresh water which flows over Teddington Weir is fed, in large measure, by vapour which has been raised far away on the Atlantic. South and south-west winds sweeping across that ocean become highly charged with watery vapour; and these warm moist winds, striking the Cotteswold Hills, deposit their freight of moisture in showers of rain, much of which reaches the Thames basin. This water is ultimately carried out to sea by the flow of the river, and mingles once more with its parent ocean, but

only to be removed in due course by further evaporation.
The waters of the earth thus move in a continued cycle,
without beginning and without end. From rain to river,
from river to sea, from sea to air, and back again from air
to earth—such is the circuit in which every drop of water
is compelled to circulate. The observer, who, looking down
upon the Thames, watches the fresh water hurrying onward
to the sea, must remember that the sea is not its resting-
place, but that most of what he sees, perhaps all, will be
distilled afresh and return to the earth in showers which
may enter into the stream of Thames again ; or swell the
affluents of some river on the other side of the globe; or be
secreted for untold ages in subterranean reservoirs. In the
words of a wise man of old—"All the rivers run into the
sea ; yet the sea is not full ; unto the place from whence
the rivers come, thither they return again."

CHAPTER VI.

THE ATMOSPHERE.

EVERY one is familiar with the common phenomenon of a piece of metal being eaten away by rust. A plate of polished iron or steel, for example, exposed to a moist atmosphere, soon loses its brilliancy, gradually becoming coated with a dull reddish-brown rust; and this process of rusting, once set up, may go on until every particle of the original metal has disappeared. But let the same piece of bright metal be preserved in a vessel of pure water so as to avoid contact with air, and it may retain its lustre unimpaired for many years; thus suggesting that the air must be directly or indirectly connected with the phenomenon of rusting. It is easy to show, indeed, that many metals rapidly rust or tarnish when exposed to even the driest air. Cut a piece of lead or of zinc, and observe the lustre of its fresh surface; it is, in fact, almost as brilliant as a piece of polished silver, but this brilliancy is rapidly lost and the surface soon bedimmed on exposure to the atmosphere. On the other hand, there are many metals, such as gold, which never exhibit rust or tarnish, however long they may be exposed. Other metals, again, although they do not rust at ordinary temperatures, may be caused to rust more or less rapidly when exposed to the air at a high temperature. This is the case, for instance, with quicksilver. The rusting of this particular metal is worth closer study, since it was the means which led, about a century ago, to the discovery of the chemical composition of the atmosphere.

Quicksilver, or mercury, as seen in the weather-glass, is as brilliant as solid burnished silver, and this brilliancy is retained even after long exposure to air and moisture. But if the liquid metal be kept, for some time, at an elevated temperature in contact with air, small reddish scales slowly appear upon its surface, and ultimately the metal may be entirely converted into this substance. The red rust of mercury thus obtained is identical with a substance long known in pharmacy as "red precipitate,"—a substance which is prepared commercially by other processes more convenient and rapid than that of heating mercury.

It is especially notable that during the rusting of quick-silver, as indeed of all other metals, there is a very appreciable increase of weight in the substance operated on. A pound of metal produces considerably more than a pound of its rust. In point of fact, every 100 lbs. of quicksilver will produce not less than 108 lbs. of red rust. This increase of weight shows that, during the operation of rusting, some-thing must be absorbed by the metal; and as the mercury can be converted into rust when heated in contact with nothing but air, it is obvious that the additional matter must have been absorbed from the atmosphere. The nature of this absorbed matter may be determined by a simple experiment.

Let a small quantity of red precipitate, or rust of mercury, be strongly heated in a tube of hard glass, represented at A, Fig. 20. If the tube be heated for a sufficient time the red powder may entirely disappear. But by making a bend in the tube, as at B, you may catch anything that distils over; and it will be found, at the end of the experiment, that this part of the tube contains metallic mercury. If 108 grains of the red powder be heated in A, you may obtain in B 100 grains of the liquid metal; in other words, you have expelled all the matter which has been absorbed from the atmosphere during the process of rusting, and have regained the original weight of quicksilver. The matter which has been thus expelled from the powder by heat need not be lost; for by attaching to the apparatus a tube C, which dips

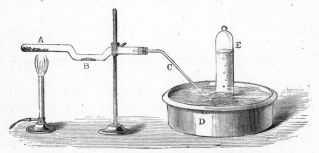

FIG. 20.—Decomposition of red oxide of mercury.

beneath water in a vessel D, it will be found, on heating the powder in A, that bubbles of gas rise in the water; and these bubbles may be conveniently collected in the bell-jar E. In this way you obtain a colourless and transparent gaseous body, not to be distinguished by the eye from ordinary air. Yet you have only to plunge a lighted taper into it in order to see at once that you are dealing with something distinct from common air. The taper burns in it with unusual brilliancy; and even if extinguished before entering the gas, so that only the merest point remains in a state of glow, this glowing point will be rekindled and the taper burst again into full flame. The gas is, in fact, what is known to chemists as *Oxygen*. The red powder is a combination of this oxygen with mercury, and is known therefore as *red oxide of mercury* or *mercuric oxide*. When strongly heated, it is completely decomposed or split up into its constituents; every 108 grains of the red oxide yielding 100 grains of metallic mercury and 8 grains of the gas oxygen.

It was on the 1st of August, 1774, that oxygen was originally discovered by Dr. Priestley. He obtained it from the red mercurial powder just as we have obtained it, excepting that he heated the powder by means of a large burning glass. Various other methods were soon discovered for obtaining the gas, and its properties were fully examined, especially by the Swedish chemist, Scheele, and the French chemist, Lavoisier. It was Lavoisier who gave to this curious kind of air or gas the name of *Oxygen*[1] by which it is now universally known; and it was he, too, who first showed, by the most conclusive experiments, what was really the composition of atmospheric air. His determination of the constitution of the air was made in the year 1777. It is therefore only within the last century that chemists have become acquainted with the exact nature of so common a body as the air we breathe.

Lavoisier took a weighed quantity of mercury and exposed it to strong heat in a vessel containing a confined volume of atmospheric air. In the course of twelve days the metal was completely calcined, or converted into the red rust or oxide. During this conversion the air diminished in bulk while the quicksilver increased in weight; in fact, the

---

[1] *Oxygen*, from ὀξὺς, *oxus*, acid; γεννάω, *gennao*, to produce; a name based on the supposition that substances burnt in oxygen always produce acid compounds.

mercury had taken oxygen from the air, and combined with it to form the red oxide, from which, by stronger heating, the oxygen gas could easily be recovered in a state of purity. It remained, however, to inquire what was the character of the air left in the vessel which had been thus robbed of its oxygen. On plunging a taper into the residual air it was at once extinguished; and on introducing a living animal into the air, the creature was suffocated. The latter property suggested to Lavoisier the propriety of giving to this foul kind of air the name of *Azote;*[1]—a name which it still retains in France, but which has been superseded elsewhere by the term *Nitrogen.*[2]

On accurately examining a given measure of atmospheric air, it was found that it contained about one-fifth its bulk of the gas oxygen and four-fifths of nitrogen. To speak with more accuracy, 100 volumes of pure air contain 20·8 vols. of oxygen and 79·2 vols. of nitrogen. If instead of a given *volume*, or measure, a given *weight* of air is examined, it will be found that 100 parts by weight—whether grains, ounces, or pounds—contain 23 of these parts of oxygen and 77 of nitrogen.

Before proceeding to examine more closely into the composition of atmospheric air it may be well to note the characters of the two constituents into which it has just been seen that air may be resolved. In most of the chemical phenomena in which atmospheric air takes part it is the oxygen which is the active agent. It has been shown that a glowing taper bursts into flame when plunged into oxygen. In like manner sulphur, phosphorus, charcoal, even iron-wire, will burn with great vigour in this gas;

[1] *Azote*, from the Greek privative ά, and ζωή, *zoe*, life.
[2] *Nitrogen*, from *nitre*, in consequence of nitrogen being a constituent of the salt called nitre or saltpetre.

the combustible substances in all cases combining with the
oxygen to form oxides. Some of these oxides are solid
substances, whilst others are gaseous. Every act of combustion in air depends on the presence of oxygen. When
a piece of magnesium wire burns with its dazzling splendour,
the metal combines with the oxygen of the air to form
oxide of magnesium or *magnesia*, which, after the combus-
thus is left behind as a light white solid substance. When
a piece of charcoal burns in air, the solid disappears, with
exception of a little ash ; the charcoal has, in fact, combined
with oxygen to form an oxide which is an invisible gas known
as *carbon dioxide* or more commonly as *carbonic acid.* All
our ordinary combustibles—such as coal, wood, oil, tallow,
and wax—contain a large proportion of carbon ; and, consequently this gas is produced in considerable volume
during their combustion. In like manner, the respiration of
animals depends upon the presence of oxygen in the
medium by which they are surrounded, whether air or
water. A kind of slow combustion goes on in the body ;
and the oxygen, taken into the system through either lungs
or gills, is, in part, consumed in the formation of carbonic
acid gas,which is expelled through the same organs. Oxygen
is therefore as needful to support animal life as to support
flame, and hence it was at one time known as "vital air."
After death, again, the matter which was once living is
subject to a process of oxidation or slow combustion, by
which it is converted, for the most part, into compounds
which contain a larger proportion of oxygen. Oxygen is
therefore essential to the maintenance of combustion, respiration, decay, and many other natural and artificial processes
in daily operation. In pure oxygen, all these actions would
be carried on with undue energy, and the nitrogen of the air
plays an important part in tempering the activity of the oxygen

with which it is associated. This nitrogen is remarkable for its inertness; it extinguishes flame and it does not support life : yet it kills, not by being absolutely poisonous, but simply by excluding oxygen. A fresh supply of air is therefore constantly required by a living animal, not because the nitrogen is deadly, but because the needful oxygen is absent.

But although nitrogen is not a dangerous gas, there are other gaseous bodies always present in the atmosphere which in a pure state are active poisons. Let a saucer of clear lime-water be exposed to the air, and in a few hours the surface of the liquid will be covered with a thin pellicle of whitish matter ; this is produced by something absorbed from the atmosphere, yet neither oxygen nor nitrogen produces the effect. It is due, indeed, to the presence of the gaseous substance to which reference has already been made under the name of *carbonic acid gas ;* this gas, acting on the lime-water, forms a solid carbonate of calcium, or, as it is more commonly termed, carbonate of lime ; and it is this white solid substance which forms the thin skin on the surface of the water. Carbonic acid gas, which is thus proved to exist in the atmosphere, is a compound of two distinct substances—carbon and oxygen. The oxygen has been already described : the *carbon* is a solid body abundantly distributed through nature, though rarely occurring in a state of purity. In its purest native form, it crystallises as the diamond ; in a less pure condition it constitutes graphite or " black-lead ; " and, in chemical combination with other substances, it forms a large proportion of coal and of all other ordinary forms of fuel. It enters largely, too, into the constitution of all living matter, whether animal or vegetable ; and it is left in a tolerably pure state when these substances are charred or imperfectly burnt, as in coke, wood-charcoal, animal-charcoal, &c. During all the processes of combustion, respiration, and decay, this carbon combines with the oxygen of the air to form carbonic acid, and hence this gas is constantly being poured into the atmosphere. Breathe through a straw into a glass of clear lime-water, and you will see that the liquid becomes milky as the carbonic acid gas expired or breathed out from your lungs bubbles through the previously limpid liquid. If you then pour a little vinegar into the cloudy liquid, the milkiness immediately clears up, because the acid dissolves the solid white carbonate of lime which had been formed by your breath. Carbonic acid gas is set free by the action of the vinegar; and, if there is enough of the solid carbonate in the lime-water, you may actually see the gas escaping in little bubbles. This bubbling, or effervescence, is likewise produced when vinegar, or almost any other acid, is poured upon an egg-shell or an oyster-shell, upon a piece of chalk or limestone or marble. All these substances consist, in truth, of carbonate of lime, and are decomposed by the acid with evolution of carbonic acid gas. If Cleopatra ever dissolved the pearl, as the story tells, or Hannibal softened the rocks of the Alps with vinegar, a chemical decomposition was effected exactly like that just described. In consequence of the gas being thus, as it were, bound in various solid substances, its discoverer, Dr. Black of Edinburgh, bestowed upon it the name of *fixed air*. A taper plunged into this air is at once extinguished, and an animal is suffocated. Hence the great necessity of duly renewing the air in dwelling rooms. And it is obvious that, the greater the number of people in the room, and the greater the number of gas-burners, lamps, or candles alight, the more need is there of efficient ventilation.

As carbonic acid gas is being constantly produced by

such processes as combustion and respiration, it is clear that
the proportion of this gas in the atmosphere must vary
locally, being, for example, higher in a crowded space than
in the open country. The average proportion of carbonic
acid in the air may be estimated at from ·03 to ·04 per
cent. by volume; thus ten thousand gallons of air will
contain between three and four gallons of carbonic acid.
Dr. Angus Smith has published, in his work on " Air and
Rain," a large number of analyses of air from various
localities, with the view of determining the variation in
the proportion of carbonic acid; and, from his analyses,
the following examples are selected :—

Percentage of Carbonic Acid in Air.

On the Thames at London, mean, ...	·0343
In the streets of London, ,, ...	·0380
From the top of Ben Nevis	·0327
From the Queen's ward, St. Thomas's Hospital . .	·0400
From the Haymarket Theatre, dress circle, at 11.30 P.M.	·0757
From Chancery Court, 7 feet from ground . . .	·1930
From Underground Railway, mean, ...	·1452
From workings in mines, average of 339 samples .	·7850
Largest amount in a Cornish mine	2·5000

These figures express *percentages*, but it is obvious that
they may be read as whole numbers *per million*. For
example, instead of saying that air from the streets of
London contains on an average ·0380 per cent., it may
be said that a million gallons of the air contain 380
gallons of carbonic acid; that a million gallons of air from
the Thames contain 343 gallons of the gas; and so on.

Since the atmosphere is constantly receiving vast volumes
of carbonic acid from various sources, it might not un-

naturally be assumed that this gas would unduly accumulate, and at length vitiate the entire bulk of the atmosphere. Such accumulation is, however, prevented by the action of living plants. To show that so small a proportion of carbonic acid in the atmosphere as 0·035 per cent. is sufficient to supply the vegetable world with its carbon, it is simply necessary to calculate the weight of this gas in the atmosphere resting on a square mile of land. The weight of air on this area is about 59,012,997,120 lbs., (or 26,345,088 tons), and the carbonic acid which it contains weighs not less than 13,800 tons. The weight of carbon in this carbonic acid is about 3,700 tons. The carbonic acid, so injurious to the animal, is the source whence ordinary plants derive the whole of the carbon in their structure. Wood, for example, contains about half its weight of carbon; yet every particle of carbon in a forest of trees has been derived from the gaseous carbonic acid invisibly distributed through the surrounding atmosphere.[1]

Before leaving the subject of carbonic acid, it should be remarked that this gas is one of great density, being in fact about half as heavy again as an equal bulk of atmospheric air. It might, therefore, not unfairly be assumed that the carbonic acid in the atmosphere would tend to settle down in a stratum near the ground. If we shake up a mixture of liquids of different densities—say mercury, water, and oil—the liquids soon settle down, after agitation, in the order of their relative weights; the heavy quicksilver sinking to the bottom, and the light oil floating on the top of the water. Such a separation does not however take place when *gases* of different densities are mixed. The following table shows the densities, or specific gravities, of the three gases which compose the atmosphere :—

[1] This subject will be further discussed in Chapter XIV

Nitrogen . . . . 0·9713
Oxygen . . . . . 1·1056
Carbonic-acid gas . . 1·5203

The term *specific gravity* is used to denote the weights of
equal bulks of different kinds or species of matter, compared
with some known standard. Air is the standard used in the
comparison just made, and it is seen from the figures that
if a given bulk of atmospheric air weighs 100 pounds, then
the same bulk of nitrogen weighs 97 pounds; the same
volume of oxygen 110 pounds, and of carbonic acid 152
pounds. Hence it might be assumed that the atmosphere
would consist of three strata or layers (like the mixture of
quicksilver, water, and oil), with the nitrogen as the top
layer, and the carbonic acid at the bottom. As a matter of
fact, however, this is not the case. All gases tend to inter-
mingle with each other, so that when different gases are
mixed they soon produce a uniform mixture, in spite of
differences in their relative weights; in fact, the particles of
the heavy gas rise and the particles of the light gas fall,
until they are completely diffused through each other. In
consequence of this property, the composition of the
atmosphere is kept practically uniform, although local
variations, within narrow limits, may be detected.

In addition to the oxygen, nitrogen, and carbonic acid, the
atmosphere always contains other constituents, but only in
subordinate and variable proportions. The gas called *ammonia*, well known as the pungent gas which escapes from
"spirit of hartshorn," is constantly present in the air, being
indeed evolved from decomposing animal and vegetable
matter. Yet the proportion of ammonia is always excessively
small; for example, twenty grains have been obtained from a
million cubic feet (or 536 million grains) of air. This ammonia

is a compound of nitrogen with a gas called hydrogen, which
will be described in the next chapter; it is necessary however
to refer briefly, in this place, to the composition of ammonia,
since this gas, though present in only such minute proportion,
directly or indirectly furnishes to plants a large part of
their nitrogen, just as the carbonic acid gas supplies them
with their carbon.   Traces of *nitric acid*, the substance
known commonly as *aquafortis*, are occasionally found in the
atmosphere, especially after thunderstorms; this nitric acid
readily combines with the ammonia to form nitrate of ammonia, the presence of which may frequently be detected in
rain water. *Sulphuretted hydrogen*, an offensive gas given
off during the putrefaction of animal and vegetable matter,
may also be often found in the air; and a few other gases
are sometimes present, especially in air taken from the
neighbourhood of large towns.   Nor should mention be
omitted of the *organic germs*, which constantly float in
the atmosphere, but of which it is beyond our present purpose to speak.   As to the *watery vapour*, which is ever
present in the air, it is unnecessary to say anything here,
since the subject was fully discussed in the last Chapter.

This watery vapour differs from the other constituents of
the atmosphere principally in the ease with which it may be
condensed or liquefied.   Hence it is generally called a
vapour rather than a *gas*.   Yet there is really but little
distinction between the two classes of bodies; a vapour
being nothing more than an easily-condensible gas.   Steam,
for example, is liquefied by a comparatively slight reduction
of temperature, while carbonic acid and a number of other
gases require a great reduction of temperature or a great
pressure, or even a combination of cold and pressure, in
order to assume the liquid form; and, until quite recently,
several of the gases had resisted all attempts to liquefy

them, and were therefore termed *permanent gases*. In
the closing months of 1877, however, M. M. Pictet and
Cailletet succeeded in bringing even the most refractory
gases, such as oxygen, hydrogen, and nitrogen, into the
liquid state.

When a liquid is evaporated, or converted into gas or
vapour, it undergoes a great increase of bulk, but its *weight*
remains unaffected. A pound of water, for example, produces neither more nor less than a pound of steam. It is
clear, therefore, that gases and vapours, although generally
invisible, must possess weight; but this weight is necessarily
small compared with that of the same bulk of matter in
the liquid or solid state. Atmospheric air is, in fact, about
800 times lighter than an equal bulk of water, and as much
as 11,000 times lighter than an equal volume of quicksilver.
Yet the weight of air, small as it seems, amounts to something considerable when we are dealing with a large bulk,
or even with such a quantity as is contained in an ordinary
dwelling-room. It is found by actual weighing that 100
cubic inches of air, under ordinary conditions, weigh about
31 grains; in other words, it requires 13 cubic feet of air to
weigh a pound avoirdupois. Suppose then that we have a
room measuring 10 feet long, 10 feet wide, and 10 feet high:
this will contain 1,000 cubic feet of air, and the weight of
this air will be about 77 pounds. But the room just taken
is a very small one, and if the calculation be extended
to a large public building it will be found that the air
which it contains weighs more than is commonly imagined.
Thus, Westminster Hall has a length of 290 feet, a
width of 68 feet, and a height of 110 feet; its contents
must therefore be 2,169,200 cubic feet, and the weight of
the air in this hall reaches the enormous amount of nearly
75 *tons !*

Since air possesses weight, it necessarily presses upon any object exposed to its influence. The atmosphere forms an ocean of air bathing the entire earth; and, on the floor of this ocean, man, in common with all terrestrial beings, has his dwelling. Everything around us on the earth's surface must therefore bear the pressure of the air above, just as anything on the bed of the ocean is pressed upon by the superincumbent water. The depth, or rather the height, of this aërial sea has never been determined, but there are reasons for believing that the atmosphere extends to at least 50 miles upwards from the earth's surface. Hence it is clear that all terrestrial objects must be subjected to enormous pressure. The roof of a house, for example, has to bear the pressure of a column of air resting upon its surface and extending upwards to the limit of the atmosphere. Now, it is found that our atmosphere exerts a pressure of nearly 15 lbs. (14·73 lbs.) on every exposed square inch of surface. The roof is consequently pressed upon by a weight of many tons. Yet the most delicate structure may be freely exposed to the atmosphere without the slightest danger of being crushed. This arises from the fact that *fluids*[1] transmit pressure in a manner entirely different from that in which it is transmitted by solid bodies. A solid presses downwards only, but a fluid presses equally in all directions, upwards as well as downwards. The air in a room, for instance, presses on the ceiling not less than on the floor; and on each of the walls not less than on the ceiling. Under ordinary conditions, therefore, the atmosphere has no power to crush, because its pressure downwards is exactly neutralised by

---

[1] *Fluid*, from *fluo*, I flow; a term embracing both *liquids* and *gases* or *vapours*, since the particles of both classes of bodies flow freely over each other.

its pressure upwards. Extend your hand, and you feel no
pressure, though it is certain that every square inch of its
surface bears a pressure of nearly 15 lbs., and the entire
hand must therefore sustain a very large total pressure;
but the weight upon the upper surface is counteracted by
the upward pressure of the air on the under surface, the
two equal and opposite pressures neutralising each other.
Nor is there any tendency for the hand to be crushed
between these opposing pressures, for the air and other
fluids in the vessels and various tissues of the body press
equally in all directions, so that any pressure from without
is perfectly counterbalanced by an equal pressure from
within. The thinnest soap-bubble sails safely through the
air, though its outer surface must sustain a pressure of
many pounds; the elasticity of the air within the bubble
causes it to press forcibly against the inner wall, and thus
resist the external atmospheric pressure, and effectually
prevent collapse. In the common toy known as "Jack
in the Box" a spring inside the figure presses upwards
against the lid when tightly shut down; and in like manner
the walls of a closed vessel containing air are pressed
outwards by the elastic force of the confined air. If the
air be removed from the interior of a closed vessel, so as
to leave a space altogether empty or vacuous, the pressure
of the external atmosphere becomes at once evident, since
it is no longer counterbalanced by any force from within;
a thin glass vessel, for example, may easily be shattered by
sucking the air from its interior.

It is easy to measure the amount of this atmospheric
pressure by a simple experiment, first made in 1643, by an
Italian philosopher named Torricelli. Take a glass tube,
rather more than 30 inches in length, closed at one end
and open at the other; fill this tube with quicksilver, and

closing the open end with the thumb, as shown in the right-hand figure of Fig. 21, invert it in a basin of mercury so that the open end may dip beneath the liquid ; it will

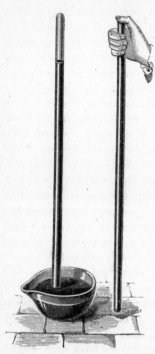

then be found that the mercury falls for a short distance in the tube, but that a column about 30 inches in length remains suspended, as shown in the left-hand figure. Torricelli argued that this column must be supported by the pressure of the external atmosphere on the surface of the mercury ; the downward pressure of the column of mercury being exactly balanced by the upward pressure of the atmosphere transmitted through the quicksilver. Indeed, if we admit air by making a hole in the top of the tube, the column immediately falls, since it is then pressed down by the atmosphere above; but when the tube is closed there is no atmospheric pressure on the top within the tube, for the

FIG. 21.—Torricelli's experiment.

space above the column of mercury is completely empty, or rather contains only mercurial vapour, whence it is called the *Torricellian vacuum.* Since the column of mercury inside is balanced by the atmosphere without, it follows that if we know the weight of the mercury we know also the weight of a column of air standing on a similar base and extending upwards to the extreme limit of the atmosphere. Now a column of mercury 30 inches long, in a tube of one square inch in sectional area, weighs about 15 lbs.; hence it is found, as before stated, that the weight or pressure of the atmosphere is about 15 lbs. on every square inch.

If instead of using a dense liquid, like mercury, the experimentalist took a lighter one, such as water, he would naturally expect that the column required to balance the weight of the external atmosphere would be proportionally longer. As a matter of fact it is found that, when water is used, the suspended column is something like 33 feet in length : in other words, as water is about $13\frac{1}{2}$ times lighter than mercury, bulk for bulk, the column of water will be about $13\frac{1}{2}$ times longer than the mercurial column. It was indeed, by observing a body of water raised in the suction pipe of a pump at Florence, that Torricelli was led to his experiment with quicksilver. In working a common pump, air is sucked out of the tube communicating with the source of water below, and the pressure of the atmosphere then forces the water up the pipe in order to supply the place of the air which has been removed. But, when the pipe reaches a length of more than about 30 feet, the column of water which it contains balances the atmospheric pressure, and consequently if the tube be longer than this no more water rises, and the pump ceases to act. In seeking to find out why water cannot rise higher, Torricelli was led to make the experiment to which reference has been made, and to construct the instrument which is represented on the left-hand side of Fig. 21. It is called a *Barometer*.[1]

---

[1] *Barometer*, from βάρος, *baros*, weight, and μέτρον, *metron*, measure; an instrument for measuring the weight of the atmosphere. *Thermometer*, from θερμός, *thermos*, hot; an instrument for measuring temperature.

Various forms have been given to the barometer, but with the exception of the *aneroid*[1]—an entirely distinct instrument—they all depend on the same principle, namely, that of causing a column of liquid to be balanced against the weight of the atmosphere. Almost any liquid may be employed, but as a matter of convenience, mercury is the only substance in common use.[2]

As the pressure of the atmosphere in any given locality varies from day to day, and even from hour to hour, the height of the mercurial column is subject to corresponding fluctuation. The great use of the barometer, in fact, is to indicate these changes of atmospheric pressure—changes which are of vast importance to the meteorologist, since they are related to general changes in the weather. Not that the barometer forms a " weather-glass " as popularly understood: it does not indicate absolutely the character of the forth-coming weather, and the indications given on the dial of common instruments are scarcely of any scientific value. But still the changes in atmospheric pressure point to changes in the winds ; and these are the prime movers in effecting changes in our weather. Hence, the readings of the barometer form the chief element in the weather-charts and reports issued of late by most of the London daily papers, and as these are forced every morning upon the

[1] *Aneroid*, from the privative *à*, and νηρὸς, *neros*, moist ; an instrument in which the pressure of the atmosphere acts upon a thin elastic metal case, the movements of which are transmitted to a dial.

[2] Water-barometers have occasionally been constructed, but their great length renders them unwieldy, and they are also open to other objections. One of these instruments may be seen in the Museum of Practical Geology in Jermyn Street. Glycerine has also been used by Mr. J. B. Jordan, as may be seen in an instrument erected by him at South Kensington. But for all ordinary purposes mercury is invariably used.

reader's attention it may be worth while to explain the kind
of information which they give, and how they are to be
interpreted.

Fig. 22 is a reproduction of the weather-chart given in the

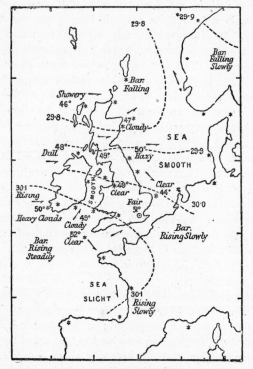

Fig. 22.—*Times* weather chart.

Times of to-day (March 31, 1877), and it shows the state
of the weather at 6 P.M. yesterday. The most striking
feature in the chart is the series of dotted curved lines,

which are called *isobars*.[1] An isobar is simply a line con-
necting all those places which have, at a given time, the
same barometric pressure. Thus the first isobaric line,
reckoning from the bottom of the chart, passes through the
south of Ireland and the south-west of England, and then
sweeps in a bold curve through France into the Bay of
Biscay. At all points along this course the barometer stood
at 30·1 inches, as indicated by the figures at each extremity
of the curve. The next isobar, passing across the north of
Ireland and England, is marked 30 inches, so that between
the two lines there is a difference of pressure equal to that
of one-tenth of an inch of mercury. Another isobar
stretches across Scotland, and indicates a pressure of 29·9
inches; and the last curve on the chart is drawn through
the north of Scotland, where the mercury stood at 29·8
inches. The chart therefore shows at a glance the distribution of atmospheric pressure over the area represented,
and from this we can learn a good deal about the character
of the winds. Between two successive isobars there is a
difference of pressure represented by one-tenth of an inch
of mercury, and the distance between these two lines gives
us the *gradient*. This term is familiar enough in engineer-
ing; if a railroad, for example, rises one foot for every
100 feet of distance, the line is said to have a "gradient" of
1 in 100. The gradient is therefore the engineer's expression for the slope of the ground; in like manner it is the
meteorologist's expression for what has been called the slope
of the atmosphere. Only, in talking about meteorological
gradients, it must be borne in mind that the vertical
scale is measured in hundredths of an inch of barometric
pressure, while the horizontal scale is measured in miles of
distance, the unit being one degree, or 60 nautical miles.

[1] *Isobar*, from ίσος, *isos*, equal; and βάρος, *baros*, weight.

Hence a gradient of 4 means that over a distance of 60 nautical miles the barometer rises $\frac{4}{100}$ or $\frac{1}{25}$ of an inch. If the isobars run close together it shows that the gradient is high, and therefore the winds will be strong; if they are wide apart the gradient is low, and the winds are light. Thus, in Fig. 22, the isobars indicate only light winds.

Although much may be learnt about winds by studying the isobaric lines, it must not be supposed that the air blows *directly* from regions of high pressure to those of low pressure. Prof. Buys Ballot of Utrecht has however laid down a law which gives the exact relation of winds to pressure, and which may be thus expressed : " Stand with your back to the wind, and the barometer will be lower on your left hand than on your right." Thus expressed, however, the law is true only for the northern hemisphere ; in the southern it will be reversed, the barometer being lower on the right hand than on the left. The same principle may be enunciated in another form. If you stand with the high barometer to your right and the low barometer to your left, the wind will blow on your back. The course of the isobars in the chart therefore indicates the *direction* of the wind, just as the distances between these lines indicate its *strength*.[1] Every Thursday the *Times* issues a weather diagram giving a graphic representation of the meteorology of the week, sufficiently explained, however, by the description which is annexed to it.

Whilst the *Times* publishes daily charts with isobaric curves, the other morning papers give their meteorological reports in different shapes. Fig. 23 is copied from the *Daily News* of to-day (March 31, 1877). It represents

[1] The arrows on Fig. 22 fly with the wind ; the asterisks indicate the position of meteorological stations ; and the figures give the shade temperature. For further information see Mr. Scott's " Weather Charts." 1876.

the upper part of the scale of the barometer, ranging from 29 inches to 30½ inches. The height of the mercury is seen at a glance by the thick black lines, and we thus not only learn what it was in London at 1 A.M. on the morning of issue, but can compare this with the readings for the same hour on the three preceding days. Thus it is seen that on the 31st, the barometer stood at about 30·05 inches; on the 30th, it was 29·86; on the 29th, 29·81; and, on the 28th, it stood at 29·58 inches. It is evident, therefore, from

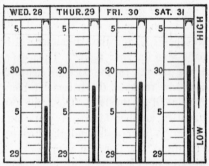

Corrected to sea-level, and reduced to 32°F.

Fɪɢ. 23.—*Daily News* barometer chart.

this report that the mercury has been steadily rising. Such comparative readings are of great value, inasmuch as the character of the weather is dependent, not so much on the absolute height of the barometer, as on whether the mercury is rising or falling, and whether moving slowly or rapidly. It should be added that the recent barometer charts of the *Daily News* indicate the extreme variations of the instrument by means of dotted lines.

The barometer chart published by the *Daily Telegraph*

for the same day is given in Fig. 24. This shows, by a
graphic method, the movements of the barometer for four
days, ending at midnight of March 30-31. The thick
curved line, running across the diagram, represents the
variations of the mercurial column, and it is seen, as before,
that the barometer has been slowly rising; the line taking,
in fact, a steady upward course from 29·15 to 30·06 inches.
It should be explained that, in all these charts, the actual
reading of the barometer has been reduced to certain
standards, in order to secure the requisite uniformity for

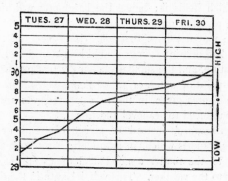

FIG. 24.—*Daily Telegraph* barometer chart.

comparison. These corrections refer to the height at
which the instrument is placed, and to the temperature at
which the reading is taken. It is obvious that the barometer will be affected by its height above the sea-level; for,
as we ascend, we leave a portion of the atmosphere below
us, and, consequently, the pressure is lessened and the
mercury falls. Hence a barometer at the top of a house
always reads lower than one on the basement; the instrument is, indeed, often used for the approximate measurement
of heights. Barometric readings from different stations

H

cannot therefore be compared together until we know
at what elevations the instruments are situated ; one observer
may live on high ground and another on low, one may have
his barometer up stairs and another down stairs.   Hence it
has come to be understood that all barometric readings
shall be reduced to what they would be if the instrument
were at the sea-level, which gives, of course, a fixed datum
line.   Then, again, the barometer needs correction for
temperature.   Mercury, in common with other liquids,
expands by heat, and expands much more than the glass
tube which holds it ; hence the barometer will rise on a
hot day and fall on a cold day, although the atmospheric
pressure may not have changed.   It is essential therefore
that all barometric readings should be reduced to the same
temperature, and the standard taken for this purpose is the
freezing-point of water, or 32° of Fahrenheit's thermometer.
All the figures given in the newspaper charts are consequently reduced to sea-level and to 32°.

The *Standard*, instead of giving diagrams or charts,
publishes reports which, in addition to barometric readings,
convey to the reader a good deal of useful information
relating to the weather.   This will be seen in the following
example extracted from to-day's issue (March 31st, 1877) :—

Date.	Barometer reduced to Sea Level, and 32° F.	Direction of Wind.	Dry Bulb.	Wet Bulb.	During the past 24 hours.			
					Max. Solar Radia. in Vac.	Max. Shade Temp.	Min. Temp.	Rain-fall.
Mar. 25	29˙09	ESE.	50	45	—	55	44	1˙01
,, 26	29˙19	SSE	47	45	—	48	38	—
,, 27	29˙43	N	45	43	—	54	42	0˙23
,, 28	29˙87	W	50	47	—	57	41	0˙18
,, 29	29˙90	NW	54	49	—	59	44	—
,, 30	30˙13	NNE	51	47	—	55	48	0˙47

₄ At Two A.M. the Barometer had risen to 30˙17.

This gives the readings of the barometer for six consecutive days, taken daily at 7 P.M., and duly corrected as just explained. The table also gives the direction of the wind at the same hour each day; and indicates the humidity of the atmosphere, by a comparison of the wet and dry bulbs of Mason's hygrometer, represented in Fig. 19. It likewise gives the highest and lowest temperature during the day, and the depth of rain which had fallen in the course of the twenty-four hours. The column left blank, but headed " Maximum solar radiation *in vacuo*," is intended to receive the readings of a radiation thermometer. This generally consists of a delicate thermometer, having a dull, blackened bulb, and inclosed in a glass tube, from which the air has been removed. The instrument is freely exposed to the heat of the sun, and its maximum reading is registered. The greatest amount of solar radiation which occurs during the day is then indicated by the excess of this temperature over the maximum temperature of the air in the shade.

Although, in this chapter, the subject of atmospheric pressure has been dwelt upon at some length, it must not be supposed that we have travelled away from our specific purpose—the study of the basin of the Thames. It has been pointed out that differences of atmospheric pressure give rise to the winds, and the character of the winds determines the supply of atmospheric moisture by which the river is fed. It is, therefore, hardly too much to say that, in the long run, the flow of the Thames is regulated by the changes in the atmosphere which are registered by the barometer.

Moreover, every phenomenon of oxidation and combustion and the well-being, and even the very existence, of every living thing upon the surface of the Thames basin are absolutely dependent upon the composition of the air which covers it.

CHAPTER VII.

THE CHEMICAL COMPOSITION OF PURE WATER.

HAD the question, "What is water?" been asked a century ago, the wisest chemist of the day could have returned no answer, save that which might have been given thousands of years earlier. He would have replied, in short, that water, like air, is one of the elementary principles of Nature. And, yet, there had not been altogether wanting observations which suggested that, after all, water might not be a simple substance. Thus, the sagacity of Sir Isaac Newton led him to infer from his optical studies, that water might consist of ingredients which were unlike each other, and that one or more of these might be inflammable. Such conjectures, however, could not be verified until considerable advance had been made in chemical science; and it was reserved for the chemists of the last quarter of the eighteenth century, soon after they had determined the composition of atmospheric air, to demonstrate the true chemical constitution of water. Cavendish and Watt in this country, and Lavoisier in France, not to mention other chemists, have been put forward as competitors for this honour, but the weight of evidence appears strongly in favour of the claims of Cavendish. With-

out entering, however, into the famous " water controversy,"
let us see what are the simplest means by which the
composition of so common a substance may be ascertained.

In these days of electric telegraphy every one is familiar
with the instrument known as the *galvanic* or *voltaic battery*.

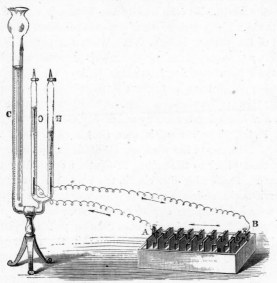

FIG. 25.—Decomposition of water by electricity.

In the year 1800, Messrs. Nicholson and Carlisle discovered
that, when a current of electricity from a galvanic battery is
sent through water, the liquid is at once split up into its
constituents.   Fig. 25 represents an ingenious apparatus,
devised by Dr. Hofmann, for effecting this decomposition.
It consists of a U-shaped tube of glass, OH, connected

with a long upright tube C, which springs from the base of
the U. Each limb of the U-tube has, at the top, an orifice,
closed by a stopcock. This tube, and part of the ascending tube, are filled with water, made slightly sour
by addition of a little oil of vitriol in order to render it a
better conductor of electricity ; but, it should be borne in
mind, that the acid does not otherwise affect the result of
the experiment. In each limb of the U-tube is a piece of
platinum, which communicates, by means of a wire, with one
end of the galvanic battery, AB. When the battery is in
action, a current of electricity passes in the direction indicated
by the arrows. Starting from one end A of the battery, it
passes through the wire to the tube O, where it enters the
water through the platinum plate. This plate forms one of
the *electrodes* [1] or entrances by which the electricity reaches
the liquid. The current is then conducted through the
acidulated water to the platinum electrode in the tube H,
and thence back to the battery at B, thus completing the
circuit. But, during this circuit, the current has wrought
a curious change in the water through which it has passed.
As soon indeed as the electric current traverses the liquid,
streams of little bubbles rise from the two platinum plates,
and the gases thus produced accumulate in the upper part
of the closed tubes, whilst the displaced liquid is forced
into the tube C, where the column consequently rises.

These bubbles of gas result from the decomposition of
the water. The electricity, in fact, splits the water into two
distinct kinds of matter, both gaseous ; one gas appearing at
the pole where the current enters, and the other gas where
it leaves the water. Our apparatus enables us to collect
each constituent separately and to examine its properties.
On opening the stopcock at the top of the limb O, the

---

[1] *Electrode*, from ὁδός, *hodos*, a way ; otherwise called the pole.

head of water in C will force the gas out of the narrow
orifice, and it can be examined as it escapes. On applying
a match with its end in a state of glow, it bursts suddenly
into flame, and burns vividly (Fig. 26), just as it did in the
oxygen described in the last chapter; we have in fact now
obtained *oxygen* by the decomposition of water. On applying a flame to the gas which issues from the other tube, H,
it catches fire and burns with a pale flame; this is the gas
which was formerly known as *inflammable air*, and is now
called *hydrogen*.[1] The longer the current of electricity is

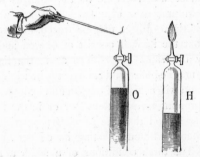

FIG. 26.—Oxygen and hydrogen from decomposition of water.

allowed to pass, the more oxygen and hydrogen are
generated; and, if the current could be continued for a
sufficient time, all the water might be thus decomposed,
and resolved into these two gases. This experiment therefore shows that pure water consists of oxygen and hydrogen.
But it teaches more than this. You cannot fail to observe,
from the figures, that the quantity of gas generated is not
the same in each tube. In fact, a careful examination
shows that twice as much hydrogen as oxygen is obtained.

[1] *Hydrogen,* from ὕδωρ, *hudor,* water; γεννάω, *gennao,* to produce.

If a cubic inch of oxygen is generated, two cubic inches of hydrogen will be obtained in the same time; and it is found that these proportions are exactly preserved, where-ever and whenever water is subjected to decomposition. It is seen, then, not only that water is composed of the two substances, oxygen and hydrogen, but that they exist in water in a constant proportion; so that, when they are set free and assume the gaseous state, there is always one volume of oxygen to two volumes of hydrogen gas.

This experiment gives a clear insight into the essential constitution of water. None of the changes which were described in preceding chapters had in any way affected this constitution. Water may be frozen, for example, into solid ice, but the ice will consist of oxygen and hydrogen in exactly the same proportions as in the liquid water. The water may be boiled and become the invisible gas, steam, but the steam will consist of oxygen and hydrogen in exactly the same proportions as in the water or in the ice. It will thus be understood that the *physical* properties of matter may be altered without affecting its deeper *chemical* con-stitution. The three conditions of a solid, a liquid, and a gas—represented respectively by ice, water, and steam —are physical states dependent mainly on temperature, and the chemical constitution of steam remains unaltered by a temperature far above the boiling point, while that of ice is not affected by any known degree of cold. It frequently happens, however, that the application of heat, instead of effecting merely physical change, produces chemical alteration in the substance. This was the case, it will be remembered, with the red oxide of mercury referred to in the last chapter (p. 77); when heated it did not melt, or fuse, or liquefy, but was at once split up into its constituents —mercury and oxygen. And, in like manner, under certain conditions, water may be resolved into its elements by the application of heat alone, just as it may be decomposed by means of electricity. This interesting fact was discovered by Sir W. R. Grove, more than thirty years ago. He found that if a piece of the metal platinum, such as a small solid ball, be made white hot, as may be done by the intense heat of the oxy-hydrogen blowpipe, and then be suddenly plunged into water, the liquid is at once decomposed into its constituent gases. But although this process is of great theoretical interest, it is not one which in the present state of science can be advantageously applied to the decomposition of water.

Having obtained oxygen and hydrogen by the decomposition of water, it may naturally be inquired whether these substances cannot in turn be decomposed. To this question it can be simply replied that the most skilful chemists have hitherto failed to effect such decomposition. They have found it impossible to obtain from oxygen anything but oxygen, or from hydrogen anything but hydrogen ; and, in the present state of our knowledge, these bodies are consequently regarded as *elementary* or *simple* substances. Nitrogen, which was obtained from the atmosphere (p. 79), is another of these elements ; and altogether chemists are acquainted with not fewer than sixty-four of these simple bodies, a large proportion of which are metals. Everything existing around us is consequently regarded by chemists either as an *element* or as a *compound*. Oxygen, hydrogen, and nitrogen are elements ; carbonic acid, ammonia, and water are compounds. These compounds generally have properties very different from those of their constituents ; thus, in none of its physical forms, does water possess the properties of either hydrogen or oxygen ; even as steam, it differs markedly from these, being neither combustible like the one, nor a supporter of combustion, like the other. When two substances are simply mixed together, without entering into chemical combination, they produce a mixture, having properties which partake of those of its components. Thus if four volumes of nitrogen are mixed with one volume of oxygen, a mixture is obtained which resembles atmospheric air, and is precisely what we should expect to produce; the activity of the oxygen being tempered by dilution with nitrogen. For this, and other reasons, chemists believe that atmospheric air is a *mechanical mixture* of gases; whilst water is a true *chemical compound*.

In the methods hitherto described for the decomposition of water, purely physical forces have been employed; in the one case it was electricity, in the other case heat. But a similar decomposition may be effected by means of chemical agencies. It has just been shown that water is a compound of oxygen and hydrogen; if, therefore, a body be presented to it which has a very strong attraction for one of these components, say the oxygen, it seems likely enough that we shall be able to draw this away, and leave the other constituent free. And such in truth is the case. Many of the metals have powerful attraction for oxygen; and, under proper conditions, are capable of removing it from water, and thus eliminating the hydrogen. There is, for example, a metal well known to chemists as *potassium*, so called in consequence of its existence in common "potashes." Potassium so eagerly combines with oxygen that the moment it is exposed to the atmosphere its surface becomes covered with a film of oxide. Throw a small piece of potassium upon water, and immediately a brilliant little violet flame bursts forth upon the surface of the liquid, and darts hither and thither until all the metal is spent. By this means the water is broken up; and the potassium has displaced a part of the hydrogen so energetically that sufficient heat has been produced to ignite the gas thus set free.

Certain other metals closely related to potassium will also effect the decomposition of water, but the action is less energetic than with potassium. The metal *sodium*, one of the constituents of common "soda," rends the water asunder, combining with its oxygen and turning out the hydrogen ; but the liberated gas does not catch fire spontaneously, at least if the water be cold. Cautiously hold a piece of sodium under water by means of a little wire-gauze

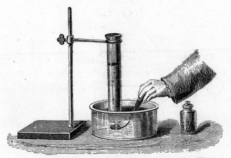

Fig. 27.—Decomposition of water by means of sodium.

spoon (Fig. 27), and bubbles of gas will immediately arise from the neighbourhood of the metal ; this gas may be collected in a small inverted vessel filled with water, and will be found to burn with the characteristic flame of hydrogen. If a fragment of sodium be thrown on to the surface of *hot* water, it is at once surrounded by flame, just as the potassium was, but the flame in this case is yellow, instead of being violet-coloured.

Potassium and sodium are metals but little known outside the chemical laboratory. The decomposition of water may,

however, be effected by the aid of some of the common
metals of every-day life. Iron, for instance, answers the
purpose well enough, provided the metal be sufficiently
heated to stimulate its attraction for oxygen until it can
overcome the union of the oxygen and hydrogen.
Fig. 28 represents a common method of effecting the decomposition of water by means of iron. A is an iron tube,
such as a gun-barrel, strongly heated in a furnace B; water
is boiled in the vessel C, and its vapour conducted
through the iron tube; in traversing the heated iron the

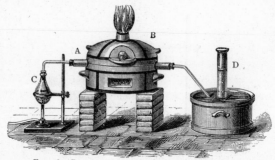

Fig. 28.—Decomposition of water by means of heated iron.

steam is broken up, its oxygen combining with the iron to
form an oxide, whilst its hydrogen is set free and may either
be burnt directly, or collected in D. This experiment shows
that steam, or water-gas, has the same chemical composition as liquid water. A gaseous compound of oxygen and
hydrogen goes in at A, and free hydrogen comes out at D;
the oxygen having been fixed by the iron which forms an
oxide, not indeed the same as that which exists in iron-rust,
but an oxide identical with that which forms the natural
loadstone, whence it is called *magnetic oxide of iron*.

In these experiments the hydrogen only has been set free;

and, in order to complete the demonstration of the chemical decomposition of water, it is necessary to explain how the oxygen may be liberated. To obtain the oxygen in a free form, it is clearly necessary to present to the water some substance which has a strong attraction for hydrogen. Such a substance is found in the gaseous element known to chemists as *chlorine*. This body exists largely in common salt, and in the well known substances " spirit of salt " and " chloride of lime." When set free it is an extremely poisonous gas, differing from all the gases to which we have hitherto referred, in that it possesses a very marked greenish-yellow colour, whence its name (χλωρὸς, *chloros*, green).

One of the most characteristic properties of chlorine is its powerful attraction for hydrogen. Mix the two gases together, and they combine with explosive violence, if exposed to sunshine ; and, even in diffused daylight, they slowly and quietly unite. This attraction for hydrogen stands us in good stead when we wish to get oxygen from water. A mixture of chlorine and steam is passed through a strongly-heated tube, and the chlorine eagerly seizes on the hydrogen to form a compound known as *hydrochloric-acid gas*, while the oxygen is set free. A similar action is indeed constantly being effected, in a less striking manner, in many of the industrial arts. Chlorine is largely used as a bleaching agent, but, in a dry state, it is powerless to bleach ; it is only when it is associated with moisture that it becomes active. When moist, however, it slowly decomposes the water, combining with its hydrogen and disengaging its oxygen ; and it is this oxygen, at the moment of its liberation, which is the really active agent in bleaching.

The proof of the composition of water, derived from the

action of chemical agencies, on one or other of its components, is now complete. On the one hand, it has been seen that certain metals remove the oxygen and set free the hydrogen; on the other hand, chlorine removes the hydrogen and sets free the oxygen. Had these experiments been conducted with great care, the balance being used at each step, it would have been possible to determine the precise proportions in which oxygen and hydrogen exist in water. In fact, the experiment with iron furnished the French chemist, Lavoisier, with the means of proving the composition of water analytically for the first time. Suppose a given weight of water in the form of steam be passed through the hot-iron tube, and that the oxide of iron which is produced be weighed to ascertain how much oxygen has been obtained; it is thus easy to tell how much oxygen exists in a given weight of water, and the rest will of course be hydrogen. In this way it has been found that 100 parts by weight of water contain 88·89 of oxygen and 11·11 of hydrogen; in other words $\frac{8}{9}$ by weight of water consists of oxygen, and $\frac{1}{9}$ of hydrogen, so that every 9 pounds of water contain 8 pounds of oxygen and 1 of hydrogen. This, therefore, is the composition of water by *weight*, and it agrees perfectly with what was deduced from our first electrical experiment with reference to the composition of water by *volume*. It was then found, in dealing with bulks, that twice as much hydrogen as oxygen was obtained from water. Now oxygen is sixteen times heavier than hydrogen, taking bulk for bulk; if therefore we obtained from a given quantity of water a volume of oxygen that weighed 16 grains, then we should find an equal volume of hydrogen weighed 1 grain; but, as a matter of fact, we obtained in our experiment twice the bulk of hydrogen, so that this quantity, instead of weighing 1 grain, must weigh 2 grains. The proportion by weight is therefore 16 grains of oxygen to 2 of hydrogen; or 8 to 1, as was expressed above. Chemists are thus led to the conclusion that water consists of a combination of hydrogen and oxygen in the definite proportions of 2 volumes of hydrogen to 1 volume of oxygen, or of 2 parts by weight of hydrogen to 16 parts by weight of oxygen.

When a compound is resolved into its components the process is called *analysis*.[1] All the processes hitherto described have been analytical processes, but to complete the discussion of the subject it is necessary to show how the composition of water may be demonstrated by *synthesis*,[2] that is to say, by putting the constituents together and building up the compound. The discovery of the composition of water was indeed made originally by synthetical, and not by analytical, processes.

Let pure hydrogen be perfectly dried, and then burnt: hold over the jet of burning gas a cold dry glass jar, Fig. 29, and the surface becomes rapidly bedewed, the moisture condensing in drops which trickle down the side, and may be collected. These drops are nothing but pure water, which has been produced by the union of the burning hydrogen with the oxygen of the surrounding air. Most of our ordinary combustibles—such as coal, wood, oil, wax, tallow, and gas—are rich in hydrogen, and they consequently produce water during their combustion. Hold a cold bright mirror near to a flame, and the moisture is instantly condensed upon its surface.

Instead of the hydrogen being burnt in air, and thus caused to combine with atmospheric oxygen, let the hydrogen be mixed with pure oxygen in the proper proportions

---

[1] *Analysis*, from ἀνά, *ana*, again; λύσις, *lusis*, a separation.
[2] *Synthesis*, from σύν, *sun*, together; θέσις, *thesis*, putting.

to form water. Such a mixture of gases may remain for
any length of time, without combination being effected; they
will form merely an intimate mechanical mixture of the gases,
but no water will be produced as long as there is no chemical
union. The moment, however, that a flame is applied to
the gases, a violent explosion occurs; chemical combination
is immediately brought about, the gases cease to exist as
oxygen and hydrogen, contraction ensues, and water is
produced. If the temperature were maintained sufficiently
high, this water would retain the condition of steam, and it

Fig. 29.—Formation of water by combustion of dry hydrogen.

would then be found that every three volumes of mixed
oxygen and hydrogen produced only two volumes of steam
or water-gas; in other words, contraction occurs to the extent of one-third of the original bulk. A pint of steam consists
therefore of a pint of hydrogen and half a pint of oxygen in
a state of chemical combination, whereby the pint and a half
of mixed gases becomes condensed to a pint of water-gas.
But, at ordinary temperatures, the steam rapidly condenses
to a liquid; a cubic foot of steam condensing to about a
cubic inch of water. If oxygen and hydrogen be exploded

in a dry vessel, its interior becomes bedewed with the condensed moisture.

It may seem unsatisfactory to look at a few drops of limpid liquid obtained by the union of oxygen and hydrogen at the lecture-table, and believe that they are really pure water. Experiments on a large scale have, however, been made, and sufficient water collected to place the matter beyond possibility of doubt. The grandest experiment of this nature was made by three eminent French chemists, Fourcroy, Vauquelin, and Seguin. The experiment commenced on the 13th of May, 1790, and was completed on the 22nd of the same month. During this time the apparatus was constantly watched, the experimenters sleeping alternately, for a few hours, on mattresses in the laboratory. The combustion was maintained almost uninterruptedly for 185 hours; 25,964 cubic inches of hydrogen and 12,571 of oxygen were consumed, and the union of these gases produced 7,244 grains of liquid. With this quantity at their disposal, they tested the liquid in every way that could be suggested, and found it to be identical with distilled water.

There is yet another means of determining the chemical composition of water, which needs to be briefly explained, since it furnishes the most accurate of all methods for determining this important question. Transmit a stream of pure dry hydrogen gas over a weighed quantity of pure oxide of copper (a compound of oxygen and the metal copper) heated to dull redness. Under these circumstances the hydrogen takes oxygen from the oxide, and forms water, which can be collected and weighed, whilst the loss of weight which the oxide suffers must represent the quantity of oxygen which this amount of water contains. It is needless to enter into the details required to secure accuracy in so delicate an experiment; but, in the hands of modern chemists, it has yielded the most trustworthy results which we possess on this subject. These results agree substantially with those which have been stated before. Indeed there is no fact in the whole range of chemical science better established than this,—that water is a definite chemical compound of oxygen and hydrogen, in the proportions by weight and measure previously given in this Chapter.

And thus we arrive at the last word of science, in its present state, respecting the origin of the river Thames. So far as its flood is pure water, we can trace that water to the ocean. And the pure water which forms the chief component of the sea has certainly been formed, some time or other, by the union of two bodies, oxygen and hydrogen, which, in their free state, are known only in the physical condition of gases.

CHAPTER VIII.

OUR study of the chemical constitution of water, in the last Chapter, led to the conclusion that this liquid consists of two gases, oxygen and hydrogen, united in definite proportions. Such indeed is the composition of absolutely pure water, but such is not the composition of any water known upon the surface of the earth. As a matter of fact, absolutely pure water is never found in the economy of nature. The great stream of water called the Thames is far from being absolutely pure in any part of its course. In the neighbourhood of the metropolis, it is, as every one knows, contaminated with impurities to such an extent as to acquire its proverbial turbidity. The muddiness, however, is due to the presence of solid particles which are mechanically suspended in the water—particles which would in great measure subside if the water were left free from disturbing causes, and which could be more or less completely removed by the simple process of filtration. Apart, however, from these mechanically suspended impurities, the Thames water, like the water of every other river, contains certain chemical compounds in a state of solution. Such impurities.

I 2

though present in very large proportions, may entirely elude observation by the eye, the water remaining clear and colourless. These soluble constituents, unlike the suspended impurities, will not be deposited when the solution is allowed to stand, nor will they be removed by the mere act of filtration. All natural water—whether brook or river, lake or sea—contains such dissolved matter, chiefly in the form of the various compounds called *salts;* but it varies considerably, in character and in quality, in different varieties of natural waters.

It is not necessary to go far to seek the source of these dissolved impurities. All the rocks of the earth, over which the waters flow, or through which they drain, contain mineral constituents more or less soluble in water. Water is, in fact, an almost universal solvent, whether of solids, liquids, or gases. River-water must therefore be regarded, not as absolutely pure water, but rather as an extremely weak solution of certain chemical compounds. What these compounds are will now be explained.

When natural water is evaporated, all its impurities, except those which are volatile, are left behind, and the vapour which rises is very nearly pure water. When the vapour of water is condensed it reproduces pure water. But such water rapidly absorbs both oxygen, nitrogen, carbonic acid, and ammonia; and, hence, the rain when it reaches the earth is no longer pure water; it has absorbed some of the atmospheric gases. Rain-water, therefore, although the purest of all forms of natural water, contains certain impurities which it has washed out of the atmosphere. The oxygen of the air is more soluble than the nitrogen; the carbonic-acid gas is much more soluble than either oxygen or nitrogen; and the ammonia is far more soluble than any of the other gases. Thus, under normal conditions of temperature and pressure, 100 volumes of water dissolve 1·48 volumes of nitrogen, 2·99 volumes of oxygen, 100·2 of carbonic acid, and 78270 of ammonia. All the constituents of the atmosphere will therefore be found in a state of solution in rain-water; while other bodies, such as nitric acid, also derived from the atmosphere, are not unfrequently present. In fact, whatever soluble constituents exist in the air will be absorbed by the rain. Hence, in the neighbour-hood of towns, where the atmosphere is impure, the rain-water will wash out more or less of its impurities, and, consequently, the rain collected in populous districts is less pure than that collected in an open country. Moreover, the rain which falls at the beginning of a shower is more contaminated than the later rain; and rain, which falls after a long drought, is more impure than that which falls towards the close of a rainy season. But, even after a long continuance of wet weather, the rain will still contain atmospheric gases to the extent of about $2\frac{1}{2}$ cubic inches to 100 cubic inches of water.

When the rain reaches the surface of the earth, it im-mediately commences to attack the rocks on which it happens to fall. Whether it dissolves much or little will depend upon whether the earth contains more or less soluble matter. But, whatever the character of the ground, some-thing will certainly be always dissolved. Every runnel, every brook, every rivulet, thus washes out some of the soluble constituents of the rock over which it flows, and carries them onwards to the river. The river consequently becomes the common receptacle for all the soluble matter delivered by its tributary streams. As it flows along, it grows richer in these soluble constituents, deriving them partly from the wear of its own bed and partly from that of its banks. It is not, however, by merely running over the surface of the ground that the river and its lateral streams derive their supply of soluble impurities, much more being probably due to the springs by which the streams are chiefly fed. Spring-water is, in fact, much richer than river-water in these soluble constituents. Nor is it difficult to see why.

To form a spring, the rain-water must sink to a greater or less depth in the ground. During its underground passage it exerts its solvent action upon the surrounding rocks. In some cases, the water sinks to great depths, traversing long and tortuous passages ; and, in such cases, it is only to be expected that, when it reappears at the surface, it will be highly charged with soluble constituents. Under pressure, at great depths, it may absorb large volumes of such gases as carbonic acid and sulphuretted hydrogen ; or it may dissolve saline matters of various kinds, and thus acquire peculiar properties which confer upon it medicinal value.

Analysis of the water of the Thames Head Well, near Cirencester, shows that it contains 27·44 parts of solid impurity dissolved in 100,000 parts of the water ; in other words, 0·02744 per cent. The most notable of the mineral constituents which affect the quality of the springs in the Thames basin is carbonate of lime.

A large part of the course of the river lies, indeed, through limestone rocks. In the upper part of the basin, it is the limestones of the Oolitic formations that furnish most of the springs ; whilst, in the lower part, it is chiefly the chalk. All limestones, from the softest chalk to the hardest marble, consist essentially of carbonate of lime ; and as this compound is slightly soluble in water, the springs and streams of limestone districts always hold it in solution. It is true that the proportion of carbonate of lime dissolved by *pure* water is extremely small ; not more, it is said, than two grains in a gallon of water. But, when water is charged with carbonic acid gas, the carbonate of lime is dissolved with facility; and, since most spring-water contains this gas, it is easy to understand how it can act with great effect upon limestone rocks. It has been seen that carbonic acid gas is dissolved out of the atmosphere by rain-water; and, in like manner, every piece of water exposed to the air must absorb it. Hence, all natural waters can dissolve carbonate of lime, with more or less ease, and thus erode the limestone rocks through which they drain.

When such calcareous waters are used for domestic purposes, they are found to curdle soap, and are consequently termed *hard* waters. A portion of the soap is wasted, inasmuch as its fatty acids form insoluble salts with the lime. As long therefore as this curdling continues, the soap is being wasted, and a lather cannot be produced. It is clearly convenient to have some means of comparing the relative hardness of different waters. To this end, Dr. T. Clarke, many years ago, proposed a scale in which each degree corresponds to one grain of carbonate of lime in a gallon of water. According to this scale, the water of the Thames Head Well has a hardness of 23 degrees; that is to say, it contains salts of lime equivalent to 23 grains of carbonate to the gallon.[1] But it is possible to improve the condition of such hard water by an easy process of softening, introduced likewise by Dr. Clarke. This consists in simply adding lime-water to the water the hardness of which is to be corrected; the lime combines with the excess of carbonic

[1] The imperial gallon contains 70,000 grains. In many official reports the proportion of carbonate of lime is given, not as grains per gallon, but as so many grains in 100,000 grains of water. The conversion of one form of result into the other is of course a mere question of proportion.

acid to form the almost insoluble carbonate of lime ; which is then precipitated, in company with the original carbonate of lime, thus rendered insoluble by removal of the carbonic acid that held it in solution.   In this way, the hardness of the water of Thames Head Well may be reduced from 23° to 5°.   Such a process of softening is carried on upon a large scale at several water-works, as at Caterham and at Canterbury.

The hardness which is thus capable of correction is termed *temporary* hardness, to distinguish it from that which cannot be removed by treatment with lime, and which is consequently termed *permanent* hardness.   Such permanent hardness is due to the presence of sulphate of lime.   It may therefore be said that the water of Thames Head has a hardness of 23°, of which 18° represent temporary hardness and 5° permanent hardness.   The upland waters of the West of England usually contain much more sulphate than carbonate of lime.   Sulphate of lime occurs crystallized in nature, and is known to the mineralogist under the rather fanciful name of *Selenite*,[1] whence waters containing much sulphate of lime are termed *selenitic waters*.   If a water be described simply as *calcareous*, it is generally assumed that the particular salt of lime which it holds in solution is the carbonate.

Waters flowing through limestone districts are generally charged with this salt ; in many cases to so great an extent that, if the water be exposed to the air, the carbonate of lime is spontaneously thrown down in a solid form.   Such springs are vulgarly called *petrifying springs*.   To " petrify," however, means literally to turn into stone ; it should therefore be distinctly understood that all such springs are able to do is to simply cover the objects which receive the water with a crust of carbonate of lime, and not actually to con-

[1] *Selenite*, from σελήνη, *selene*, the moon.

vert them into mineral matter. Thus, at Matlock, in Derbyshire, the water flowing through the Carboniferous Limestone
is caused to deposit its carbonate of lime upon various
objects exposed to its action, and in this way the so-called
petrified bird's nests and other curiosities are produced.
Thick deposits of carbonate of lime are frequently formed

FIG. 30.—Bridge of travertine at Clermont, Auvergne (Scrope).

by calcareous springs where they issue into the air. Fig. 30
represents a natural bridge of carbonate of lime formed
by calcareous water at Clermont in the Auvergne, described
many years ago by the late Mr. Poulett Scrope.[1] Here, the

[1] *The Geology and Extinct Volcanoes of Central France.* By G.
Poulett Scrope, M.P., F.R.S. Second Edition, p. 22. 1858. (By
permission of Mr. Murray.)

water has formed for itself an aqueduct, 240 feet in length, which terminates in a large arch spanning the stream into which the water at one time flowed. All this solid mass must have existed originally in an invisible state of solution in the water of the spring. Such deposits of carbonate of lime are commonly termed *travertine*, a word supposed to have been derived from the old name, *Lapis Tiburtinus*, which was formerly applied to the stone, in consequence of its deposition on a large scale from the calcareous waters of the River Anio at Tivoli, the ancient Tibur, near Rome. At the Falls of the Anio, the travertine has formed bed after bed, to the thickness of four or five hundred feet.

In consequence of the comparative ease with which limestone yields to the solvent action of water holding carbonic acid gas in solution, this rock is frequently worn by water into holes and caverns. When calcareous water finds its way into the roof of a cavern it slowly deposits its burden of carbonate of lime, or at least a portion of it, in a solid form; and, by long continuance of this action, ultimately produces a conical or cylindrical body hanging like an icicle from the rocky roof. Pendent rods of this kind are termed *stalactites*.[1] From the point of the stalactite, water slowly drops down upon the floor, and, as this water likewise contains carbonate of lime, another calcareous deposit is formed as a little conical mass seated on the floor; this mass is termed for distinction sake, a *stalagmite*.[2] As the stalagmite grows in height, it approaches the stalactite above, which continues to grow downwards; and, ultimately, the two may meet and thus form a solid pillar stretching from floor to roof. Fig. 31 will give some idea of the com mon shapes assumed by stalactites and stalagmites. It

---

[1] *Stalactite*, from σταλάσσω, *stalasso*, to drop.
[2] *Stalagmite*, from στάλαγμα, *stalagma*, a drop.

represents a cavity, described by Professor Boyd Dawkins as the Fairy Chamber, in a limestone cavern on the isle of Caldy opposite to Tenby in Pembrokeshire.[1] In the formation and decoration of such caves, water is the main agent from beginning to end. Finding its way through the cracks

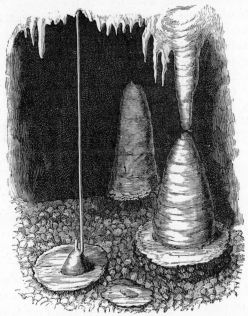

Fig. 31.—Stalactites and stalagmites, Isle of Caldy.

and crannies of the solid rock, it first eats away the limestone so as to form the cavity, and then bedecks the roof, the floor, and the walls, with calcareous deposits of most fantastic shapes. Even without going into a limestone

[1] *Cave Hunting.* By W. Boyd Dawkins, M.A., F.R.S. P. 64. 1874.

cavern, examples of these stalactites may readily be seen. It is, in fact by no means uncommon to see small stalactites hanging down, like icicles, from the roof of the arches of a railway bridge, where they are produced by the rain-water dissolving the calcareous matter contained in the roadway, or in the materials of which the arch is composed.

Calcareous salts, although the most common, are by no means the only mineral compounds which occur in natural waters. Some springs, such as those at Epsom, are rich in sulphate of magnesia; whence this salt is popularly called *Epsom salts*, while the springs themselves are said to be *saline*. Others may contain salts of iron, and form *chalybeate* springs, as mentioned at p. 26. It is notable that many mineral springs have a temperature higher than that of the locality in which they issue ; thus the warm springs of Bath have a temperature of nearly 120° F. In volcanic districts, such thermal sources are extremely common, and as water when hot dissolves most substances more freely than when cold, these springs are often rich in mineral matter. The famous *geysers* of Iceland and of Colorado are intermittent boiling springs, containing in solution a good deal of silica, or the matter of which flint and rock crystal are composed. (See Chapter XIII.)

Springs, such as have been referred to above, are of course exceptional; but, it should be remembered, that all spring water contains more or less mineral matter in solution. On comparing the composition of *river* water with that of spring water, it will generally be found that the river contains less saline matter. In fact, the water discharged into the river by springs becomes diluted by direct influx of rain, and this dilution more than compensates for loss by evaporation ; so that, on the whole, the proportion of salts diminishes. Moreover, the organisms inhabiting the river derive their needful supply of mineral matter, directly or indirectly, from the surrounding medium, and thus the fresh-water shell-fish and crustaceans appropriate a large quantity of carbonate of lime, to form their shells, from the river in which they live. Much of this, however, must be returned to the river by the decay of the shells after the death of the animals. In these and other ways, it is easy to account for the proportion of saline constituents being less in river than in spring-water. If the river drain a country composed of hard and almost insoluble rocks, the water will contain but little mineral impurity. Thus the water of the Dee, of Aberdeen, which draws its supply from a granite district, contains only about three grains of saline matter in the gallon. It is a very different case, however, with a river like the Thames, which collects its water from the drainage of comparatively soft and soluble rocks. The composition of the Thames water may be seen by the following analysis :—[1]

COMPOSITION OF THAMES WATER AT LONDON BRIDGE IN GRAINS PER GALLON OF 70,000 GRAINS.

Carbonate of Lime	8·1165
Chloride of Calcium [2]	6·9741
Chloride of Magnesium	·0798
Chloride of Sodium	2·3723
Sulphate of Soda	3·1052
Sulphate of Potash	·2695
Silica	·1239
Insoluble Organic Matter	4·6592
Soluble Organic Matter	2·3380
	28·0385

[1] "Analysis of Thames Water." By John Ashley. *Quarterly Journal of the Chemical Society*, vol. ii. p. 74.

[2] Probably the calcium exists rather as sulphate of lime, and the chlorine as chloride of sodium.

Although the proportion of mineral matter held in solution in Thames water, appears, from such an analysis as that just cited, to be extremely small, it must yet be remembered that, taking into consideration the great volume of the Thames, the total quantity of matter removed in this way from the land and carried seaward is something enormous. Professor Prestwich, taking the daily discharge of the Thames at Kingston at 1,250 million gallons, and the salts in solution at 19 grains per gallon, calculates that the quantity of mineral matter carried down in solution, at that locality, amounts to 3,364,286 pounds, or 1,502 tons, every twenty-four hours; or say, roughly, a ton a minute. Of this amount about 1,000 tons will consist of carbonate of lime, and 238 tons, of sulphate of lime. The total quantity of saline matter carried invisibly away by the Thames from its basin above Kingston, will thus reach, in the course of a year, to the enormous amount of 548,230 tons.

Although it has been shown that river-water contains a smaller proportion of saline matter than is present in spring-water, it would yet be a great mistake to assume on this ground that the river-water is more pure and wholesome. On the contrary, the river-water, though poor in mineral matter, is usually rich in organic impurities, and is therefore much less fitted for drinking purposes. Most of the water from *deep* wells and springs in the Thames basin contains the merest trace of organic matter; but the river itself derives a large proportion of organic impurity from the decomposing vegetable matter, spread over the large surface of country which it drains. A more serious source of contamination, however, is to be found in the sewage-matter, which is allowed to be run into it from the centres of population seated on or near its banks. It must, nevertheless, be borne in mind that, by the constant exposure of fresh surfaces

of polluted water to the action of the atmosphere, which
is accomplished in a running stream, the organic matter
is oxidised, and may thus be eventually converted into
products which are perfectly harmless ; in other words,
a river is competent to effect its own purification unless
overtaxed with pollution.

Although the organic impurities, or those derived from
animal and vegetable sources, thus suffer considerable alteration as the river flows along, the saline matters, on the other
hand, remain unaffected, save in so far as they may be
consumed in supplying mineral matter to the organisms
which inhabit the river. The mineral matter is therefore,
for the most part, borne onwards by the river and finally
discharged into the sea. The sea consequently becomes
the ultimate receptacle for all the saline matter washed out
of the land and brought down by rivers. And yet the water
of the sea differs considerably in chemical composition from
that of rivers or of springs. Whilst a gallon of Thames
water contains in solution about 21 grains of saline matter,
a gallon of sea-water will contain something like 2,400
grains. In fact, the proportion of solid matter in sea-water
reaches as high as $3\frac{1}{2}$ to 4 per cent. It is needless to
remark that most of this saline matter consists of common
salt, such as we use at table,—a salt known to chemists as
chloride of sodium, since it consists of two elements, namely,
the gas *chlorine* and the metal *sodium*. Out of the 2,400
grains of mineral matter in a gallon of sea water, nearly
2,000 grains will consist of this common salt.

As an example of the composition of sea-water, the
following analysis[1] of water from the British Channel may

[1] An analysis, by Schweitzer, in the *Philosophical Magazine*, vol. xv.
p. 58. Recalculated to bring it into comparison with the analysis of
Thames water on p. 125.

be quoted. The density of this water was found to be
1027 :—

COMPOSITION OF WATER OF THE BRITISH CHANNEL IN GRAINS
PER GALLON OF 70,000 GRAINS.

Chloride of Sodium . . .	1964·165
Chloride of Potassium . . .	53·585
Chloride of Magnesium . . .	256·655
Bromide of Magnesium . . .	2·044
Sulphate of Magnesia . . .	16·069
Sulphate of Lime	98·462
Carbonate of Lime	2·310
Iodine and Ammonia	traces
	2393·290

Every tide brings this sea water into contact with the
fresh water of a tidal river, like the Thames, and the two
kinds thus become mixed. On going down the Thames
from London Bridge, it is found that the water gradually
loses its freshness. A little below Gravesend, it begins to
acquire a saltish flavour, and this saltness increases until the
water becomes decidedly brackish and undrinkable. Going
still farther out into the estuary, the saltness becomes more
pronounced; and, by the time Whitstable is reached, the
water is hardly to be distinguished from that of the sea
itself.

The fresh water brought down by a river does not however immediately mix with the salt water, but rather tends
to float upon its surface. For, since the sea water is rich in
solid matter, its density is proportionally high; that is to say,
sea-water must weigh considerably more than fresh water
when equal bulks are compared. A gallon of water from
the Nore weighs rather more than a gallon of water from
the Thames at Teddington. If a given measure of pure

water weighs 1,000 lbs. the same measure of water from Margate will weigh 1,027 lbs. As a consequence of this high density, it is easier to swim on salt than on fresh water. Hence, too, the fresh water carried down by a river tends to float for a time upon the surface of the dense sea-water; and, off the mouths of some great rivers, the water is found to be nearly fresh for some distance out to sea.

From the vast surface exposed by the sea, water is continually being evaporated by the aid of solar heat. But it is practically pure water which is thus drawn up into the atmosphere, the saline constituents of the sea water being left behind. Pure water condenses from this vapour, and falling upon the land as rain, charged to a certain extent with the constituents of the atmosphere, it washes out more or less of the soluble constituents of the rocks, which are ultimately carried down to the sea, where they accumulate. There is consequently, a never-ceasing transference of solid matter from the land to the ocean—a transference, however, which entirely escapes cognizance by the sight, since the matter is carried down in a state of invisible solution. But, as was remarked at the commencement of this chapter, in addition to the dissolved mineral matter which thus eludes observation, the Thames, like other rivers, bears a vast quantity of other solid matter in a state of mechanical suspension, and therefore readily recognized by the eye. This mechanical transport of solid matter from earth to sea will form the subject of the next Chapter.

K

CHAPTER IX.

THE WORK OF RAIN AND RIVERS.

Take a gallon or two of water out of the Thames at London Bridge, and allow it to stand quietly in a clean vessel. If you look at it, after it has stood for several hours, you will find that the water is much clearer, and that a quantity of muddy matter is spread over the bottom of the vessel, the quantity being greater or less according to the condition of the river at the time you happen to examine it. This mud was previously held in suspension by the water, and was the main cause of its turbidity, so that, as soon as the muddy particles settled, the water became clearer. While the water was in the river, the fine solid particles were kept in constant agitation by the current of the stream, and were thus prevented from settling down. The more rapid the stream, the greater is its power of carrying this suspended matter ; but, as the river approaches its mouth, the flow becomes slackened and the sediment subsides. Hence, in the lower part of the course of the Thames, especially in the " reaches," or bends in the river, near Woolwich, there are large mud banks ; and this mud is systematically dredged up and removed, in order to prevent obstruction. Those particles of mud which are very light may be kept suspended in the water until they are carried by the river right out to sea; but a time at length comes, when even these will quietly settle down upon the sea-bottom. If a little of the muddy sediment, deposited by the water, be dried by exposure to the air, it will be found to harden into a substance not unlike *clay*. Clay is, in fact, nothing but such mud, hardened and perhaps otherwise altered.

Very little thought is necessary to convince any one that the fine particles of solid matter, which form mud, are produced by the mechanical waste of the land. After a heavy shower of rain has fallen in the street, you observe dirty streams coursing along the gutters, and every one knows that the muddy matter in these streams is merely the dirt washed from the roofs of the houses and the stones of the street. In like manner, every shower of rain that falls in the open country washes something off the surface of the land. This removal of matter is termed *denudation*, since the rocks are laid bare by having their superficial covering thus peeled off. The particular kind of denudation effected by means of rain is called *pluvial*[1] denudation. A heavy shower, falling upon a field, washes away some of the soil, and carries it off in muddy runnels to the nearest stream, whence it passes to the river. Where the rain comes down in a deluge, as often happens in the tropics, its power as a denuding agent is almost incredible; and even in this country, especially among the hills of Wales and Cumberland, we occasionally hear of torrents of rain tearing up rocks and sweeping everything before them. It has been held by Mr. A. Tylor and some other geologists, that the rainfall was formerly very much greater than it is at present; and, if this be admitted, it follows that the work done by rain in destroying

[1] *Pluvial*, from the Lat. *pluvia*, rain.

the land, must have been much greater than that which is now witnessed.

The detrital matter which is worn away from the land, and carried along by rivers, contains materials of every degree of coarseness. It often happens that fragments of rock, perhaps of considerable size, are loosened from cliffs near a river by the action of rain and frost, and tumble down into the stream. There they get slowly worn down, by constantly knocking against each other, and may ultimately be rubbed into the form of smooth round pebbles. In the basin of the Thames, it is common for the hard flints from the chalk to get broken and rolled about in the water, and it is in this way that *gravel* is formed. The substance which is strewn over our roads and garden-walks consists, chiefly, of little bits of flint, which have been so rolled about in water that the sharp points of the broken stones are rounded off. All gravel has not however been subject to the same amount of rough usage, so that whilst the pebbles are in some cases well rounded, in other cases they retain more or less of their angularity, though the corners are never quite sharp. The small pieces worn off the fragments of rock, as they rattle together on the bed of the stream, get rolled about until they form small rounded grains known as *sand*. As a rule, both the gravel and the sand consist, chiefly, of the substance called *silica*, or the material of which flint is formed, and which is chemically the same as the matter of pure rock-crystal (p. 58). The gravel and the coarser sediment are pushed along the bottom of the river by the motion of the stream, whilst the finer sand may be carried in suspension, though it will not travel so far as the lighter particles of mud. The heavier pieces naturally fall to the bottom first, so that if a quantity of mixed gravel, sand and mud be shaken up in water, it will be found that the gravel is the first to fall; then the sand subsides, and finally the mud settles down.

If a river has a steep bed it generally possesses great carrying power. Mountain-torrents, for example, rush down steep slopes and not only transport vast quantities of gravel, sand and mud, but often move stones of considerable weight. During floods, too, ordinary rivers acquire great mechanical power. Thus we read of floods sweeping away bridges, tearing up rocks from the banks of the river, and carrying along stones weighing several tons. Sir T. D. Lauder, in describing the great floods which occurred in Morayshire in August 1829, records the destruction of many farms and hamlets; while no fewer than 38 bridges were swept away by the flooded rivers. A huge mass of sand-stone, measuring 14 feet in length, 3 feet in width, and one foot in thickness, was carried for a distance of 200 yards by the swollen stream of the river Nairn.

In estimating the carrying-power of running water, it must be borne in mind that the weight of a stone is considerably less in water than in the atmosphere. When a body is immersed in water, it appears to lose a certain proportion of its weight, the proportion depending upon its specific gravity. If a stone be twice as heavy as an equal bulk of water, it will lose one-half its weight; if three times as heavy, it is lightened by one-third; and so on. It is generally said that if a stream flow at the rate of six inches per second it has power enough to carry off fine sand; if at 12 inches per second it can sweep away fine gravel; and if at 36 inches per second it can transport pebbles as large as hen's eggs. It should not be forgotten, however, that the *shape* of the fragments greatly affects the ease with which they may be moved in water.

Hitherto, the work of the river has been regarded as

chiefly that of transporting solid matter which has been carried into it by rain and other denuding agents. But the river is, itself, a powerful agent of direct denudation— *fluviatile* denudation as it is sometimes termed. It is true that running water, alone, can do but little towards abrading a hard rock : but the pebbles, sand and other detrital matter carried along by the stream, rub against every hard point with which they come in contact, and thus enable the river to wear away the hardest rocks in its course, as surely as though they were being ground and scoured with sand-paper. The grinding action of pebbles, when set in motion by water, is strikingly shown in the formation of *potholes*. These are roundish cavities, perhaps several feet in depth, not uncommon in the hard bed of a mountain-stream. A few pebbles, lodging in a small cavity, get whirled round and round by the eddies of the stream, until, at length, they excavate deep holes of considerable size. In such cases, the grinding effect of the pebbles is generally assisted by the sand and finer particles in the water, which scour the walls of the hole as effectually as though they were well rubbed with fine sand-paper.

Aided by its burden of detrital matter, the river frets away the rocks along its banks and thus tends to widen its channel ; while, at the same time, the coarse sediment scratching along the bottom, helps to tear it up and thus deepen the bed of the river. Every stream, with sufficient fall, is in this manner continually at work, gnawing away the rocks through which it flows, so that a channel which is, to begin with, narrow and shallow may gradually become widened and deepened. The amount of excavation which can be wrought in a given time, by means of running water, is well seen in volcanic regions, where rivers have cut through sheets of lava which have been poured forth at known dates.

But perhaps the grandest results of river-denudation are to be witnessed in the vast chasms through which some of the rivers in Colorado flow.   These narrow gorges, bounded by steep wall-like cliffs, are known under their Spanish name of *cañons* (Fig. 32).[1]   The Colorado River of the West, which runs from the Rocky Mountains to the Gulf of California, flows, during part of its course, at the bottom of a profound chasm ; being hemmed in by vertical walls which, in some places, are more than a mile in depth.   There is no reason to doubt that this gigantic furrow has been cut down by the river which runs through it.   The tributary streams flowing into the river run, in like manner, through smaller ravines, known as side-cañons ;   and, in fact, the general arrangement of the cañons at once suggests that of the drainage system of a country.   Nothing can show the amount of *vertical* erosion, effected by running water, better than these gorges.   Probably they owe the preservation of their peculiar form to the fact that the country in which they occur is comparatively rainless ; for, if there were much rain, the sides could not retain their position as perpendicular walls, and denudation would gradually convert the chasm into an ordinary river valley.

To understand how running water usually effects denudation, it is instructive to watch, at the sea-shore, the behaviour of the water which drains off a flat coast of mud, or fine sand as the tide retreats.   Flat and smooth as the beach may seem to the eye, the water soon finds out some slight inequalities of surface, and runs down even the gentlest declivity.   Particles of sand carried down by the water begin to scour out little grooves, and then to enlarge them into wider furrows. Several streams may be seen uniting into one larger stream.

---

[1] From Powell's *Exploration of the Colorado River of the West.* Washington, 1875.

and, at length, a complex system of branches is established, all tending to a common channel which runs down towards low water. Even without going to the sea-side, one may often see similar effects near a way-side puddle which receives the muddy drainage of the road. No imagination is needed to compare the miniature system of branching streams, produced in either of these cases under one's eyes, with the drainage system of a river basin. The model is in fact complete in almost every point. There is the main stream, with its side feeders, running down to the sea; and, it may often be seen, that one little system of streams is separated from another by an intervening space which represents a water-parting.

Suppose now that a portion of the sea-bottom were to be upheaved, and appear above the surface of the water as a great mud-flat. From what has just been said, it is easy to judge at once how it would be drained. When rain fell upon this new-born land, it would be sure to find some slight rise and fall of the surface, and the gentlest fall is sufficient to determine that the rain shall run in this direction rather than in that. The very fall of the pattering rain-drops would produce little dimples on moist ground, and thus give rise to superficial irregularities. As the water flowed off in runnels, it would wash away fine particles of the mud; and thus every shower would find better channels scooped out to receive the drainage. The streams would certainly not run down to the sea in parallel straight lines, but a number of neighbouring streams, all tending to the lowest level, would soon be gathered together in a common channel, something like that shown in Fig. 33. If the action went on for a long time, the water-channels would get worn wider and deeper, while the sides of the streams would be washed by the rain into sloping banks. So close indeed is the

Fig. 32.—The Grand Cañon, Colorado.

similarity of a system of drainage established in this way
to what is found in a large river basin, that those who have
thought most upon the subject believe that one may be
taken to explain the other; that, in point of fact, the present rivers have gradually scooped out their own channels,
and that our river-valleys are, mainly, the result of work per-
formed by rain, rivers, and similar agents of denudation.

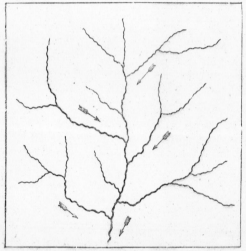

FIG. 33.—Self-established drainage system.

At first sight, it may seem incredible that a great river-
system, like that of the Thames, should have been shaped
by the action of instruments which seem so insignificant.
Yet the more one thinks upon it the less are the difficulties
that beset such an explanation. No one can deny that
little water-courses may be eaten out of solid rock by a
running stream, for the very origin of such gulleys may

often be witnessed. And, from these, it is possible to pass, by insensible steps, to brooks and streams of larger size, until, at length, you come to a true river. If it be admitted that the little stream has worn out the gutter in which it runs, it is hard to deny that the larger stream has not done similar work on a larger scale. The whole affair is indeed a mere question of time. The smallest cause can produce a vast effect if it is only allowed to work long enough.

It needs but little boldness to apply such reasoning to the valley of the Thames. On looking at the two opposite sides of the valley it may often be seen that the rocks exactly correspond; a bed of gravel on one

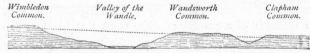

Wimbledon   Valley of the   Wandsworth   Clapham
Common.   Wandle.   Common.   Common.

FIG. 34.—River-valley worn through gravel and London clay.

bank, perhaps, has its counterpart on the other. Fig. 34 is a section from Wimbledon Common to Clapham Common.[1] Here it is seen that the surface of Wimbledon Common is covered by a bed of gravel spread over the London clay. On descending from the summit of the common to the valley of the river Wandle, the gravel is seen to be abruptly cut off and succeeded by the underlying clay; but, on going up the opposite slope of the valley, the gravel again appears, at about the same level, and covers the surface of Wandsworth Common; and similarly the gravel will be found on the surface of Clapham Common. There can be little doubt, then, that the gravel once spread in a continuous sheet over these three commons, as indi-

[1] From Prof. Prestwich's *Ground Beneath Us.* 1857.

cated by the dotted line, and has been cut through by
running water. The Wandle is a tributary of the Thames,
and what is true of this small river is also true of the larger.
In some places the Thames has cut through similar high-
level gravels [1] and through the London clay. In other
parts of the river, again, the chalk forms the two sides of
the valley through which the water flows. In the case of
the chalk, it is evident, from what was said in the last
chapter, that the mechanical erosion would be greatly
assisted by chemical solution, the carbonate of lime being
easily soluble; while the flints, so commonly found embedded in the chalk, would resist such chemical action
and, to a great extent, would also withstand mechanical wear.
Hence their broken fragments will be found still rolling
about as flint-gravel; and every bit of such gravel is, in fact,
a memorial of a quantity of white chalk that has long ago
been dissolved and washed away by running water. In
other parts of its course, the Thames flows through rocks of
a different character, which will be subsequently described;
but they are all affected by the mechanical or by the chemical
action of the river, in the way just explained.

Passing from the study of the Thames Valley to that
of the general surface of the country, abundant evidence
is to be found that rain and running water have been
actively at work. Indeed there is good reason to believe
that these almost silent workers have been the chief
instruments in producing the present physical features
of the ground. They have eaten out river-courses and
worn away valleys, leaving masses of rock which stand out
as hills and crags. But, while giving them credit for effecting

[1] The meaning of the term "high-level gravels" will be explained
in Chapter XVII.

such work as this, it is necessary to recognize the co-
operation of other forces, the effects of which will be discussed in subsequent chapters.

If running water is thus wasting away the land, year after
year and age after age, what ultimately becomes of the great
quantity of matter which must be removed? To this question
a partial answer has already been incidentally given. The
coarser detrital matter is pushed along the bottom of the
stream, and thus slowly moved towards its mouth; whilst
the finer detritus, being held in suspension, is carried more
rapidly away by the flow of the running water. When the
flow is checked, the sand and mud settle down, the coarser
particles being naturally the first to subside. In the miniature river-system, self-established in the muddy bank left by
the receding tide, a minute stream may often be seen entering a quiet pool of sea-water, and depositing its burden of
sand, particle by particle, upon the floor of the little pond.
Exactly the same kind of thing occurs, on a much larger
scale, at the mouth of every river. In some cases, a river
during its course opens out into a lake, and then the
resemblance to our model on the sea-shore is even more
striking. On entering the lake, the flow of the stream
becomes suddenly checked, and a part of the suspended
sediment falls to the bottom; so that, by the time the stream
emerges, its waters have become purified. The effect of
a sojourn in the lake is somewhat like that of allowing
muddy water to stand in a glass; in either case, much of
the sediment slowly subsides.

A striking example of the purifying effect of a lake is
seen in the Lake of Geneva, through which the Rhone
flows. The river enters the upper end of the lake as a
turbid stream, laden with detritus brought down from the
Alps; but, at the lower end of the lake, it issues forth well

purged of its impurities. During its passage through the lake, the mud which it held in suspension is deposited upon the bottom ; and, accordingly, at the entrance of the river, new land is being slowly formed by the growth of this sediment. In fact, Port Vallais, the *Portus Valesiæ* of the Romans, which was originally situated on the margin of the lake, is now nearly two miles inland ; the intervening ground having been formed, at the expense of the lake, by accumulated sediment delivered by the river. In this way, a lake may grow shallower and smaller, until at length it becomes completely silted up ; and a marshy tract is formed, through which the river flows in a meandering course. Such land is generally called *alluvium*.[1]

It often happens that, without flowing into a lake, a river may get relieved of much of its burden of sedimentary matter. When an unusual supply of water is suddenly delivered into a stream, by heavy rainfall or by rapid thaw of snow, the swollen stream rises above its banks, and floods the adjacent land. In a flood, or freshet, the water is always highly charged with detritus ; and, on the overflow of the river, some of this is deposited as a fine layer of mud evenly spread over the flooded soil. The overflow being repeated season after season, the layers of mud accumulate until they form a low alluvial tract on each side of the stream. Most rivers are bordered by strips of rich meadow-land, which have been formed in this way, Such low-lying alluvial meadows are common along the banks of the Thames ; and in the lower part of the basin, where the river is broad, especially between London and Tilbury, there are great expanses of flat marshy ground : the Isle of Dogs, for example, is such an alluvial tract. Periodical deposition of

---

[1] *Alluvium*, from the Lat. *ad*, and *luo*, I wash ; land which is added to by the wash or flow of water.

sediment by means of river-floods is, however, best illustrated by reference to the overflowing of the Nile. After
the rainy season in the southern part of the course of the
river, there is a sudden rush of water, charged with detritus,
which spreads far over the banks of the river in its lower
course, and deposits the rich alluvial mud of Egypt.

When a river approaches the sea, the inclination of its
basin usually diminishes, its speed is slackened ; and, consequently, it deposits more or less of the matter which it
holds in suspension. If the sea, near the mouth of the river,
is not much disturbed by currents, as in a protected bay, the
sediment will accumulate, and form a tract of alluvial land
which is generally fan-shaped. In Lower Egypt, the Nile
has, in this way, produced an enormous alluvial tract, which
was called by the Greeks the *Delta*, in allusion to its shape
resembling that of their letter Δ. About 120 miles above
its mouth, the Nile divides into two main streams, of which
the western is known as the Rosetta branch, and the eastern
as the Damietta branch, these names referring to two towns
situated at their respective mouths. The two streams inclose, with the Mediterranean sea on the north, a triangular
tract of alluvial land, intersected by a network of channels.
The apex of this triangle, forming what is called the *head*
of the delta, is situated about 25 miles below Cairo. Fig.
35 shows the form of the Nilotic delta.

From being originally applied to the triangular land
about the mouths of the Nile, the term "delta" has come
into general use and is now extended to all similar alluvial
deposits. Even the land, which has been described as
formed in the Lake of Geneva by deposits from the Rhone,
may be called a *lacustrine delta.* If the silt is thrown down
under tranquil conditions, on a tolerably level bed, it will
fall in nearly horizontal layers, regularly spread one upon

another. Could a clean cut be made through the ground
in such a delta, the cut sides would expose the edges of a
number of beds or layers, of which the lowest must needs
be the oldest or earliest formed, and the uppermost the
youngest or latest formed ; the materials of the delta, are, in
fact, *stratified*.

In following a river from its mouth towards its source, it is
generally found to be continually branching out into smaller

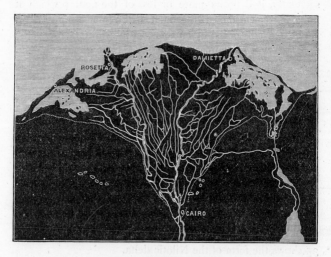

FIG. 35.—Delta of the Nile.

and smaller streams, not unlike the ramifications of a tree,
until, at length, it is lost in a multiplicity of little rills. And,
in tracing a river downwards into its delta, it is found in like
manner that it divides and subdivides, till at last it is split
up into a network of channels, and reaches the sea through
a number of separate openings. The arrangement of
branches in the delta is therefore similar to that in the

catchment-basin, but exactly opposite in direction. In the catchment-basin all the branches *converge* to the main stream; in the delta they all *diverge* from the trunk channel. The difference between the catchment basin and the delta is shown in Fig. 36.

In many deltas, the alluvial land is swampy, or washed by the sea at high tide; and the alluvium may, in some cases, be traced beneath the level of the sea, in the form of shoals and sand-banks, which are made up of the lighter particles of detritus swept out beyond the true delta. The great Indian rivers, the Ganges and Bráhmapútra, form together

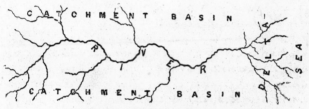

FIG. 36.—Catchment-basin and delta of a river.

a vast delta, consisting, for the most part, of marshy land supporting a growth of mangroves and nipa palms. The delta of the Mississippi (Fig. 37) is an enormous tract of swampy ground in the Gulf of Mexico, furrowed by numerous streams and lakes. Holland may be regarded as an old delta, formed by the Rhine and the other rivers that pass through it. And, on the coasts of this country, we frequently find tracts of alluvial land, such as that forming Romney Marsh. Occasionally, the estuaries of our rivers become silted up, more or less completely, and thus impede navigation. In the times of the Romans, the Isle of Thanet was separated from the Kentish coast by a channel suffi-ciently wide to admit the Roman fleet; but this channel is

L

now choked up, and the so-called island is united by an alluvial tract with the mainland. But, as a rule, the rivers of this
country are not large enough, and have, comparatively, too
rapid a fall, to produce deltas.   Moreover, in tidal rivers, the
regular to-and-fro motion of the water in its estuary hinders

FIG. 37.—Delta of the Mississippi.

deposition of sediment. The scour of the ebb-tide co-
operates with the rapid flow of the river to sweep away any
sediment thrown down during the flood-tide, when the
downward current of the river is arrested. In some estuaries,
the tidal current is so charged with muddy matter that it is

artificially carried over low land, in order to cover it with a fine silt, called *warp;* this is done in the estuary of the Humber.   In cases where an actual delta is not formed, a *bar*, or shoal, may be thrown across the mouth of the river, and thus interfere with navigation.   A river exposed to full tidal action, like the Thames, has little chance to form a delta ; and, although alluvial deposits are to be found on its banks, and shoals in parts of its estuary (Fig. 48), there is sufficient scouring out of the mouth to keep its channel open.

But, although the Thames forms no delta, the quantity of detritus which it carries down from the surface of its basin and discharges into the sea is far from being insignificant. The proportion of solid matter suspended in water varies considerably in different rivers ; and, in the same river, at different seasons.   Thus, Bischof, in examining the Rhine, found that, when the river was turbid, it contained $\frac{1}{4878}$ of its weight of solid matter in suspension ; but, at another season, when the water was clear and blue, it contained only $\frac{1}{57800}$th part.   The Ganges, which has formed such an enormous delta, is said to hold, on a yearly average, as much as $\frac{1}{510}$th by weight of suspended detritus.   No river has been more carefully examined than the Mississippi, and it has been determined that the average proportion of sediment in this great stream is $\frac{1}{1500}$ by weight, or $\frac{1}{2900}$ by volume ; so that the weight of mud actually carried to sea, in the course of a year, reaches the enormous amount of 812,500,000,000 pounds.

With regard to the Thames, it has been estimated that it discharges annually 1,865,903 cubic feet of sediment (Geikie).   Add to this the quantity of mineral matter washed away in solution, to which reference was made in the last chapter, and it will be found that the total quantity of solid matter carried to sea by the Thames is really

enormous. At Kingston, as has been stated at p. 126, the
dissolved matter is estimated at about 548,230 tons per
year. Now reckoning 15 cubic feet to the ton, which is
about the average weight of chalk, this weight is equivalent
to upwards of 8 million cubic feet. But this is only at Kingston, and it is certain that much more is dissolved before the
river reaches the sea. Nor must we forget to add something considerable to represent the quantity of coarse sediment pushed along the bed of the river. On the whole,
then, we shall probably not be far wrong in saying that
the Thames carries down to the sea, every year, 14 million
cubic feet of solid matter.

Imagine a huge die-shaped mass of stone measuring 100
feet in length, 100 feet in width, and 100 feet in height :
this would contain one million cubic feet. No fewer, then,
than 14 of these gigantic cubes appear to be quietly stolen
from the surface of the Thames basin by means of running
water, and transported to the sea, in the course of a single
year. But the Thames basin covers a very large area, and
it will be found on calculation that, admitting the abstraction
of this vast mass, the entire surface of the basin would be
reduced in level by only $\frac{1}{800}$th part of an inch every year.
At the present rate of wear and tear, therefore, denudation
can have lowered the surface of the Thames basin by hardly
more than an inch since the Norman conquest ; and nearly
a million years must elapse before the whole basin of the
Thames will be worn down to the sea-level. This method
of showing the amount of work effected by rain and rivers
in wearing away the land was suggested by Mr. A. Tylor,
and has since been applied with interesting results by other
geologists. Thus, Prof. Geikie has calculated[1] that, at the

"On Modern Denudation." By Archibald Geikie, F.R.S. *Trans-
actions of the Geological Society of Glasgow*, vol. iii. p. 153.

present rate of denudation, it would require about $5\frac{1}{2}$
million years to reduce the British Isles to a flat plane at
the level of the sea.   It must be remembered, however,
that such calculations are beset with grave difficulties, and
that the results can only be put forth as rough approxima-
tions.   Nevertheless, they are not without their value in
enabling us to form a conception of the great wearing down
of land which must be effected by rain and rivers.

CHAPTER X.

ICE AND ITS WORK.

ALTHOUGH our attention was restricted in the last chapter to the action of rain and rivers, it would be a great mistake to suppose that these are the only agents by which denudation is effected. Rain and rivers unquestionably do much in the way of destruction, but they work with far greater effect when aided by the action of frost. Bare faces of hard rock may be exposed to the action of rain, year after year, without suffering any marked change : the water may fill the pores and fissures of the rock ; yet, unless the mineral components happen to be easily decomposed, it will eat its way into the stone with extreme slowness. But when a frost comes on, the conditions are entirely changed, and a fresh element of destruction is introduced. The water with which the rock is charged freezes into ice and, during its solidification, it tends to expand, as explained in a previous chapter. If the water be confined in the pores and cracks of the rock, the tendency is resisted ; but the particles, in freezing, push each other apart in all directions, with such force, that the strongest rock is sooner or later compelled to yield. Just as a water-pipe bursts during a frost, so the rock ultimately gives way. Fragments of stone, often of large size, are thus rent from the rock and ready to tumble down at the next thaw, exactly as the flakes peel off a stuccoed wall after a hard frost. Nor should it be forgotten that frost does excellent work for the farmer in breaking up hard ground. A stiff soil is more or less loosened after a thaw, and is thus brought easily within the reach of other denuding agents.

In addition to the mechanical force exerted by water during freezing, there are other ways in which ice assists in the destruction of the land. In a country with a mild climate, like that of Britain, the effects of ice are extremely feeble ; yet they are not altogether wanting, even within the basin of the Thames. It has been explained in Chapter IV., that when a body of water is cooled, it shrinks in bulk, like other substances; but it shrinks only when cooled down to a certain temperature. In fact when water is reduced to about 39° Fahr. (4° Cent.) [1] its molecules are packed more closely together than at any other temperature, so that whether you raise or lower the temperature above or below this point, precisely the same effect is produced ; the bulk of the liquid is increased. At 39° Fahr., therefore, water

[1] The thermometer commonly used in this country is graduated according to a plan introduced by Daniel Gabriel Fahrenheit, a native of Dantzic, who settled at Amsterdam in the beginning of the last century, and became famous as a thermometer maker. In Fahrenheit's instrument the distance between the freezing and boiling points of water is divided into 180 equal parts, or degrees, and the zero or starting-point of the scale is arbitrarily placed 32 degrees below this freezing point. On the Continent another scale is commonly used, known as the *centigrade* scale, since the distance between the freezing and boiling points of water is divided into one hundred degrees. The centigrade scale is now frequently used in scientific investigations in this country. As a given temperature is indicated by different numbers on the two scales, they are distinguished by addition of " Fahr." and " Cent." to the readings or simply by the initials F. and C.

is said to have its *maximum density*. This can easily be observed by repeating an old experiment devised originally by Dr. Hope. Insert two thermometers (Fig. 38), at different levels into a cylinder of water, and chill the water by applying ice around the middle of the vessel. As the water becomes cooled it grows denser, and therefore sinks to the bottom, so that the *lower* thermometer falls until it reaches 39° Fahr. Further cooling then *expands* the water, instead of condensing it, and consequently the cold water rises, so that now the *upper* thermometer, which has mean-

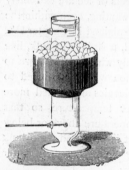

while been almost stationary, begins to fall, and continues falling until, like the upper one, it reaches 39° Fahr. The whole body of water is then at its maximum density, and any further reduction of temperature causes expansion, the cold water becoming specifically lighter and rising to the surface. Gradually, the upper thermometer sinks to the freezing-point, and then a layer of ice begins to form upon the surface. This experiment roughly imitates what occurs in a natural piece of water, such as a lake: the surface freezes, while the bottom-water remains several degrees warmer.

FIG. 38.—Hope's experiment on the contraction of water.

At the moment of freezing, when the particles of water are trying to arrange themselves in those crystalline forms which were noticed in Chapter IV., there is an increase of bulk much greater than that just described.

Ice, being thus relatively much lighter than water, floats upon the surface. Yet there are certain conditions under which ice may be actually formed at the bottom of a stream, and remain there for some time. This formation of *ground-ice* is occasionally seen in parts of the Thames.

Dr. Plot, the first keeper of the Ashmolean Museum at Oxford, published in the year 1677 a famous work on the Natural History of Oxfordshire, in which he refers to the freezing of the Thames in the following words :—" I find it the joint agreement of all the watermen hereabout that I have yet talked with that the congelation of our river is always begun at the bottom, which, however surprising it may seem to the reader, is neither unintelligible nor ridiculous. They all consent that they frequently meet the *ice meers* (for so they call the cakes of ice thus coming from the bottom) in their very rise, and sometimes in the underside including stones and gravel."

To explain the formation of such ground-ice, it has been suggested that the action of the running stream mechanically mixes the cold surface-water with the warmer water below until the temperature becomes uniform throughout ; and when the air is very cold the whole mass may thus be reduced to the freezing-point. The formation of ice will then be determined at the bottom, in consequence of the greater tranquillity of the water and the contact of cold stones and other objects which have become chilled by free radiation. This ground-ice is generally found in little masses clinging to stones and weeds ; and, when the temperature rises after sunrise, the loose bodies are lifted to the surface by the ice, just as if buoyed up with corks. The ice then floats down the river, bearing its little freight of gravel, which is dropped on the bed of the river when the ice is broken up or melted. The Rev. J. C. Clutterbuck, who has paid great attention to the study of the Thames, tells us that he has seen "pieces of rock, eight pounds in weight, raised by a mass from the bottom and carried down the river."[1]   Here then is a geological agent not to be neglected, since it assists the transporting power of streams in carrying solid matter from the land seawards.   But, if the geological importance of ice is to be fully realized, attention must be turned from these trivial illustrations to the grand spectacles which are presented by masses of moving ice in mountain regions beyond the limits of our own islands.

When a snow-storm occurs in this country, the snow does little or nothing in the way of denudation, beyond what it may effect indirectly, by giving rise to floods when a rapid thaw takes place.   In fact, the snow, as snow, protects rather than destroys.   But the result is different in a mountainous country, such as that of the Swiss Alps.   The greater part of the snow which falls there above the snow-line, as explained in Chapter IV., lies all the year round unmelted ; and, therefore, every fall must needs add to the thickness of the heap piled upon the mountain-top.   It is true that the snow evaporates, but the evaporation is extremely slow, and is far from equal to the additions constantly received ; and, though the heat of the sun during the day, may melt the surface layer, the water thus formed sinks in and becomes frozen in the interior of the mass. Occasionally, the accumulation is relieved by a great mass of snow sliding down the mountain slope, as an *avalanche*. Usually, however, the pressure of the heaped-up snow gets rid of the surplus by gently squeezing it into the valleys below, where it moves down with extreme slowness.   Yet it does not come down as a mass of white opaque snow. It has been shown in an earlier part of this work (p. 64) that snow is white and opaque in consequence of the

[1] *Report of the Thames Commissioners*, Appendix i. 1866.

air entangled among its crystals. In squeezing a handful
of snow into a snowball, some of this air is forced out, and
the loose crystals begin to adhere to one another; while, by
compressing snow very tightly in a hydraulic press, it may
be rendered almost homogeneous and thus brought nearly
to the condition of ice (see p. 158). In this way, the great
pressure exerted by the piles of snow in the Alpine snow-
fields compresses the lower layers, and converts them more
or less completely into ice. The imperfectly consolidated
substance, partly snow and partly ice, is known in Switzerland as *Névé* or *Firn*. Moreover, the water produced by
temporary thaw, during sunshine, becomes frozen into ice;
and, in these and other ways, the water, which fell on the
mountain-top as loose white snow, is ultimately sent down
into the valleys in the form of solid ice. The river of ice
which thus drains the high snow-fields is termed a *glacier*
(Fig. 39).[1]

Although we have just spoken of a "river of ice," it is not
easy, at first, to believe that a substance so solid and rigid can
really move in any way like a mobile liquid. Yet the fact
that the glacier does so move can easily be demonstrated.
Drive a row of stakes firmly into the ice across a glacier and
opposite to some well-marked point, as at A in Fig. 40, so
that you may know exactly their position. If you examine
these stakes a week or two afterwards, you will find that they
are no longer at A, but at some point lower down the glacier,
say opposite to B. The ice has therefore moved during this
time from A to B, carrying the stakes with it.

From this experiment it is seen that the ice really moves.
But the experiment teaches something more than this; for
it will be observed that the stakes have not only moved
down, but have changed their relative positions. Instead of

[1] From Agassiz's *Études sur les Glaciers.* Neuchatel, 1840.

FIG. 39.—Glacier of Zermatt.

forming a straight line across the ice, as at A, they now form
a curve at B; the stakes in the middle of the row have got
farther from A than those at the sides, and it is therefore
clear that they must have moved faster.   But the movement
of the stakes is due simply to the movement of the ice, so
that if the middle stakes move faster than the side ones, it
shows that the middle of the glacier moves faster than its
sides.   Exactly the same thing
may be observed in a river: light
bodies floated on a stream move
like the stakes carried down by
the glacier.   Nor is it difficult to
see why a river should flow more
rapidly in the middle than at its
sides.   The particles of water at
the sides rub against the banks,
and consequently are not so free
to move as the particles in the
middle of the stream.   In like
manner, friction against the rocky
walls on the flanks of a glacier
causes the ice at the sides to

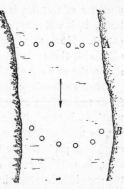

FIG. 40.—Motion of a glacier.

move more sluggishly than the ice in the middle.   Again,
it is known that, in a river, the particles at the bottom drag
along the bed and move less rapidly than those at the
surface.   The ice of a glacier behaves in precisely the same
way.   It is concluded, therefore, that the motion of a glacier
is like the motion of a river.   If the glacier enters a gorge,
it becomes contracted and the flow is rapid : while, if its
bed widens, it spreads out and the movement becomes
slower.   In truth, in all points, the motion of a glacier
resembles that of a river; the movement is essentially
the same in kind but different in degree, the rate of

movement of the glacier being perhaps only a few inches
or, at most, a yard or two, daily.

This sluggish motion of a glacier, and the way in which it
accommodates itself to all the inequalities of the surface
over which it travels, long ago gave rise to the supposition
that ice is a plastic or viscous substance, something like
dough or even treacle, so that it can sink into a depression,
or ride over a ridge, without losing its continuity. Yet, as
a matter of fact, ice is so brittle that if you pull, or try to
bend, it, it will snap, without stretching to any appreciable
extent. How, then, can the apparent plasticity be recon-
ciled with the undoubted brittleness? Prof. Tyndall[1] has
shown the way out of this difficulty.

When a schoolboy makes a snowball, he squeezes a handful or two of light snow into a hard compact lump; and it is
worth noting that, if the snow be just on the point of thaw-
ing, he will be able to weld it into a firmer mass than if he
employed perfectly hard and dry snow. Snow, as we have
seen, is nothing but a confused mass of ice-crystals; and
the snowball becomes hard, partly, because it contains less
air, and, partly, because the little pieces of ice of which it
is composed, instead of remaining loose, stick firmly to one
another. But why do they thus become welded together?
Experiment shows that when two pieces of damp ice are
pressed together, they immediately freeze into one solid
mass. Faraday observed this curious fact five-and-twenty
years ago, and the phenomenon has been termed *regelation*.
Hence, when snow is strongly squeezed, the icy particles
freeze together into a compact substance; and, hence, the
snow from which a glacier takes its birth, is pressed by the
weight above into a hard mass, more or less like true ice.

[1] See *The Glaciers of the Alps*, by John Tyndall, F.R.S.   1860.

A number of pieces of ice, powerfully squeezed together in a hydraulic press, are readily united into a solid lump, or a single mass may be crushed, and the fragments built up into a differently shaped body. In a similar manner, when a glacier is forced over an obstacle, the ice, being brittle, cracks and snaps, but the enormous pressure of the sliding mass behind, squeezes it together again, and regelation immediately heals the fractures. The glacier therefore accommodates itself to irregularities in its bed, not by virtue of any real plasticity, but by being successively fractured and frozen. In fact, by suitable means, ice may be artificially moulded at will, as though it possessed true plasticity; and a similar operation is doubtless carried on in nature.

As it creeps down the valley, the glacier transports, from higher to lower levels, any detrital matter that may happen to fall upon its surface. From the neighbouring rocks, fragments are constantly being loosened by atmospheric agents, and these, sooner or later, tumble down upon the glacier. In this way, a line of débris fringes each side of the glacier, some of the stones being perhaps several tons in weight. Such accumulations of detritus are known as *moraines;* and, as those which are now being described, occur on the two sides of the ice-river they are distinguished as *lateral moraines.* As the glacier moves along, the moraine-matter is carried forwards, until, at length, it reaches the end of the glacier; and thus fragments of rock may be transported down the valley, far from the heights above. The water which issues from the melting ice, at the end of the glacier, is unable to carry off this burden of stones which the ice has deposited; and, hence, we generally find, across the end of the glacier, a confused heap of rubbish, known as a *terminal moraine.* When two streams of ice unite, the lateral

moraines unite also, as in Fig. 41, where A B C D represent
the four lateral moraines of two glaciers. It is clear that,
after the union of the two branch-streams, the outer moraines,
A and D, will continue to occupy the sides of the trunk-
glacier; while the two inner moraines will unite at the fork
E, and form only one ridge of detritus, which will be carried
along the middle of the main glacier. This middle line of
stones is therefore distinguished as a *medial moraine*. If a

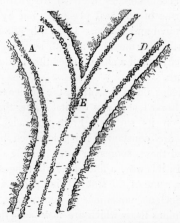

Fig. 41.—Lateral and medial moraines.

glacier receives in its course many side-branches, each con-
tributing its moraines, the entire surface of the ice may
ultimately become strewn with rubbish.

A glacier resembles a river, not only in its power of thus
transporting detritus from a higher to a lower level, but also
in acting as a direct agent of denudation. Just as a river
wears away its banks and its bed, so the ice acts on the sides
and bottom of the valley along which it travels. If the

ice has to turn a sharp corner, or make an abrupt descent, it is forced to split, and in this way yawning chasms, perhaps hundreds of feet in depth, are produced in the glacier. Such rents are termed *crevasses*. Stones, sometimes of great size, fall with a crash down these clefts, and reaching the bottom of the glacier get frozen into its base. As the glacier moves, these stones, pressed by the weight of ice above, scratch and score the rocky bed in the direction of the ice-flow; while the stones themselves, jammed in between the ice and its floor, get bruised in turn, so that by the time they are discharged at the terminal moraine they may be covered with parallel scratches.

At the same time, the smaller fragments worn off the rocks by the passage of a glacier get ground down into fine gravel, sand, and mud, which may be carried in suspension by the stream of water which flows over the bed of the glacier. For it should be noted that the bottom layer of ice, pressed by the weight above, and grinding along the floor, is generally in a state of thaw ; and, moreover, water finds its way from the surface to the bottom through crevasses. Hence, a little liquid stream separates the bottom ice from the rocky bed; and at the end, or snout, of the glacier this water issues forth, not indeed as a clear bright spring, but as a thick stream laden with detritus. The Rhine, the Rhone, the Po, the Ganges, and many other large rivers, may be traced back to muddy streams springing from glaciers. The fine detrital matter which the water thus carries along polishes the surface of the rock over which it flows. The action of a glacier is consequently twofold : the fine sandy matter polishes the surface, while the large stones scratch furrows. It is, in fact, as though some giant hand had rubbed the surface of the rock with fine emery powder, and at the same time rasped it with a huge file.

M

All rough points of rock in the path of a glacier are thus rubbed down, and projecting masses are smoothed to the form of rounded bosses. The flat-domed hummocks of rock produced in this way are termed *sheep-backs* or *roches moutonnées* (Fig. 42), since, if seen in the distance, they bear

FIG. 42.—Roches Moutonnées Creek, Colorado (Hayden).

some resemblance to a flock of sheep. Hence, the passage of a glacier across a country gives rise to peculiar features not produced by any other agent of denudation; and, by these peculiarities, we may tell, with certainty, that ice has been at work in a district where there is, perhaps, not a vestige of ice at the present day. Thus, in many of the valleys of Switzerland, not now occupied by glaciers, the rocks are rounded, polished, and scratched, showing that the Swiss glaciers must formerly have been of gigantic proportions and that they extended far beyond the limits retained by their present successors.

On travelling northwards, the snow-line is found to descend until, in the Arctic Regions, it comes down to the very sea-level. Hence, in such regions, the entire surface of land may be enveloped in a mantle of ice. This ice-sheet creeps down towards the shore, until its foot at length advances into the sea. Huge masses of ice then become detached, and are sent drifting away as icebergs. These mountains of ice often assume most fantastic shapes ; and their vast mass produces so great a depression of temperature in the neighbouring air that, when they are carried into the Atlantic, they are usually obscured by a shroud of mist The icebergs, like glaciers, are laden with fragments of rock worn from the land over which the ice-sheet travelled ; and when, on reaching warmer waters, they melt, they discharge this freight of stones and earth, which may thus get carried far from their original home. When blocks of rock are borne along by running water, they become rounded by the friction to which they are subjected ; but, when a fragment of rock is transported on an iceberg, it may retain much of its angularity and be dropped upon the sea-bed in an almost unworn state. The finer detritus which the berg carries will be diffused through the water in which the ice melts ; and currents may transport it far away into southern latitudes. If a glacier descends to the edge of a lake, exactly the same thing occurs as in the formation of an iceberg. A tongue of ice is pushed into the water, and bergs break off and float away, carrying their burden of moraine matter to be strewn over the bottom of the lake on the melting of the floating ice. If the bottom of the lake, or of the sea, should at any time be upheaved, the glacial mud and gravel, with angular blocks and ice-scratched boulders, may be exposed to view ; and may thus furnish evidence of glacial denudation in countries which are now free from anything like glaciers or icebergs.

Other evidence of ice-action is afforded by the peculiar position of large angular blocks of stone, poised perhaps upon the very edge of a precipice, or balanced upon a mere point. Such stones, known as *perched blocks* or *blocs perchés*, could hardly have been brought into their strange position by mere rolling, or by the action of running water ; but it is easy to see that they might have been dropped by an ice-berg, or left stranded by the gradual melting of a glacier on which they were originally seated.

It is now more than a quarter of a century since the late Prof. Agassiz, who had been a diligent observer of glacial action in Switzerland, visited this country, and in company with Dr. Buckland pointed out the evidence of former ice-action in many parts of Britain. The traveller in Scotland, Ireland, Cumberland, or North Wales, will have no diffi-culty in detecting *roches moutonnées*, perched blocks, and occasionally the remains of old moraines ; while here and there, where the rocks have been protected, the glacial polish and striations are still preserved. Such evidence conclusively proves that ice must have flowed over the sur-face of the country. It is believed, indeed, that at one period of geological history, known generally as the *Glacial Period*, Britain must have been buried beneath a vast sheet of ice, similar to that which now covers Greenland. This ice played its part in rasping and grinding and polishing the surface of the land ; and it has even been suggested by Prof. Ramsay that many of the rock-basins which contain lakes

have been scooped out by the action of huge masses of
moving ice. Nor is it only the effects of land-ice which
the glacialist sees marked upon the rocks of Britain. During
part of the Glacial Period, the land must have been submerged beneath the waters of an icy sea ; and icebergs,
drifting from the north, scattered their freight upon the
rocky floor which has since been upheaved as dry land.
Even in the very neighbourhood of London, as at Finchley,
deposits of gravel and clay may be found crowded with ice-
borne boulders, which still retain their glacial scratches.
This *drift*, as it is termed, not to cite other evidence, sufficiently shows that there must have been a time when ice
played its part, as an agent of denudation, within the basin
of the Thames.

CHAPTER XI.

THE SEA AND ITS WORK.

At Margate, where the estuary of the Thames ends in the North Sea, even a blind man could not stand long upon the shingly beach without knowing that the sea was busily at work. Every wave that rolls in from the open ocean hurls the pebbles up the slope of the beach; and then, as soon as the wave has broken and the water has dispersed, these pebbles come rattling down with the currents that sweep back to sea. The chatter of the beach thus tells us plainly that, as the stones are being dragged up and down, they are constantly knocked against each other; and, it is evident, that, by such rough usage, all angular fragments of rock will soon have their corners rounded off, and become rubbed into the form of pebbles. As these pebbles are rolled to and fro upon the beach they get worn smaller and smaller, until, at length, they are reduced to the state of sand. Although this sand is at first coarse, it gradually becomes finer and finer, as surely as though it were ground in a mill; and, ultimately, it is carried out to sea as fine sediment, and laid down upon the ocean-floor.

On examination of the chalk cliffs, which back the beach, it is easy to see how these suffer by the constant dash of the waves. Rain, frost, and other atmospheric agents, playing their part in the work of destruction, attack the clift and dislodge masses of rock which come tumbling down to its base, where they accumulate as a line of rubbish. As soon as the fragments are brought within reach of the waves, they are rolled against the cliff, bruising and battering the face of the rock, while the fragments themselves are apt to get shivered in the fray.

During violent gales the breakers acquire unusual power, and are able to move rocks of enormous weight. On the western coast of Britain, where the Atlantic breakers roll in upon the shore, they have been known to exert a pressure of between three and four tons on every square foot of surface exposed to their fury. Even in summer, these waves break upon the coast with a pressure of about 600 pounds per square foot; and, in winter, this force is often trebled. It is easy to believe that such masses of moving water can carry with them huge blocks of stone, and hurling these against the shore, can breach it just as effectually as though it were attacked by the blows of a battering-ram. In fact, whether in storm or in calm, a cannonade, more or less sharp, is constantly kept up against the coast, the ammunition being supplied by the ruins of the coast itself.

Were the waves to break upon the shore without the aid of any fragments of rock, the mere weight of water would naturally effect some amount of destruction; but, there is reason to believe that, in most cases, this would be comparatively slight. It has been already shown that a river erodes its channel, not so much by its own friction, as by that of the sedimentary matter which it sweeps along in its course. In like manner, the wear and tear of the waves themselves is insignificant compared with that wrought by the boulders and pebbles, the gravel and sand, which they bring to bear upon the coast. Every wave carries, as it were, a number of stone hammers, with which it bruises and batters the cliffs ; and, as this action is persistently repeated by wave after wave, the hardest rock is at length forced to yield.

Almost any part of our coast-line will serve to show the destructive effects of the sea. It is true, the action is much less marked in some directions than in others; while, at certain points, the sea may be engaged, not in destroying, but in actually forming land, by deposition of sedimentary matter resulting from the destruction of the shore elsewhere. As a rule, however, abundant evidence of marine waste may be seen on any visit to the seaside. Bays and coves may be hollowed out in one part of the coast, and a headland may be worn away in another: here, caves are being ex- cavated in the base of a cliff; there, tunnels are drilled through some projecting rock; while, in many places, wall- like masses are partially detached from the cliffs so as to stand out as buttresses, or are even completely isolated in the form of " needles," " stacks," and " skerries." A good example of marine denudation is furnished by the well- known Needles off the Isle of Wight (Fig. 43). A ridge of chalk runs across the island from east to west, and it is evident that the outstanding wedge-shaped masses were once connected with this main body, though now completely surrounded by the sea. The headlands of chalk have been beaten about by the waves until a passage has been forced at a weak point, here and there; and pillars of chalk have thus been separated from the mainland.

Where cliffs are formed partly of hard, and partly of soft, rocks, the latter will naturally be more easily attacked by the waves. The fantastic forms which sea-cliffs assume may often be explained on this principle ; the harder beds, or

dykes, of rock standing out in bold relief when the neighbouring softer rocks have been eaten away. The oldest,
and, as a rule, the hardest rocks of Britain are developed in
the western and northern parts of the island, and hence the
sea acts with less effect upon them than upon the softer
rocks in the east and south of England. Even cursory
inspection of a map of England and Wales serves to show
how the flowing outlines of the chalk coasts of Norfolk,

Fig. 43.—The Needles, Isle of Wight.

Lincolnshire, and Yorkshire, contrast with the sharp outlines
and bold headlands formed by the old rocks of western
Cornwall, Pembrokeshire, and Carnarvonshire.

In the estuary of the Thames, the rocks are comparatively
soft, consisting for the most part of sands, clays and chalk.
Within the Thames Basin, then, there should be no difficulty
in obtaining evidence of marine waste. Thus Sir C. Lyell

has pointed out that the Isle of Sheppey has suffered considerably by the inroads of the sea, fifty acres of land having been lost within the short space of twenty years, though the cliffs there are from sixty to eighty feet in height. Herne Bay, on the Kentish coast, has lost land to such an extent that it no longer retains its shape as a bay. Going yet further out into the estuary of the Thames, we find a notable illustration of marine destruction at Reculver. This was the old Roman station of *Regulbium*. Not only has the sea entirely destroyed the military wall, but the church, which in the time of Henry VIII. was nearly a mile inland, is now on the very brink of the cliff; and, indeed, it has only been saved from actual destruction by artificial means. As the two towers of the church form a well-known landmark to mariners, a causeway has been constructed on the beach to arrest the progress of the sea.

If the sea were a body of water in perfect repose, it would be utterly incapable of effecting mechanical erosion. But every one knows that the sea is never absolutely at rest, and that, even in the calmest weather, its surface is ordinarily more or less troubled with waves. It is easy to understand how these are formed. When you blow upon the surface of a basin of water, the mechanical disturbance of the air is immediately imparted to the liquid, and the surface is thrown into a succession of ripples. In like manner, every disturbance of the atmosphere finds its reflex on the surface of the natural waters. Each puff of wind catches hold of the water, and heaps it up into a little hill with the face to leeward; then the crest falls, and the water sinks down into a trough, as deep below the mean surface as the hill was high above it; but the next column of water is then forced up, only however to be pulled down again, and in this way the motion of the wave may be propagated across a broad expanse of water. Drop a stone into a pond, and the same kind of action will be seen : the water all round the spot where the stone falls is first depressed in a little cup, and then rises again, the motion being taken up by the neighbouring water ; and a succession of circles, each wider than the last, spreads over the pond, until the ripples at length die away upon the shore. If any light object, such as a cork, happens to be floating on the surface, it will serve to indicate the the motion of the water below. As the waves reach it, the cork rises and falls, but it is not carried forward by the movement of the water. Exactly the same kind of action may be witnessed at sea. If a gull, for example, is seated on a wave it is simply rocked up and down, and not moved onwards.

Such simple observations are sufficient to show that the motion of the water is a movement of undulation and not of translation ; it is merely the form of the wave, and not the actual water, that travels. The motion is transmitted from particle to particle, to a great distance ; but the particles themselves perform very small excursions, merely vibrating up and down, or rather revolving in vertical circular paths. The general effect is similar, as has often been pointed out, to that witnessed when a gust of wind sweeps across a field of corn. Notwithstanding the impression produced on the observer, he knows that any movement of translation is here quite out of the question ; the stalks are not uprooted and carried across the field, but each stalk simply bends down before the wind and then returns to its erect position. Similarly, in the open sea, the wave, or pulsation, is propagated, but the mass of the water at any given spot remains stationary, except in so far as it vibrates up and down. The mechanical force of the wind, however, urges the surface-water forwards to a small extent. A fresh breeze tears off the water from the crest of a wave, and scatters it as spray, and a heavy gale converts this into blinding showers of salt rain. The wind too catches the top of the wave, and causing it to move faster than the water below, urges it to leeward in the form of a graceful curl, the edge of which breaks into foam. On reaching a shore, the retardation of the deeper part of the wave by friction against the sea bottom, increases the relative velocity of the superficial part, and the latter rolls over; the water bursts with great force upon the land, and then sweeps back, as a powerful "undertow," to the sea.

However agitated the surface of the sea may be, there is reason to believe that the disturbance never extends far downwards. The more violent the wind, the greater of course will be the agitation which it is capable of producing; but, even during a storm, the waves never attain to anything like the height which is often popularly ascribed to them. It is not uncommon to hear of the sea running "mountains high;" yet, in a strong gale in the open ocean the height of a wave, from crest to trough, rarely exceeds forty feet. In the shallow seas around our own islands, they are far from attaining to such a magnitude; the largest waves, even in a storm, not exceeding eight or ten feet in height. The disturbance produced by such waves extends downwards to only a comparatively small depth. In fact, the motion of the largest waves is almost imperceptible at a depth of about 300 fathoms, or 1,800 feet; while the agitation produced by ordinary waves must be quite insignificant at one-third of this depth. So far, then, as the destruction of the land by the sea depends on the mechanical action of such waves, it must cease at about 100 fathoms. Indeed it is probably very feeble at depths much less than this; and, in most cases, on our own shores, it is not very marked below the limit of the lowest tide.

Winds not only agitate the sea and produce irregular waves, but where they are constantly blowing over the ocean in a definite direction they cause the surface-water to take a similar course, and thus produce steady *drifts* or *currents*. Dr. Croll has shown that the direction of the great ocean currents agrees very closely with that of the prevailing winds. Bottles thrown overboard from ships in the open ocean may be carried by these currents for hundreds of miles, and ultimately cast upon distant shores. Pieces of wood, and nuts and seeds, known to be native to the West Indies and tropical America, are occasionally drifted across the Atlantic, and are washed on to the western shores of England, Scotland and Ireland, and even across to Norway. In like manner, the Portuguese men-of-war (*Physalia,Velella*) and those oceanic snails with violet shells called *Ianthinæ*, are now and then brought as visitors to our coasts, though usually confined to warmer seas far to the south and west.

Perhaps the best known of these oceanic currents is the *Gulf Stream*, which is a broad body of warm water sweeping out of the Gulf of Mexico, through the Strait of Florida. After running northwards, nearly parallel to the coast of the United States, it strikes across the Atlantic Ocean in a north-easterly direction. Warm currents, which continue the direction of the Gulf Stream, set on to the western shores of Britain and even extend to the coast of Norway; while, other currents, parting with these in mid-ocean, turn to the south and sweep round the coasts of Spain and Northern Africa. The cause of the Gulf Stream is undoubtedly to be sought in the so-called "Trade Winds," which,

constantly blowing more or less from the north-eastward,
give a westerly impulse to the inter-tropical surface waters of
the Atlantic, and thus create the current, which sets into the
Gulf of Mexico. But, whether the stream, after it leaves
the coasts of the United States, retains sufficient impetus to
carry it to our shores ; or whether, as some believe, the true
Gulf Stream is lost in the middle of the Atlantic, and any

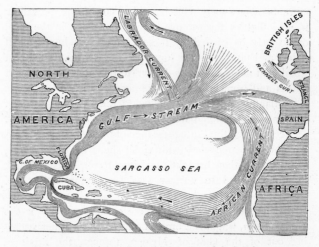

FIG. 44.—Map of the Atlantic, showing course of the Gulf Stream.

warm currents felt on our own coasts are due to the predominant south-westerly winds of the temperate part of the
Atlantic, is as yet uncertain.

The general course of the Gulf Stream is shown in Fig.
44. Where the water issues from the Gulf of Mexico, through
the Florida Narrows, it has a temperature of upwards of 80°
Fahr. and moves at the rate of between four and five miles
an hour. In passing across the Atlantic. the current widens,

and its speed is slackened, but it cools with extreme slowness, so that it carries along a considerable store of heat.

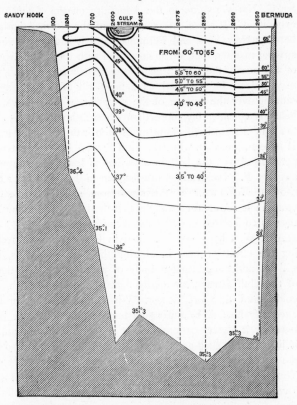

FIG. 45.—Section of the Atlantic Ocean between Sandy Hook (near New York) and
    Bermuda, a distance of 700 nautical miles. The figures above the dotted lines
    indicate depths in fathoms. Drawn to true scale this diagram would be about
    five feet wide.

The stream forms, in fact, a sharply-defined river of warm
water flowing over the colder water of the ocean.

That the Gulf Stream is an extremely shallow body of water is well seen in Fig. 45, which is reduced from one of Sir G. Nares' reports to the Admiralty on the *Challenger* expedition. It represents a section of the North Atlantic, between New York and Bermuda; and it shows in a very striking manner, that, when compared with the great depth of the ocean, the Gulf Stream is extremely superficial. It may indeed be regarded as a mere rill of warm water running over the surface of the sea; for, while the water below is considerably more than 2,000 fathoms in depth, the Gulf Stream itself is not more than 100 fathoms deep. It is seen, too, that, while the Gulf Stream has here a temperature of 75°, the bottom water has as low a temperature as 35°3 F. Incidentally, the diagram in Fig. 45 serves to show the character of the sea-bottom along the line of section; it shows, for example, that the island of Bermuda rises as an isolated peak from water of great depth.[1]

After what has been explained in Chapter IV. respecting the effect of heat in altering the bulk of bodies, it will be understood that a body of warm water, like that of the Gulf Stream, can easily float upon water which is colder and therefore denser. When a mass of water is unequally heated, by raising its temperature below, or by lowering it above, currents are at once established; and, if light matter, such as sawdust, be suspended in the liquid, the direction of these currents becomes very evident. Thus in Fig. 46, where heat is applied at the bottom of a vessel, the liquid becomes specifically lighter and therefore rises, whilst the surrounding colder water being denser, runs down in streams to supply the place of that which has ascended to the surface. This is, in fact, the ordinary way

---

[1] The caution which has already been given respecting the exaggeration of the vertical height in the diagrams, must not be forgotten.

in which heat is propagated through a body of liquid, and the process is called *convection*,[1] to distinguish it from *conduction*, or the method by which heat is propagated through solid bodies. In conduction, the heat is passed on from particle to particle, and thus travels through the mass, while, in convection, the heated particles themselves move. Again, if a piece of ice be dropped into a tumbler of slightly warm water, a system of currents will also be established, as in Fig. 47. From the bottom of the piece of ice a clear

FIG. 45.—Currents in water by heat.   FIG. 47.—Currents in water by cold.

stream of heavy cold liquid flows down the middle of the glass, like a stream of clear oil, while the neighbouring water, which is comparatively warm, flows upwards in currents nearer to the sides of the vessel.

Unequal cooling or heating of the great natural masses of water will be competent to produce a circulation similar to that just described. During the recent voyage of the *Challenger* the temperature of the sea at different depths

---

[1] *Convection*, from Lat. *con*, and *veho*, I carry, the heat being carried by currents through the fluid mass.

was very carefully examined by means of instruments specially constructed to avoid sources of error. These observations show that, as a rule, the temperature diminishes as you descend, just as was shown to be the case in the North Atlantic. Reference to Fig. 45 shows that the bottom-water of that part of the ocean has a temperature only a little above 35° F.; while, in other places, it is still lower, and may even descend below the freezing-point of fresh water.[1] It appears that the presence of such cold water in the deeper parts of the ocean, even in tropical regions, can hardly be explained otherwise than by assuming a grand movement of water from the polar towards the equatorial regions. Dr. Carpenter has brought forward much evidence to prove the existence of such a general oceanic circulation, and he refers the movement mainly to differences of density due to differences of temperature. The cold polar waters sink by their density and form a deep layer, which creeps along the ocean-floor towards the equatorial regions; while the warmer and relatively lighter water floats on the surface in a contrary direction, or from equatorial towards polar areas.[2] By such means, a complete

[1] The freezing-point of water is lowered by the addition of common salt, and ordinary sea-water does not freeze until reduced to 28°·4 F.

[2] The character of this circulation will of course be greatly modified by the shape and depth of the sea-bottom over which the cold water creeps. Thus, the southern part of the Atlantic basin communicates freely with the Antarctic Sea, and the influx of cold water is therefore unimpeded; but the northern part of the basin is contracted, and the principal channel through which Arctic water can flow southwards is the shallow channel between Greenland and Iceland; hence the underflow of glacial water from the North will be much less than that from the South. This is still more strikingly shown by the shape of the great Pacific basin, where the communication with the Northern Polar seas is confined to the narrow and shallow channel of Behring's Strait, through which very little glacial water can flow to the south.

circulation might be established; and it has consequently been said that every drop of water in the open ocean may, in course of time, be brought up from the greatest depths to the surface. Other meteorological conditions, however, may exert an influence of the same kind, as great as, or even greater than, that produced by difference of temperature. Sir Wyville Thomson regards the influx of cold water into the Pacific and Atlantic Oceans from the south as an indraught due to " the excess of evaporation over precipitation in the northern portion of the land hemisphere, and the excess of precipitation over evaporation in the middle and southern part of the water hemisphere." [1]

It seems probable that ocean-currents are of no great importance as agents of denudation or of transport. A slow circulation of the entire mass of the ocean, brought about by such comparatively slight differences of density in the water of different parts of the ocean, as are here under consideration, might perhaps facilitate the dispersion of the finest sedimentary matter. Again, where the surface-currents strike upon the shore they must do something in the work of denudation, though as a rule this will be extremely slight; the effect of currents, indeed, is not so much to abrade the land as to carry off the results of its abrasion by other means, and to distribute the finely-suspended matter, far and wide, over the floor of the ocean.

In addition to the movements of the sea which have been already noted in this chapter—the wind-waves, the surface-currents, and the general circulation—it must not

Hence it is believed by Sir Wyville Thomson that the greater part of the cold bottom-water in the North Pacific, and a good deal of that in the North Atlantic, is an indraught from Antarctic, and not from Arctic seas.

[1] *Proceedings of the Royal Society*, vol. xxiv. No. 170, p. 470.

be forgotten that the ocean is subject to that grand rhythmical movement which was referred to in the first chapter. We saw, when standing on London Bridge, that the water regularly ebbed and flowed; and, what it does there, it does at every point along our coast. Twice in every four-and-twenty hours the margin of the sea rises, and twice it falls, so that its level is constantly shifting up and down. And yet it is a common practice to say that a given elevation is so many feet above the sea-level. Such a statement assumes that the standard taken is neither high-water mark nor low-water mark, but the mean level between the two; the water rising, at one time, as much above our standard level as it falls, at another time, below it. The Ordnance Survey has fixed its *datum line*, or standard from which all heights are measured, as the mean tide-level at Liverpool. The level of high water at London Bridge, which is sometimes taken as a standard, is called, from the Trinity House, " Trinity High-water mark."

As the cause of the tides is to be found outside our earth, its explanation must be deferred to a later portion of this work. It is sufficient to remark, in this place, that the great tidal-wave, which travels round the earth, is an oscillatory wave, and not a wave of translation ; the water simply rising and falling, but not moving onwards. While, however, this is true of the tidal wave in the ocean, it must be borne in mind that, in narrow seas, it becomes converted into an actual wave of translation. Where the channel is contracted, as in a narrow strait, the tide may produce a rapid rush of water, or a *race*. If, again, the tidal wave rolls into a narrow estuary, the water becomes heaped up, and produces a sudden rush into the channel of the river : such a wave is called a *bore*, and is well seen in the Bristol Channel, at the mouth of the Severn, where at certain seasons the head of water attains to as great a height as forty feet.

In the estuary of a tidal river, the tide periodically agitates the water; and thus hinders deposition of sediment. The flow of the river seawards is, however, checked every time the tide comes in, and sediment is then deposited; hence, *bars*, or banks of sand, are common at the mouths of rivers; and, even in the estuary of the Thames, the shifting shoals indicate similar depositions. But, it has been shown in a former chapter, that the ebb-tide, by scouring out the estuary, prevents the formation of a true delta. The position of the principal sands in the estuary of the Thames between the Nore and Margate, is shown in Fig. 48, which is reduced from a part of the Admiralty chart.

The sediment which the tidal water carries away from the mouth of a river at one part of the coast may be deposited at another point, and thus the sea may become a constructive agent charged with the formation of new land. Usually, however, the suspended matter swept away by the ebb-tide is carried out to sea, where it may be caught up by currents and thus drifted to a great distance. Hence the tides and currents assist greatly in distributing the solid matter derived from the waste of the land.

Putting together what has been said in this chapter with reference to the action of the sea upon the land, it may be concluded that its work, on the whole, is a work of destruction, yet not exactly like that of rain and rivers. To observe this difference, it must be borne in mind that marine denudation is not equally active at all depths of the sea. The waves, as explained above, indicate only superficial agitation, and have no effect on deep water. Most of the destruction wrought by the sea is consequently confined

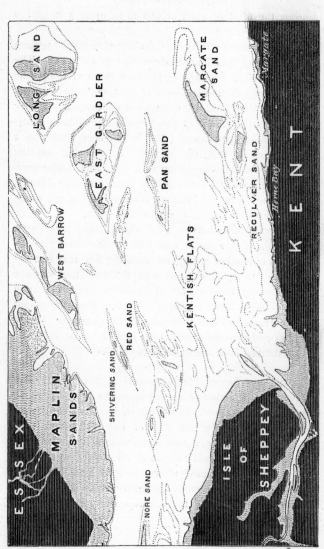

FIG. 48.—Chart of the estuary of the Thames between the Nore and Margate.   Scale about six miles to one inch.

within narrow limits, not extending deeper than a few hundred feet, and being for the most part restricted to the zone of coast between high and low water-marks. At great depths, the abrasion by slow under-currents must be extremely small, for dredgings have shown that, in deep seas, there are no large fragments of rock to assist in the work of demolition; and, even if there were, the force of the current would probably be insufficient to move them. The great business of the sea is therefore confined to eating away the margin of the coast, and planing it down to a depth of perhaps a hundred fathoms. If this action went on for a sufficient time, the entire coast would be nibbled away, and Britain reduced to a great plain

FIG. 49.—Plain of marine denudation.

below the sea-level. The comparatively smooth surface which would be formed in this manner has been called by Prof. Ramsay a *plain of marine denudation*. Were such a submarine plain to be upheaved above the surface of the water, it would immediately be attacked by rain, frost and other atmospheric agents, and would eventually be chiselled, by these means, into a variety of physical features. It is believed that old plains of marine denudation may yet be detected in certain districts. Thus, if Fig. 49 represents a section across a country where the highest points may be connected by a plane, the edge of which is A B; this plane surface, with a gentle slope seaward, probably coincides with the original plain of marine denudation, or is at least parallel

to it, the present irregular surface of the country being
due to subaerial denudation. Denudation by the sea differs
then from that effected by other agents, in that it tends to
produce an approximately level surface, while subaerial
denudation gives rise to superficial irregularities.

CHAPTER XII.

ALL the natural agents described in the last three chapters, however much they may differ among themselves, agree in this—that they are, upon the whole, slow and certain agents of destruction. Rain and river, frost and thaw, wind and wave—all work in the same direction, persistently attacking the solid land and sweeping away its superficial substance. Not that a particle of this substance is annihilated. Every grain stolen from the land is sooner or later carefully deposited somewhere in the sea. But, still, this gradual transference of matter, from land to water, must ultimately result in the lowering of the general level of the land to that of the sea by the action of the rain and rivers; and, in the subsequent paring down of the plain, thus formed, to the depth at which marine denudation becomes insensible. If, therefore, no hindrance were offered to the action of these agents, not only would a time come when every foot of the British Isles would be buried beneath the sea; but, inasmuch as the volume of the sea is very much greater than that of the land which rises above the sea-level, if sufficient time were granted, all the dry land in the world would ultimately disappear beneath one universal sheet of water.

It is not difficult, however, to detect in the operations of nature, counterbalancing forces which are capable of upheaving the deposits that have been formed on the sea-bottom, and of piling up fresh stores of solid matter upon the surface of the earth. Among these elevatory, and therefore reparative, agents, the most important place must be assigned to those which give rise to earthquakes and volcanoes. After the occurrence of an earthquake, it is by no means uncommon to find that the level of the land has been shifted. Sometimes, it is true, the surface is depressed, but more commonly the movement is in the direction of elevation.

Perhaps the best recorded example of such upheaval is that which was observed by Admiral Fitzroy and Mr. Darwin when examining the western coast of South America. This region is peculiarly subject to subterranean disturbances, and in 1835 a violent earthquake, which destroyed several towns, was felt along the coast of Chile, extending from Copiapo to Chiloe. It was found, after the shock, that the land in the Bay of Concepcion had been elevated to the extent of four or five feet. At an island called Santa Maria, about twenty-five miles south-west of Concepcion, the upheaval was easily measured, vertically, on the steep cliffs ; and the measurements showed that the south-western part of the island was raised eight feet, while the northern end was lifted more than ten feet high. Beds of dead mussels were, in fact, hoisted ten feet above high-water mark ; and an extensive rocky flat, previously covered by the sea, was exposed as dry land. In like manner, the bottom of the surrounding sea must have been elevated, for soundings all round the island became shallower by about nine feet. It is true, there was a partial subsidence shortly afterwards, but this was far from sufficient to neutralize the upheaval, and the net result showed a permanent elevation. It is considered probable, that the greater part of the South American coast has been raised several hundred feet by a succession of such small upheavals.

When an area is thus raised, the addition suddenly made to the mass of dry land may be very considerable, and will compensate for the effects of denudation continued through a long period.   It was calculated, for example, by Sir C. Lyell, that, during an earthquake which occurred in Chile in 1822, a mass of rock more than equal in weight to a hundred thousand of the great pyramids of Egypt was added to the South-American continent.   If a single convulsion of this kind can thus raise such an amount of solid land from beneath the waters, it is obvious that these movements must be of great service in renovating the surface of the earth, and in bringing new material within reach of the ever-active agents of denudation. It is proper to remark, that an earthquake-wave is a vibration of the solid crust of the earth, which may, and constantly does, occur, without giving rise to any permanent change in its form.   Nevertheless, the wave is often accompanied by movements of elevation, or of depression, which produce permanent alterations of level of considerable magnitude.

An earthquake is just such a disturbance of the ground as would result from a sudden shock, or blow, given upwards in the interior of the earth, from which, as from a centre, waves or tremors may be propagated in all directions through the solid ground.   In many cases, the shock is preceded or accompanied by a rumbling noise, like that of distant thunder, or by other sounds produced by the subterranean disturbance.   The earthquake-wave, as it travels along, causes the ground to rise and fall, and frequently produces irregular fissures, which may close again and thus bury whatever has been engulfed, or may remain open as yawning chasms, and thus modify the drainage of the country.   The impulse may be transmitted through the earth to an enormous distance; the great earthquake which destroyed Lisbon in 1755, having made itself felt, directly or indirectly, on the waters of Loch Lomond in Scotland. If the centre of disturbance is near the sea, the water is affected even more than the land, and the water-waves may be far more destructive than the earth-waves. News has recently reached this country of the terrible devastation wrought by the great tidal wave which followed the earthquake at Lima, Arica, Iquique and other points of the coast of South America in May, 1877.

A good deal of attention has been paid by Mr. R. Mallet to the study of earthquake phenomena, or *Seismology*,[1] and he is led to conclude that the origin of the disturbance is usually not deep-seated in the interior of the earth, probably never exceeding a depth of thirty miles; while in many cases, it is certainly much less. Thus he ascertained that the great Neapolitan shock of 1857 had its origin at a depth of only eight or nine miles beneath the surface. Dr. Oldham has since found that a great earthquake at Cachar, in India, in 1869, had its focus, or centre of impulse, at a depth of about thirty miles.

Although earthquake-shocks are happily of rare occurrence in this country, it must be remembered that, in many parts of the world, they are by no means rare phenomena; and, probably, it is not overstating the case to say that earthquake shocks occur, on an average, about three times a week. During the year 1876, for example, no fewer than 104 earthquakes are recorded in Professor Fuchs's Annual Report; and, in the preceding year, as many as 100 days were marked by the occurrence of shocks. But, in addition to these, there are no doubt many slight disturbances, in

---

[1] *Seismology*, from σεισμὸς, *seismos*, a shock or earthquake.

unfrequented districts, which are never recorded in such reports. The total effect produced by the causes of such disturbances must consequently be far from insignificant, even in the course of a single year.

Subterranean disturbances which commence merely with quakings of the ground often terminate with the forcible ejection of heated matter from the interior of the earth. A rent may be produced at some weak point, and this crack then serves for the passage of large volumes of steam and other vapours, with showers of red-hot ashes, accompanied or followed by streams of molten rock. The solid materials are shot forth into the air, and fall in showers around the mouth of the orifice; where they form, by their accumulation, a cone-shaped mound or hill. Such a hill is called a *volcano*,[1] or popularly a " burning mountain." It must be borne in mind, however, that it does not " burn," in the sense in which a fire burns, but it merely offers a channel through which heated matter is erupted from below. It differs again from an ordinary mountain, in that it is simply a heap of loose materials and melted matter, which has been piled up, layer after layer, around a hole leading down to the interior of the earth. Hence, if a volcano were cut through, it would probably present a section something like that shown in Fig. 50. Here a channel, *a*, has been opened through strata, *b, b*, originally horizontal, and the ejected matter has fallen all round the orifice in conical layers, each forming a mantle thrown irregularly over the preceding layer, and sloping in all directions away from the central chimney.

At the mouth of the volcanic pipe, there is usually a funnel-shaped opening known as the *crater*. Fragmentary materials falling back into this cup, or rolling in from the sides, form layers which slope *towards* the vent and there

[1] *Volcano,* Italian *vulcano,* from Vulcan, the Roman god of fire.

fore in the opposite direction to the dip of the volcanic beds which make up the mass of the mound. A section of a cone of loose cindery materials is given in Fig. 51, and shows the difference of dip just referred to. The molten matter which wells up the throat of a volcano, cements the loose ashes and cinders into a compact mass, where it comes in contact with them, and thus forms a hard stony tube lining the volcanic chimney.

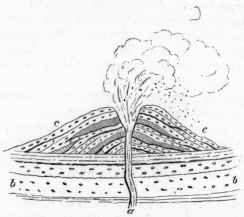

Fig. 50.—Diagrammatic Section of a Volcano

At the beginning of an eruption, clouds of steam are copiously belched forth, showing that water has its part to play even in these fiery phenomena. The steam generally issues spasmodically, each puff giving rise to clouds which shoot up to a great height, and are either dissipated or condensed in torrents of rain. Associated with the steam are various gaseous exhalations, most of which, however, are not combustible. Hence, the appearance of a column of flame, often said to be seen issuing from a volcano, must generally

be an illusion, due to illumination of the vapours, partly by
the sparks and red-hot stones and ashes shot out at the
same time, and partly, by reflection from the glowing walls
of the pipe and from the surface of the molten matter
below.   In the early stages of an eruption, huge fragments
of rock may be ejected ; for when, after a period of repose,
the pent-up steam and gases at last gain vent, they violently
eject the materials which have accumulated in the throat of
the chimney, and choked its opening.   Masses of rock, some
as much as nine feet in diameter, are said to have been cast
forth from the great volcano Cotopaxi, in Quito, during the

F ɪɢ. 51.—Diagrammatic Section of a Cinder Cone.

eruption of 1553, and to have been hurled to a distance of
more than fifteen miles from the mountain.

During an eruption, ashes are commonly ejected in great
quantity, but it must be borne in mind that the materials
so-called are very different from the partially-burnt fuel of
the domestic hearth.   Volcanic ashes are, in fact, nothing
but fragments of lava, or partially-fused rocky matter.   When
jets of this lava are shot forth from the volcano, the liquid is
broken up by the air, and so splashed about that it falls in
drops, which harden into small spongy fragments, resembling
ashes and cinders.   In some cases, the lava is broken into
such fine particles that it is known as *volcanic dust* or sand ;

dense showers of such dust have been known to darken the sky for miles around the volcano, and have been wafted by winds for even hundreds of miles. It is an interesting fact, shown by the examination of the sea-bottom by the *Challenger*, that volcanic detritus is almost universally distributed over the floor of the deep sea.

When the steam, which is abundant in most eruptions, condenses in torrents of rain, the volcanic dust is frequently worked up into a hot mud which rolls down the hill in a sluggish stream, burying everything before it. Herculaneum was sealed up by a crust of volcanic mud discharged from Vesuvius; while Pompeii was overwhelmed by a vast accumulation of dust and ashes during the same eruption.

The partially-molten rock called *lava* rises up in the volcanic pipe, and may eventually run over the lip of the crater, or force its way through cracks in the hill, forming red-hot streams which generally present a consistence something like that of treacle. These lava-torrents are often of great magnitude ; thus, it was estimated that in the famous eruption of Skaptár Jokul, in Iceland, in 1783, the mass of lava brought up from subterranean regions was equal to the bulk of Mont Blanc. The lava rapidly cools on the surface, though long retaining its heat beneath the protecting crust ; and, ultimately, the entire mass solidifies, forming a hard rock, more or less like a slag from an iron-furnace. In different specimens, however, the lava exhibits great variations ; some being dark-coloured and comparatively heavy, while others are lighter in colour and much less dense; in some cases the rock is compact, while in others it is spongy or cindery, when it is said to be *scoriaceous*. The little cavities, or vesicles, in this *scoria*,[1] or cellular lava, are formed by the disengagement of bubbles of gas or vapour,

---

[1] *Scoria*, volcanic cinder, from Lat *scoria*, "dross."

when the matter is in a pasty condition ; just as the porous texture of a piece of bread is due to the presence of bubbles of gas evolved by the fermentation of the yeast. The stone largely used for scouring paint under the name of *pumice*[1] is a lava of very porous texture ; its name recalling its origin as the froth or scum of lava.   Sometimes, the masses of lava, which are tossed into the air, are rotated during their flight, and fall as more or less rounded bodies, known as *volcanic bombs*. Occasionally a very liquid lava may be caught by the wind, and drawn out into delicate fibres, like spun glass ; this beautiful form is very abundant at Kilauea, a volcano in Hawaii, one of the Sandwich islands, where it is known as *Pélé's hair*, its name being borrowed from that of an old goddess who was supposed to reside in the crater. Other lavas again are vitreous, and strongly resemble dark-coloured bottle-glass, when they pass under the name of *obsidian.* This kind of lava was largely used by the ancient Mexicans for making rude knives and other cutting instruments ; and a hill in northern Mexico, formerly worked for this material, is still known as the *Cerro de Navajas* (Spanish " Hill of Knives.")

It often happens that the lava which wells up in the pipe of a volcano, breaks by its sheer weight through the rim of the crater, or even breaches one side of the conical hill. Thus Fig. 52 represents a group of small extinct volcanoes in Central France, showing cones which have been broken through in this way.   In some cases the flanks of the cones are rent, and lava is then injected into the cracks, forming, when cold, huge rocky ribs known as *dykes*.   In other cases, the chimney gets choked by a plug of hard lava, and new vents may then be opened on the side of the cone.   Fig. 53

---

[1] *Pumice*, from the Lat. *pumex*, formerly *spumex*, allied to *spuma*, " froth."

is an ideal section of a volcano, showing the dykes of lava running through the stratified deposits, and also showing two minor cones *a b*, thrown up at points where the volcanic matter has been able to force its way to the surface. Mount

FIG. 52.—Breached Volcanic Cones, Auvergne.

Etna is remarkable for having its flanks studded with parasitic cones, some of which are of considerable size, one being upwards of 900 feet in height.

After a volcano has long been silent and the large crater

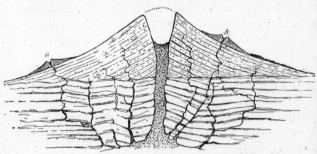

FIG. 53.—Diagrammatic Section of Volcano, with Dykes and Minor Cones.

has been more or less filled, partly by ejected materials which had fallen back into the cavity during the last eruption, and partly by matter washed in by rain, renewal of activity through the old channel may give rise to the

formation of a new cone seated within the old crateral
hollow. Great changes may indeed be effected in the
character of a volcano by successive eruptions, new cones
being thrown up at one time, and old ones obliterated at
another. Fig. 54, shows the summit of Vesuvius as it
appeared in 1756, when there were no fewer than three
separate cones, one within another, encircling as many
craters. But about ten years afterwards the summit presented the form shown in Fig. 55, where a single cone rises

FIG. 54.—Summit of Vesuvius in 1756.

from the floor of the great crater. The curious stages
through which a volcano may pass are well illustrated by the
story of Vesuvius.

Rather less than two thousand years ago, that mountain
was as peaceful as Primrose Hill is at the present day. It
seems from all accounts to have had a very regular conical
shape, with a crater about a mile and a half broad. Yet its
shape led hardly any one to suspect that the mountain was a
slumbering volcano. Wild vines were growing over the

sides of the crater, and it was in the natural fortress formed
by this great amphitheatre that Spartacus the Thracian, with
his little band of gladiators, took up his position at the
beginning of the Servile War in the year 72 B.C. Earthquakes, as already pointed out, are often the heralds of
volcanic eruptions ; and the first notice which the old
dwellers around Vesuvius received of its renewed activity
was from a series of earthquakes which began, as far as we
know, in A.D. 63, and continued intermittently for about

FIG. 55.—Summit of Vesuvius in 1767.

sixteen years. These disturbances culminated in the great
eruption of A.D. 79, which has been described in two letters
written by Pliny the Younger to Tacitus. The elder Pliny,
the author of the famous *Historia Naturalis*, was, at that
time, in command of the Roman fleet off Misenum. On the
24th of August a cloud of unusual size and shape was seen
hanging over the mountain. It is described as having had
the form of a huge pine-tree ; and similarly-shaped masses
of cloud usually accompany the eruptions of Vesuvius. An

enormous column of steam, mingled with ashes and stones, shoots up from the crater to a height of a thousand or twelve hundred feet, where the clouds spread out in horizontal masses, some miles in breadth, while the ashes and stones fall down in showers. Attracted by so curious a sight, the elder Pliny went to Stabiæ, about ten miles from Vesuvius, but his eagerness to witness the spectacle cost him his life. His nephew, who stayed at Misenum, describes the scene—the showers of ashes, the ejection of redhot stones, the movement of the land, the retreat of the sea, and other phenomena characteristic of the eruption of a volcano attended by an earthquake. So vast were the quantities of ashes and other fragmentary matter ejected, either dry or mixed with water, that the unfortunate cities of Herculanæum, Pompeii, and Stabiæ were buried beneath deposits, in some places, thirty feet in thickness. It is doubtful, however, whether any true lava was erupted on this occasion. From that date to the present day, Vesuvius has been more or less active, though sometimes quiet for considerable intervals. During the great eruption just referred to, the south-western side of the original cone was destroyed, but the half which was then left has remained in existence up to the present time, and forms the semi-circular hill known as Monte Somma. Fig. 56 is a view of Vesuvius half encircled by the cliffs of this ancient crater.[1]

When a volcano is situated near the coast—and by far the larger number of existing volcanoes are so situated—the ashes may be showered into the sea, or be borne thither by the wind, and may, in this way, get mixed with the detrital matter which is spread over the sea-bottom. A curious series

[1] Figs. 51 to 57 are taken, by Prof. Judd's permission, from the late Mr. Poulett Scrope's work on *Volcanoes*.

of deposits may thus be produced, consisting partly of materials worn away from the land by the action of the water, and partly of matter ejected from subterranean

Fig. 56.—Vesuvius and Monte Somma.

sources. In some cases, volcanic outbreaks take place actually beneath the sea, and the matter thrown up becomes mixed with the remains of shell-fish and other marine organisms. Submarine volcanoes occasionally give rise to

Fig. 57.—Graham Island, 1831.

new land, the erupted matter being piled up in sufficient quantity to form an island rising above the waters. Thus, in the year 1831 an island, which Admiral Smyth named

Graham Island (Fig. 57) appeared in the Mediterranean, between Sicily and the coast of Africa, where there had previously been more than 100 fathoms of water. The pile of volcanic matter forming this isle must have been upwards of 800 feet high, for the highest part of the island was 200 feet above water; while the circumference of the mass of land was nearly three miles. After it had stood above the waves for about three months, the island entirely disappeared.

It is obvious that a great deal of the force by which volcanic products are brought to the surface is due to the conversion into steam of water which, in some way or other, obtains access to the deep-seated molten rocks; but, whether this is the sole source of volcanic energy or not, is uncertain. Numerous hypotheses have been advanced to explain the source and origin of the molten matter itself. Some of these attempts at explanation refer the heat to chemical and some to mechanical causes ; while others assume that it is merely the residue of the heat which the earth originally possessed, if, as seems likely, it existed at one time in a state of fusion. Dismissing, however, these vexed questions, it is sufficient to remark that some source of heat unquestionably does exist in the earth beneath our feet.

If a thermometer be buried in the ground at a depth of only a few inches below the surface, it is found to be affected by all superficial changes of temperature, and its indications show that it is cool at night and warm in the day, cold in the winter and hot in the summer. But plunged deep into the ground, or placed in a deep cellar or cavern, these variations disappear, and one uniform temperature is registered under all circumstances. What that temperature is will depend principally on the climate of the locality, the constant temperature being nearly the mean temperature of the surface.

On going still deeper, the heat is found to increase; and, at the bottom of a deep mine, it is generally so warm that the miners are glad to discard most of their clothing. At present, the deepest mine in this country is the Rosebridge Colliery, at Ince, near Wigan, which has reached a depth of 2,445 feet. Experiments on the temperature at different depths, while sinking this pit, showed that the average increase is about 1° Fahr. for every fifty-four feet. In other sinkings, somewhat different results have been obtained, the rate of augmentation being affected by the character of the rocks bored through and by the position which the strata occupy; whether, for example, they are inclined or horizontal. Thus at the Astley pit at Dunkenfield in Cheshire the rate was found to be 1° for every seventy-seven feet, but this appears to be unusually slow. Perhaps it will not be far wrong to assume that the average increase is 1° for every sixty feet: such at least is the rate which was adopted a few years ago by the Royal Coal Commission in their calculations.

Even the deep sinking at the Rosebridge Colliery is but the veriest dent in the earth's surface compared with the actual radius of the globe. It gives therefore but scant information respecting the temperature of the deep-seated portions of the interior; but, assuming such a rate of increase to continue, it is evident that at the depth of only a few miles the heat would be sufficient to fuse any known rock. It is true that the melting-point of a solid body may be greatly modified by pressure; and it is obvious that, at great depths, the pressure must be prodigious. Nevertheless, the eruption of lava from volcanic vents sufficiently shows

FIG. 58. — Beehive Geyser, Yellowstone Park, Colorado. (Hayden.)

that, whatever the general state of the earth's interior, there must be at least local masses of molten rock.

Additional evidence of the existence of heat at great depths is furnished by the temperature of the water yielded by certain springs. Some of the hot springs at Bath, for example, have a temperature of 120° F. Still hotter springs occur in many countries ; and, in volcanic districts, even the boiling-point is occasionally reached. The most remarkable of these hot springs are those known in Iceland as *Geysers*. Jets of boiling water with clouds of steam are intermittently thrown high into the air with great force and accompanied with loud explosions. The water generally holds silica in solution, as mentioned on p. 124, and this siliceous matter is deposited around the mouth of the hole as an incrustation called *sinter*. Although the Geysers of Iceland are best known, similar springs are found in New Zealand, and also in the Rocky Mountains of North America. Fig. 58, represents a geyser in the Yellowstone Park, described by Prof. Hayden. No fewer than 10,000 hot springs, geysers, and hot lakes are said to exist within the area of the Yellowstone Park. The geyser, here represented in action, throws jets of hot water to a height of something like 200 feet.

In some localities, hot water issuing from the ground is mixed with earthy matter ; and streams of thick mud accumulate round the openings, so as to form conical hills, known as *salses*, or *mud volcanoes*. Such eruptions of mud, varying considerably in consistency and in temperature, occur, for example, in the Crimea and on the shores of the Caspian Sea. In other cases, hot vapours issue from cracks in the ground, as at the Solfatara, near Naples, where the vapours are charged with sulphur. A large industry has sprung up in the Tuscan Maremma, by utilizing the hot vapours which issue from smoking cracks, known as *soffioni*, and contain

particles of boracic acid which are used in the preparation
of borax.

Most of the phenomena just described, are probably to be
regarded as representing the lingering remains of volcanic
activity.   When a volcano has become extinct, the effects
of subterranean heat in the locality may still manifest themselves in a subdued form, in such phenomena as those of hot
springs.   Many volcanoes, however, which appear at the
present day to be perfectly quiet, are merely dormant, and
may break forth with renewed activity at any moment.   The
early history of Vesuvius, as already pointed out, shows
that a volcano, after being silent for ages, may suddenly
start forth into fresh life.

There are few better examples of an area in which volcanic
action must have been rife on an enormous scale at a comparatively recent time, than that furnished by the Auvergne
and the neighbouring districts in Central France.   There
the traveller may see hundreds of volcanic cones, known
locally as "puys," still preserving their characteristic shape,
in spite of long exposure; there, too, are the streams of
lava just as they flowed from the craters, or burst through
the sides of the cones (Fig. 52), whilst thick sheets of old
lava and beds of ash are spread far and wide over the surrounding country.   The district known as the Eifel, on the
west bank of the Rhine, between Bonn and Andernach,
offers equally striking examples of extinct volcanoes.

Even in the British Isles, it is not difficult to trace the
remains of ancient volcanic outbursts, although these are not
so fresh and well-marked as those just mentioned.   Sheets
of lava are found in the north-eastern part of Ireland, especially in the county of Antrim where the remarkable scenery
of the Giant's Causeway is due to the fact that some of the
old lava has split up into columns, not altogether unlike

those into which a mass of starch splits during drying. Similar evidence of volcanic action may be found in Scotland, whilst in North Wales there are extensive remains of eruptive rocks; the state of fiery activity which they indicate dates back, however, to a very remote period of geological history. Yet it must not for a moment be supposed that any volcanic product still exists, as a crater, amongst the volcanic hills of Wales. So great indeed has been the disturbance and de nudation of this part of the earth, that the old surface has long ago been swept away, and its present shape bears little or no relation to its form at the period of eruption. It is true, for example, that the summit of Snowdon is formed of volcanic rocks, yet the mountain, in its present form, does not in any way represent an old volcanic cone.

Without pursuing this subject further, enough has been said to prove that peaceful as our islands now are, they have again and again been the scene of violent volcanic disturb- ances. Fire, indeed, has played as important a part as water in the geological history of the British Isles; and it is highly probable that, at a depth, which, as compared with the diameter of the earth, may be justly termed insignificant, even the peaceful valley of the Thames is underlaid by an ocean of molten rock.

CHAPTER XIII.

SLOW MOVEMENTS OF THE LAND.

SUCH movements of the land as those which accompanied the South American earthquakes, referred to in the last chapter (p. 186), must have been brought about by the comparatively sudden action of subterranean forces. But the land is subject not only to a rapid rise and fall of this kind, but also to local elevations and depressions so gradual as to escape ordinary observation. Special means, indeed, are, in most cases, needed to detect these slow changes of level, and to measure their extent. Yet it is probable that such gradual oscillations of the land are, in the long run, of far greater importance in the economy of nature than those abrupt movements which occur spasmodically. It will be shown in a subsequent chapter, that every foot of solid ground within the area of the Thames basin has, at some time or other, been buried beneath the sea ; and it is therefore clear that elevatory forces must have been at work to lift up the sea-bed and expose it as dry land. Nor has such move-ment been effected once only. Any one who seeks to read the history of the rocks in the basin of the Thames will be driven to conclude that the level of the land has changed

again and again, rising at one time and falling at another.
And probably, such changes have been effected, for the most
part, quietly rather than violently ; by slowly-acting forces
working through long periods of time rather than by sudden
disturbances.

It would, perhaps, be difficult to point to any clearer proof
of such gentle oscillations of level having taken place within
the memory of man, than that afforded by some well-known
ruins on the shore of the Bay of Naples. Although this
illustration has been used by Sir Charles Lyell and other
writers, it is, nevertheless, well worth referring to again, since
it shows most instructively the kind of evidence on which
geologists rely in proof of the instability of the surface of
the land.

About the middle of the last century, the attention of some
Italian antiquaries was attracted by three stone columns,
almost concealed by a growth of bushes behind a villa very
near to the sea shore, in the western part of Pozzuoli, a town
seated on the Bay of Baiæ, about seven miles from Naples.
These columns were buried to a considerable height in an
accumulation of soil, the removal of which brought to light
the ruins of a magnificent building. A square floor, paved
with marble, and measuring seventy feet in the side, showed
the magnitude of the central court. This area had originally
been covered with a roof supported by forty-six noble columns,
some wrought in granite and some in marble, still remaining
more or less perfect. It was assumed by the antiquaries of
the day, apparently on very slender grounds, that the building had been a temple dedicated to Serapis, an Egyptian
divinity, whose worship had been introduced into Rome.
Just behind the building is a hot spring, from which water had
been carried, through a marble channel, to a number of small
apartments built around the central court. This has led to the

suggestion that the building, instead of having been a temple
of Jupiter Serapis, was nothing more than a magnificent
bathing establishment. Be that as it may, however, it is
convenient to refer to it for geological purposes under its
well-known name of the Temple of Serapis. To geologists
its interest centres in the three tall columns by which the

FIG. 59.—Marble Column from Temple of Jupiter Serapis.

building was discovered, and which are the only pillars, out
of the original forty-six, still standing.   Each column, though
upwards of forty feet high, has been carved out of a single block
of green marble, Fig. 59. Up to the height of about twelve feet
from the base, the colums are smooth ; but, above this level,
each pillar is marked by a band of deep pits, the band being

about eight feet in breadth. Each pit is a pear-shaped hole, and at the bottom of the hole, which is the widest part, there may generally be found the two halves, or *valves*, of a shell not unlike that of the common mussel. Exactly the same kind, or *species* of shell-fish[1] as that represented in the cavities of the marble, is found to-day living in the Medi-terranean, where it may be seen boring its way into lime-stone rocks, much in the same manner that the so-called " shipworm " bores into timber. There is no difficulty then, in understanding that the perforations in the columns of the temple are the work of boring shell-fish. But it is clear that the columns, when attacked, must have been washed by the sea, for the shell-fish could not have lived in the holes when left high and dry above water. The fact is thus established, that the part of the marble pillars bored by the shells must have been immersed in the sea, long enough for the creatures to have drilled the multitude of holes which are now visible.

Here then is evidence of a considerable alteration in the relative level of land and water. It is obvious, however, that such an alteration of level may have been brought about in one or other of two ways : either the sea may have been raised, or the land may have been carried down. At first sight it appears much more likely that so mobile a thing as the sea has changed its level, than that the surface of the solid earth should have shifted its position. And yet it needs scarcely a moment's consideration to show that any local alteration of sea-level cannot possibly have occurred. For, supposing the surface of the sea to have been raised so as to reach the zone of shell-burrows, the water must then have been forced up into a great heap ; but directly this heap was formed, the particles at the top would press upon those below, and thus urge them down the

[1] *Lithodomus dactylus.*

sloping sides until they reached the general level. In fact, the freedom of motion which the liquid molecules enjoy renders it impossible to produce anything like a hump of water, except temporarily. As soon as the surface of the liquid is raised at one point, it tends to fall down again until a common level is restored. Hence if the sea rose, and kept its high level around the bases of the columns, the rise could not have been confined to the Bay of Naples, but must have been part of a general rise of the surface of the ocean, to the same extent, all over the world. The difficulty, however, of finding a source for so vast an amount of additional water, as this general rise would imply, is alone an insuperable objection to this hypothesis. But geologists have abundant other reasons for the conclusion that, in such cases, it is the land and not the sea that has shifted its level.

It appears then that the marks left by the boring shell-fish on the columns of the temple of Serapis, upwards of twelve feet above sea-level, prove that the land on which these pillars stand must, at one time, have been depressed to that extent, and afterwards elevated to its present position. But the temple teaches much more than this. About five feet beneath the present marble floor of the building, there are the remains of another floor; and it seems only fair to suppose that the upper pavement was constructed after the lower one, which belonged to some earlier building, had been carried down to an inconvenient level by subsidence of the land. Such subsidence has indeed been going on in this locality within the present century; for, when the ruins were first unearthed, the upper floor stood much higher than it stands at present. Careful observations, in the early part of this century, showed that the ground was sinking at the rate

P

of about one inch in four years, and some observers have given even a more rapid rate. The ruins stand close to the sea; and, as the pavement sank, the sea flowed in, so that, it is said, in 1838, fish were daily caught within the temple, where, in 1807, there was not a drop of water in ordinary weather.

After what has been explained, it will be seen that the story of the temple may be interpreted somewhat as follows:— The present building was erected on the site of some older one, the floor of which had been carried down by sinking of the land. It may be fairly supposed that the pavement of the new building was at the sea-level, or thereabouts. Inscriptions found among the ruins prove that the temple was decorated by Septimius Severus and Alexander Severus, so that the building must have been in use during the third century of our era. But, by subsidence below the sea-level, water entered the court; and deposits of solid matter from this water were gradually thrown down around the base of the pillars, mingled, at times, with layers of volcanic ashes. Traces of some of these deposits may still be seen adhering to the shafts, below the zone of borings (Fig. 59). As the lower parts of the pillars were buried beneath these accumulations, they were not attacked by the shell-fish which burrowed into the marble during the period of greatest depression. The depression was certainly gradual, but it is probable that the subsequent elevation may have been more rapid; and it was, perhaps, partly effected during a violent subterranean disturbance in 1538, when a mountain, still called Monte Nuovo, was thrown up not far from the temple. It is certain, however, that none of the movements which have affected the temple could have been sufficiently violent to overturn the columns that are still standing.

Such appears to have been the succession of events registered by these ruins. It is true, the Bay of Naples is in a region peculiarly subject to volcanic disturbances, but the slow movements of the land are by no means confined to such districts. Few countries in the world perhaps have been more free from such disturbances than Scandinavia. Yet direct measurement has shown that the northern part of this peninsula is slowly rising, while the southern part, curiously enough, appears to be suffering depression. In such a case as this, where movements in opposite directions are simultaneously going on, it is useless to think of attributing them to any movement of the sea. For a change of sea-level implies, as already pointed out, a *general* change, whether of rise or fall; and it is therefore absurd to assume a rise in one place and a fall in another, at the same time.

In the British Isles, there is no lack of evidence to show that the level of the land has been frequently disturbed, though the oscillations within the memory of man are hardly so well marked as in the cases previously cited. Visitors to certain parts of the coast of Britain may note a terrace of sand and gravel, mixed perhaps with sea-shells, and having all the appearance of a deserted beach, which fringes the shore at a height far beyond reach of the highest tides. Such accumulations must have been formed along a line of shore, and afterwards elevated to their present position, whence they are termed *raised beaches*. A raised beach is therefore an index of elevation of the land. And it appears that this elevation must have been effected, in part at least, since the country was inhabited. For the upraised deposits of silt which skirt the estuary of the Clyde have yielded relics of human workmanship, such as rude canoes, that were originally buried in the mud and sand of the old estuary, though they are now found several feet above high-water mark.

Evidence of the depression of land in Britain is just as conclusive as that of elevation. It is sometimes possible to see, at low tide, in the estuary of the Thames, the remains of a vast forest, with the stools or stumps of the trees still rooted in the old soil, now submerged to a depth of perhaps twenty or thirty feet below high-water. The relics of this ancient forest show that it must have supported a rich growth of yew, pine, oak, alder, and other trees. Now, as these trees do not grow in water, it is evident that the land on which they flourished has been depressed. In some places, the remains of the old land-surface have been buried, to a depth of several feet, beneath alluvial deposits which have been thrown down by the river. When the marshy land on the coasts of Kent and Essex, bounding the estuary of the Thames, is cut through, the sections frequently expose the ancient peaty soil, rich in vegetable remains. This was the case, for example, during the progress of the Main Drainage Works, when deep trenches were cut through the marshes below Woolwich. It is not, however, only at the mouth of the Thames that such evidence of subsidence is to be found ; for similar submerged forests may be seen at low water at many points of the British coast, especially in Devonshire, Cornwall, and Wales.

Raised beaches and submarine forests afford as good evidence of the rise and fall of the land as any to be got from the Temple of Serapis. But they are not the only evidence which the geologist can cite, to prove that the surface of the British Isles has suffered frequent changes of level. Nor are they by any means the strongest. Indeed their value lies chiefly in the fact that the movements which they register are of comparatively recent date. That there

have been variations of level to a much greater extent, at
more remote periods, is abundantly testified by the strata in
almost any part of the country. London, for example, is
seated on clay, which, as already pointed out, must have been
deposited under water, in the state of mud. But as this
clay contains, in many parts, the remains of marine shell-
fish, such as the nautilus, there can be no doubt that the
mud in such places must have been originally thrown down
out at sea. The clays, sands, and other deposits below the
London clay, already referred to under the name of the Lower
London Tertiaries (p. 32), have been formed, some in salt and
others in brackish water, as is testified by the character of the
shells which they contain. As to the chalk, which lies in a
mass of vast thickness immediately beneath these deposits,
it will be shown, in a subsequent chapter, that it abounds
with the remains of creatures which once lived in the depths
of the sea. If, then, these rocks are, in great measure,
nothing but old sea-bottoms, it is clear that great upward
movement must have taken place to raise them into their
present situation.

But this is not all. The rocks have not only been up-
lifted, but in many cases have been subjected to some disturbing action by which they have been more or less contorted.
The section in Fig. 11, p. 31, shows that the strata beneath
London lie in a gentle hollow, purposely exaggerated in the
diagram, but still sufficiently marked in nature to suggest the
name of "London Basin." Supposing they had been originally deposited in a depression of the sea-bottom, the
layers would have been thrown down almost horizontally, as
in Fig. 60; and not in curved layers of equal thickness as in
Fig. 61, such as are really found in nature. The present
position of these rocks is therefore explained by supposing
that the strata were originally horizontal and have been

thrown into a basin-like shape since their formation. The
disturbance to which they have been subjected is yet more
strikingly seen if a section be taken across, not only this
basin, but across another area of similar character, known
as the Hampshire basin.   Fig. 62 is a section from Abingdon
in Berkshire, through Hampshire and across the Solent to
the Isle of Wight ; the vertical scale being about twenty
times greater than the horizontal scale.   Here the strata,
originally almost horizontal, have been thrown into a succession of gentle undulations, rising to a crest in one locality
and falling to a trough at another.   There can be little doubt
that the Eocene rocks, including the London clay, once
spread over the whole surface of this chalk, but have since
been removed from the high ground by denudation, leaving

Fig. 60.—Strata deposited in   Fig. 61.—Strata thrown into a
a basin.   basin-shape.

isolated tracts separated by intervening patches of bare
chalk.   In the Isle of Wight, the beds have been so greatly
disturbed that the chalk strata stand almost on end, as is well
shown by the bands of black flints which run in almost
vertical lines.   Incidentally it may be remarked that when
strata lie in this shape ⌣ they are said to form a *synclinal*,[1]
and when in this form ⌢ an *anticlinal*.[2]   The strata in the
south-eastern part of England have been but little disturbed ; but, among the old rocks of Wales and other parts
of western Britain, it is not uncommon to find the beds

[1] *Synclinal*, from σὺν, *sun*, with ; and κλινω, *klino*, to slope.
[2] *Anticlinal*, from ἀντὶ, *anti*, against ; and κλίνω.

thrown into a succession of sharp anti-clinals and synclinals.

During the disturbances to which strata have been subjected since their original deposition, it has frequently happened that the rocks have been broken and dis-located, as represented in Fig. 10, p. 30; where the series of beds, on one side of the fracture or *fault*, have been thrown down to a much lower level than that occupied by the strata on the opposite side. Even in an area so little disturbed as the London basin, such dislocations of the strata may be detected; and, indeed, a considerable fault runs along part of the valley of the Thames below London, and throws down the beds on the north to the extent of 100 feet, or even more. Before leaving this subject, it may be well to mention that contortion and dislocation of strata may be due to squeezing at the sides, and not to the direct operation of forces acting immediately from below.

From what has been said in this chapter, it will be seen that deposits, formed origi-nally on the floor of the sea, have been hoisted above water, and now form the bulk of our dry land. The land is there-fore subject to a kind of circulation similar to that which has been already pointed out in the case of water. The water, it will be remembered, passed from the river

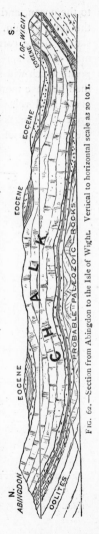

Fig. 62.—Section from Abingdon to the Isle of Wight.   Vertical to horizontal scale as 20 to 1.

to the ocean, and back again from the ocean to the river in the form of rain. In like manner, the solid land is constantly being carried, piece by piece, into the sea. Here most of it is spread out upon the ocean floor, forming deposits which will some day be raised as dry land; and will then be once more attacked by the water, as soon as it rises above sea-level. The solid earth is, therefore, subject to a cycle of changes not less complete than that exhibited by the circulation of the waters.

CHAPTER XIV.

LIVING MATTER AND THE EFFECTS OF ITS ACTIVITY ON
THE DISTRIBUTION OF TERRESTRIAL SOLIDS, FLUIDS,
AND GASES—DEPOSITS FORMED BY THE REMAINS OF
PLANTS.

It has been seen that the fresh and salt waters which run
upon, and beat against, the land, are constantly engaged in
transporting the materials of which that land is composed
from higher to lower levels. A comparatively insignificant
fraction of these materials remains in the lakes, which lie in
the course of some rivers; but, by far the greater part,
sooner or later, reaches the sea.

The solid deposits which thus accumulate on the sea-
bottom are never exactly equal to the waste of the land, but
are always of less, and frequently of much less, mass. For
all the chief constituents of the land are more or less soluble
in water; and hence, a larger or smaller proportion of the
products of denudation reach the sea in a state of solution,
and are diffused through the ocean, as the sugar in a drop of
syrup would be diffused through a pail of water. Notably,
dissolved carbonate of lime and silica are thus being constantly poured into the sea.

Supposing that no influences were at work upon the earth's

crust, except those of rain and rivers, and of the sea; then, as has been pointed out in Chap. XI., the ultimate result of their action would be the reduction of the solid land to a submarine plain. The waters covering this plain would be more or less completely saturated with the soluble materials extracted from the denuded rocks. Denudation, therefore, on the whole, not only diminishes the quantity of dry land, but also lessens the proportion of the solid to the fluid constituents of the globe.

The tendency of the forces of upheaval is in the opposite direction, though the source of the work done is still largely derived from water. The fused rocks in the depths of the earth, which are vomited forth by volcanoes, are forced to the surface by steam power, and then take on the solid form. There is a transference of matter from lower to higher levels, accompanied by an increase of the solid at the expense of the fluid constituents of the globe. Whether the proportion of dry land is, or is not, increased by volcanic action depends upon the locality of the vent, and the amount of matter thrown out from it. If the vent opens on dry land, the erupted matters will necessarily increase the mass of dry land; while, if it break out beneath the sea, they may reach the surface, or not, according to their mass and the form they assume.

Supposing that no agents were at work upon the earth's crust except volcanoes—with concomitant movements of elevation and depression—the quantity of water in the ocean would remain substantially unaltered; but, the proportion of the surface of the earth occupied by dry land to the area covered by water, might be almost indefinitely increased or diminished. It is conceivable, for example, that the whole ocean, which, at present, occupies about three-fifths of the surface of the earth, might come to be contained in a few very deep lakes; in consequence of the deepening of the existing sea-valleys, and the elevation of the intermediate land areas. Or the contrary result might be brought about, by the depression of the existing land areas, and the raising of the sea-bottom by matter ejected from submarine volcanoes.

Thus, so far as the mere transference of the matter of the crust of the globe is concerned, the tendency of volcanic action and of the elevatory forces is, on the whole, towards compensating denudation and depression; and, it is conceivable, that the two processes should go on, for any assignable time, in such a manner, that the proportion of land above the sea level to that below it should remain unchanged. But, in the operations of nature hitherto dealt with, there is nothing to compensate for the gradual conver· sion of solids into liquids by denudation; nor for such outpouring of gases into the atmosphere as occasionally, if not always, accompanies volcanic action.

Nevertheless, an agent, by which some of the gaseous and liquid constituents of the earth are, temporarily or permanently, reduced to the state of solids, is at work upon a prodigious scale. This agent is what is termed *living matter;* or less accurately, *organic matter.*[1]

The surface of the valley of the Thames is covered with prodigious multitudes, and seemingly endless varieties, of the forms of this living matter, some of which we call plants, and others animals. But, notwithstanding their obvious differences, there are so many deep-seated points of agreement among the diversified forms of life, that any plant or

[1] Less accurately, because all forms of living matter cannot be strictly said to be organised. An *organ* is a part of a living body, the structure of which fits it for the performance of some special action, which is called its *function.* The lowest forms of life possess no parts to which the term organ can be applied in this sense.

any animal will serve to illustrate the essential characters of
all plants and of all animals. Every one has seen a field of
peas, thronged with pigeons. The peas will serve very well
as examples of plants, and the pigeons as types of animals.

The pea that may be extracted from a ripe peascod is a
living body, in which, however, the vital activities are, for the
time, almost quiescent. Within the thin skin which envelops
the pea, there is inclosed a perfect, though embryonic plant,
composed of a minute stem with its root and leaves; of
which last, two, the *cotyledons* or *seed-leaves*, are so large and
solid that they make up the chief mass of the infant pea-
plant.

Subjected to chemical analysis, the embryo plant yields
certain complex bodies, composed chiefly of carbon, hydrogen, oxygen, and nitrogen, which are known as protein compounds.[1] Besides these it contains fatty matters; woody
substance (cellulose), sugar, and starch; various salts of
potash, lime, iron, and other mineral matters, including a
considerable proportion of water.

Examined with the naked eye, the soft substance of the
young plant appears to be almost homogeneous; the application of the microscope, however, shows that it is far from
being really so; but that, on the contrary, it has a very
definite and regular structure. A delicate woody framework,
or skeleton, is excavated by innumerable small cavities, each
of which is filled by a semifluid matter, termed *protoplasm*,[2]
just as the honey fills the waxen cells of a honeycomb.
Each mass of protoplasm, with its investing wooden wall, is
technically termed a *cell;* and, inasmuch as part of the protoplasm is distinguishable from the rest as a rounded *nucleus*,

---

[1] *Protein*, from πρωτεύω, *proteuo*, to have the first place.

[2] *Protoplasm*, from πρῶτος, *protos*, first ; and πλάσμα, *plasma*, forma-
tive matter.

it is called a *nucleated cell.* The protoplasm contains the protein compounds, and the larger proportion of the saline and watery constituents of the plant. The cell-wall is mainly cellulose and water. Saccharine and fatty matters probably exist, diffused through the protoplasm, in all the cells; starch, in the form of granules, is to be found in most.

The embryonic pea-plant, then, is no simple homogeneous mass, but is an aggregate, made up of a multitude of distinct nucleated cells, each of which is essentially composed of a protoplasmic body invested by a cell-wall. The fact that this cell-aggregate is alive, does not become manifest until the pea is exposed to certain conditions. But, every one knows, that if a pea is planted in the ground in moist and warm weather, it shortly bursts its coat. The seed-leaves enlarge and come to the surface; while the rootlet grows into the soil. The stem shoots up; its minute and colourless leaves rapidly enlarge and become green; new leaves are developed; and, by degrees, a tall plant rises above the ground, the bulk and weight of which soon becomes many thousand times greater than that of the embryo. Then the plant blossoms, and in the centre of each flower is found a hollow organ, the *pistil.* From the walls of this, small bodies termed the *ovules* grow out, and each ovule contains a microscopic nucleated cell—the *embryo cell.* In the fertilised ovules, the embryo cell divides and subdivides, each new cell growing until it becomes as large as, or larger than, that from which it proceeded; and, thus, by degrees, the single cell is converted into a cell-aggregate, which assumes the shape of the embryo plant. This, inclosed in the distended envelope furnished by the ovule, is the pea—while the enlarged pistil becomes the peascod.

Thus, the plant under consideration goes through a series of changes, the starting-point of which is the simple nucleated cell (the embryo cell) contained within the ovule, while its conclusion is the production of new embryo cells, every one of which may become competent to repeat the whole series. Each term of the series is a stage of what is called the development of the plant; and, if successive stages of this development are compared, it will be found that the plant becomes more complex the further its development advances. The embryo plant, in the pea, is a more complex structure than the embryo cell in the ovule; the blossoming plant is more complex than the young plant before flowering; and this increase of complexity is true, not only of the outwardly visible parts, but of the inward structure, of the growing plant. Nevertheless, it is to be observed, that the full-grown plant is as much an aggregate of nucleated cells, more or less modified, as is the embryo; and every change in the form and size of the growing plant is, simply, the expression of the mode of growth and multiplication of the individual cells of which the body of the plant is made up.

The process of evolution, from an extremely simple to a highly complex condition, thus exemplified by the pea-plant, is characteristic of living matter. For, although there is a superficial similarity between the growth of a plant and the tree-like form which some bodies assume in the act of crystallisation, as is well exemplified by the hoar-frost on a window-pane; yet, a very slight examination shows that the two processes are, in reality, altogether different. When an individual crystal grows, the new matter is added upon its exterior; and when crystalline bodies assume an arborescent form, the first crystal that is deposited does not grow into the crystal tree, but new crystals are added to the outside of the first, in such a manner, that the compound mass has a tree-like shape. But, when the embryo-cell grows, the addition of matter takes place within its own substance, just as a piece of jelly swells by taking in water. And the primitively single cell becomes a cell-aggregate, not by attachment of strange cells, from without, to that which first existed; but, by the growth and division of the primitive cell; and the repetition of the processes of growth and division in the successive generations of new cells thus produced.

There is another very striking difference between the growth of such not-living bodies as may be said to grow, and living growth. A crystal can grow, only if the materials of which it is composed exist, as such, in the liquid which surrounds it. A crystal of salt can grow only in a solution of salt; and a crystal of sulphate of soda, in a solution of sulphate of soda.

It is quite otherwise with a plant. A single pea may not only develop into a large pea-plant, but may ultimately give rise to a multitude of peas as large as itself. In other words, the pea, in the course of its development, accumulates within itself many hundred times the quantity of protein compounds, of cellulose, of starch, of sugar, of fat, and of water and mineral salts, which it primitively contained. Nevertheless, of all these bodies, it is certain that none but the water and the mineral salts exist, as such, either in the air or in the soil. In fact, strange as it may seem, the soil is a superfluity. A pea will grow into a perfect plant and produce its crop of peas, if it is supplied with water containing nitrate of ammonia and the phosphates, sulphates, and chlorides of potassium, calcium, iron, and the like, which it needs, and is freely exposed to the air and to sunshine. Under such conditions as these, it is obvious that the full-grown plant must be almost entirely composed of fluids and gases which have been transmuted into solid matters; and that it has manufactured the multifarious, and often highly complex chemical compounds, of which its body is composed, out of the comparatively simple raw materials supplied to it.

In the case supposed, the fluid with which the pea is supplied contains only hydrogen, oxygen, nitrogen, phosphorus, sulphur, and certain metallic bases; but another element, carbon, enters, largely, into every one of the manu factured articles which are to be found in the full-grown plant. The presence of this carbon, and its great relative amount, may be made manifest enough if the plant is strongly heated in a closed vessel, when the carbon remains, as a conspicuous mass of charcoal. Whence is this carbon derived? Under the conditions defined, the only possible source of supply is the carbonic acid diffused through the atmosphere; which, though it forms so small a percentage of the air, yet amounts to an enormous absolute quantity (p. 84). In fact, it is known that, under the influence of sunlight, a green plant decomposes carbonic acid into its elements; and, setting free the oxygen, builds up the carbon, together with the nitrogen, hydrogen, and oxygen, and mineral matters derived from other sources, into the complex compounds of its own living substance.

Thus the green plant transmutes the fluid and gaseous matters, which it draws from the soil and from the atmosphere, into the solid materials of its own body; and thus, to a certain extent, reclaims the solids lost by aqueous solution and igneous decomposition. Under ordinary circumstances, the restoration of solid matter to the earth, thus effected by plant-life, is only temporary. Even during life, the activity of the green plant, like all vital activity, is accompanied by the slow oxidation and destruction of its protoplasmic matter; and one of the products of this oxidation, carbonic acid, is returned to the atmosphere. After death, the process of decay is accompanied by slow oxidation. The carbon goes off chiefly in the form of gaseous carbonic acid ; the nitrogen, in the shape of ammoniacal salts ; and the mineral salts are dissolved away by rain and carried to the general store of the waters. But if, by the overflow of a river, the plant should become silted up in mud, or carried away by floods and buried in the sea-bottom, the process of decay may be so slow and so imperfect, that its carbonized remains, often infiltrated with mineral matter, may be preserved as a "*fossil*,"[1] when the mud is hardened into a stone, and thus permanently contribute to the solid land.

So much for the plant ; let us now turn to the animal. The laid egg of a pigeon answers to the ripe pea. Within the shell, and suspended in the white of the egg, is the rounded yellow mass of the yolk, and on one side of the yolk is a small round patch—the *cicatricula*.[2] Though apparently homogeneous, the microscope shows that the cicatricula is made up of minute nucleated cells ; and this cell-aggregate is an embryo pigeon, just in the same sense as the little plant within the coat of the pea is an embryo pea-plant ; though it is far less like a pigeon than the latter is like a pea-plant.

The embryo pigeon, like the embryo plant, contains protein compounds, fats, mineral salts and water. The yolk in which it lies is composed of similar materials; but no starch or cellulose enters into its composition.

The cicatricula exhibits no more signs of life than the

---

[1] *Fossil*, Lat. *fossilis*, from *fodio*, to dig ; a term applied by old writers to anything dug out of the earth, and therefore including minerals, but now conventionally restricted to organic remains.

[2] *Cicatricula*, Lat. diminutive of *cicatrix*, a scar.

young plant within the pea. It is in a quiescent state, and its activity must be roused by an external influence. This, in the case of the egg, is simply a certain amount of heat (which is ordinarily furnished by the warmth of the body of the parent), the supply of nourishment being yielded by the matter stored up within the egg itself, in the yolk and white. Under these circumstances, the cicatricula enlarges by the growth and multiplication of its cells, and rapidly extends over the surface of the yolk. Part of it rises up and becomes fashioned into a rude resemblance of the body of a vertebrated animal, in which the head, trunk, and tail gradually become more and more recognizable; while the limbs grow out like buds, at first without much likeness to either legs or wings.

As the yolk is used up in the construction of the embryo, it diminishes as the latter increases; the young bird becomes larger and larger, acquires its feathers, and puts on more and more completely the characters of a pigeon. At last, it leaves the shell, and grows to the full size of its kind. In the adult state the female bird possesses an organ termed the *ovary*, in which nucleated cells, the *primitive ova*, which correspond with the embryo cells of the plant, are developed. Each of these grows and becomes invested by the materials of the egg; and, before it is laid, it undergoes a process of division, whereby it is converted into the embryonic patch, or cicatricula, from which this series of changing forms has proceeded.

Thus the pigeon is developed from a simple nucleated cell, by a process of evolution, similar in principle, however dissimilar in its results, to that which gives rise to the pea-plant. The adult pigeon is an aggregate of modified cells, descended by repeated division from the primitive egg cell; and this aggregate assumes a series of successive forms of gradually increasing complexity. Finally, cells are given off and extruded from the body as eggs; each of which is competent to run anew through the series, characteristic of that form of living matter known as a pigeon.

Hence, there is a very close analogy between the animal and the vegetable forms of life at present under consideration, but the differences are no less striking. The pigeon cannot live on a watery solution of ammoniacal and mineral salts, however much fresh air and sunshine may be added to this diet. It has no power of manufacturing the protein compounds, or the fatty or saccharine matter of its body out of simpler substances; but, directly or indirectly, it is dependent upon the plant for all the most important constituents of its body.

Like all other animals, the pigeon is a consumer, not a producer. The complex substances, which it obtains from the peas on which it feeds, are assimilated to its own substance, and are then slowly burned by the oxygen which it obtains by the process of respiration. The animal is in fact a machine, fed by the materials it derives from the vegetable world, as a steam-engine is fed with fuel. Like the steam-engine, it derives its motor power from combustion; and, as in the case of the steam-engine, the products of the combustion are incessantly removed from the machine. The smoke and ashes of the animal are the carbonic acid evolved in expiration, and the fæcal and urinary excreta. The latter are returned to the earth in a more or less fluid, or, at any rate, soluble form; the former is diffused through the air.

When the bird dies, the soft parts rapidly putrefy, and pass off, as gaseous and fluid products, into the air and the water. The dense bones resist decay longer; but, sooner or later,

even the lime salts by which they are hardened are dissolved away ; and the·solid animal fabric returns to swell the
sum of the fluids and gases from which, through the plant,
it has been derived. But, under like conditions to those
which have been mentioned in the case of the plant, the
bones may be covered up and protected from further decay,
or may become infiltrated with calcareous or siliceous matters ;
and thus, as a " fossil bird," a pigeon may form an integral
part of the solid crust of the earth.

It will be apparent that pigeons and peas, or more broadly,
the animal and the plant, respectively represent, in the world
of life, the destructive and the reparative powers of the not-
living world—the forces of denudation and of upheaval.
The animal destroys living matter and the products of its
activity, and gives back to the earth the elements of which
such matter is composed, in the form of carbonic acid, ammoniacal and mineral salts. The plant, on the contrary,
builds up living matter, and raises the lifeless into the world
of life. There is a continual circulation of the matter of the
surface of the globe from lifelessness to life, and from life
back again to lifelessness.

If pigeons and peas were the only forms of life, the
balance of solid and fluid constituents of the globe would
hardly be affected by their existence. Every pigeon and
every pea, as has been seen, represents a certain amount
of liquid and gas transmuted into the solid form; but, under
ordinary circumstances, the solids thus withdrawn, return to
the fluid and gaseous states within a short time after the
death of the body which they constitute. It is hardly conceivable that, under any circumstances, fossil pigeons or
fossil peas should make a sensible addition to what may,
at any rate in a relative sense, be termed the permanent
crust of the earth.

But it is otherwise with plants and animals which live under conditions more favourable for preservation ; and, in which, the earthy and less perishable constituents enter in large proportion into the composition of the body.   There is much more likelihood that the remains of animals and plants which live in the sea, or in rivers, or which haunt marshes and lakes, should be fossilized, than that those of the dwellers on dry land should be so preserved.   And the greater the quantity of salts of lime, or of silica, or of other slowly soluble ingredients, in the body of an animal or of a plant, the longer will its fabric be in disappearing, and the greater the chances of its preservation.

Along the shores of the Isle of Sheppey, in the estuary of the Thames, it is by no means uncommon to find fossils which have fallen out of the clay cliffs in the course of their destruction by the sea.   Many of these fossils are the hard fruits of trees, which lived at the time when the clay was in course of formation.   The fruits appear to have fallen from the trees which bore them, and which probably grew on the banks of a river ; and then to have been carried down by the river to its estuary, where they were embedded in the fine mud which has since been hardened into the clay of the Sheppey cliffs.   This is the same kind of clay as that on which the metropolis stands—the common London clay. The vegetation of this part of the world, at the time repre-sented by this clay, must have been very different in character from that of the present day.   Many of the fruits, for instance, are the produce of palm-like trees (*Nipa*) akin to the screw-pines, and similar to those now growing in Bengal, in the Philippine Islands, and elsewhere in the East Indian Archi-pelago ; while others are the cones of plants (*Proteaceæ*) similar to those which at the present day flourish in Australia. Fig. 63 shows one of these fruits from the London clay of

Sheppey. It must be borne in mind, that such fossils form only an insignificant portion of the bulk of the rocks in which they are embedded. There are, however, other organisms which enter so largely into the composition of certain deposits as to form by far the greater proportion of their bulk.

Thus, there is a well known substance, which has been used in the arts for many years as a polishing material, under the name of *Tripoli*. It is a kind of rottenstone, which occurs in large deposits in many parts of the world, but is especially abundant at Bilin, in Bohemia, where it

forms strata of considerable extent, one bed measuring as much as fourteen feet in thickness. In some places, the tripoli is a soft friable rock, while, in other localities, it is so hard as to be known as "polishing slate." Chemically, it is almost pure silica, like the silica of rock-crystal; but examination under a microscope shows, at once, that it is not simply mineral silica. Indeed, when a little of this tripoli is sufficiently magnified, it is seen to be

FIG. 63.—Fossil fruit (*Nipadites ellipticus*) from the London clay, Sheppey.

made up, not of shapeless mineral particles, nor of minute crystals of silica, but of such beautifully-formed objects as those represented in Fig. 64. It was shown, many years ago, by the late Prof. Ehrenberg, of Berlin, that these delicate objects in the tripoli are identical with the siliceous cases characteristic of a group of minute organisms called *Diatoms*. The diatoms are found living both in salt and in fresh water, but the kinds commonly preserved in tripoli are characteristic of fresh water, and hence it is concluded that the material was probably deposited at the bottom of lakes or in marshes.

When a living diatom is examined, it is seen that the siliceous case incloses a particle of protoplasm. A diatom is, in fact, a simple vegetable cell, but its peculiarity lies in the fact that the cell is able to separate, or *secrete*, from the surrounding water, that chemical combination which is called " silica," and which exists, in minute proportion, dissolved in most natural waters.   The silica thus appropriated by the diatom forms a solid case, which incloses the protoplasm, and often exhibits a beautifully-sculptured surface.

FIG 64.—Microscopic section of diatomaceous deposit, Mourne Mountains, Ireland.   Magnified about 160 diameters.

On the death of a diatom, the protoplasm decomposes and disappears ; but the siliceous shield, although it is very slowly dissolved by water, is not easily perishable, and it therefore remains as a solid body at the bottom of the water. It is true the diatoms are very minute, but they compensate for this by their extraordinary abundance.   In some estuaries, they are so abundant that the accumulation of their hard envelopes contributes largely to shallowing the water and blocking up harbours. It was estimated by Ehrenberg that as much as 18,000 cubic feet of siliceous organisms were accumulated every year in the harbour of Wismar, in the Baltic. Sir J. Hooker refers to the enormous multitudes of diatoms in the waters and in the ice of the South Polar Ocean ; and a deposit, or *ooze*, consisting principally of their siliceous casings, was found along the flanks of the Victoria Barrier, extending over an area which measured as much as 400 miles in length and 200 in breadth. During the voyage of the *Challenger*, a similar diatomaceous ooze was found, as a pale straw-coloured deposit, in certain parts of the Southern Ocean ; and diatoms are seen in abundance on the surface of many seas, especially where fresh water is brought down by rivers. Insignificant as diatoms appear when regarded individually, it is clear that, by their vast numbers and by the comparative indestructibility of their cases, they may play a very important part in the formation of certain deposits which will eventually constitute siliceous rocks. In fact, Ehrenberg has shown that the loose siliceous particles of the diatomaceous deposit at Bilin may become altered into a compact rock by the percolation of water. This very slowly dissolves the silica and then re-deposits it, as a hard opal-like rock, in which the organic structure is well-nigh obliterated.

There are not many plants that have power, like the simple diatoms, to encase their cells in such hard material as silica. In the Grasses, however, the cells forming the coating of the stalks contain a good deal of silica, which confers rigidity upon the structure ; and one of the Horse-tails[1] is so rich in this substance that it is imported from Holland, under the name of " Dutch rushes," for use as a

[1] *Equisetum hyemale.*

polishing material.   But, even where there is no special
deposition of mineral matter in the plant-cells, the walls of
the cells themselves are commonly formed of a compact
membrane which may offer considerable firmness of texture.   The cell-membrane consists of the material called
cellulose, which differs essentially from the inclosed protoplasm, in that it contains no nitrogen, but rather resembles
starch in chemical composition.   In woody plants, the cell
walls become very much thickened ; and the accumulated
woody matter, which is insoluble in water, contributes to the
strength and support of the vegetable structure, and decays
but slowly.   Hence, the accumulation of remains of plants
may, under proper conditions, yield deposits of considerable
durability.

Accumulations of partially decomposed vegetable matter
form the substance known as *peat* or *turf*.   This is produced only under certain conditions of moisture and temperature ; damp ground, in a temperate climate, being the
situation most favourable to its formation.   In this part of
the world, the principal peat-forming plants are certain
mosses known to botanists under the generic name of
Sphagnum.   The stems of the bog-moss die away in their
lower part, while the upper portion continues to grow freely.
The interwoven dead portions form a tangled mass, which
holds water like a sponge and favours the growth of the
moss above.   Remains of other plants become mixed with
the mosses, and contribute to the formation of the peat,
while trunks of trees occasionally get embedded in the
bog.   Muddy matter is likewise washed in during floods,
and helps to consolidate the felted mass and to produce a
deposit of considerable firmness.   The rate at which the
peat grows varies greatly under different conditions, but
some notion of the rate may be gained from the fact that

Roman remains, and even Roman roads, have been found beneath eight feet of peat. In Ireland, peat-bogs are so abundant as to cover about one-tenth of the entire surface of the country; and, in some cases, the peat may be as much as forty feet in thickness. The peat is cut from the bog, in brick-shaped blocks, by means of a peculiar spade known as a "slade," and, after being dried in stacks, is used as fuel. In England, peat is not so important as in Ireland, but it is to be found in many damp localities. It was mentioned, in the last chapter (p. 212), that an old peaty soil extends for miles along the estuary of the Thames, though hidden beneath the surface.

In the deeper, and therefore older, parts of a thick peat-bog, where the decomposing matter is most compressed and altered, it usually takes the form of a brownish-black, slightly compact mass, in which the vegetable structure may be almost obliterated : the material is in fact converted into a substance not altogether unlike *coal*. Indeed, the resemblance has led to the suggestion that beds of coal may, in some cases, have been formed by the alteration of old peat-bogs. Although there are certain objections to such a view, it is nevertheless beyond question that coal owes its origin to the alteration of vegetable matter. The evidence upon which this conclusion is founded is derived, partly, from the chemical and microscopic structure of the coal and, partly, from the conditions under which the substance is found in nature.

Coal occurs in the shape of beds, or *seams*, of variable thickness, associated with shales, sandstones, and other sedi-mentary rocks. The succession of strata, or *measures*, cut through in a colliery, is generally similar to that represented in Fig. 65, but the series may include hundreds of separate beds. The "roof" of the coal, or the rock immediately above the seam, is commonly a shale, which when split into layers is very frequently found to inclose impressions of plants. Perhaps the commonest of these remains are the graceful leaves or *fronds*[1] of ferns, which are often strikingly similar to those living at the present day. Although, in these islands, ferns never attain to the size of trees, yet, in countries where the climate is very warm and moist, as in New Zealand, they form trees fifty or sixty feet in height.

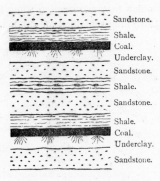

Sandstone.

Shale.
Coal.
Underclay.

Sandstone.

Shale.

Sandstone.

Shale.
Coal.
Underclay.

Sandstone.

FIG. 65.—Section of coal measures.

Such tree-ferns lived also in this country, at the time of the formation of the shales which are found in association with the coal.

In addition to the impressions of plants found in the shales above the coal seams, vegetable remains are also met with in rocks beneath the coal, forming what is called the "floor." It was pointed out many years ago by the late Sir W. Logan,

---

[1] A *frond* differs from an ordinary leaf in usually bearing fructification. The ferns have no flowers, and the fruit is generally developed on the frond.

when examining the great coal-field of South Wales, that each bed of coal is supported by a layer of shale known as *under-clay* or *seat-earth*, as shown in Fig. 65. Whatever the number of seams of coal—and in some cases they are very numerous—there is always just the same number of under-clays. Moreover these underclays usually contain such bodies as that figured in Fig. 66, which are never found in the roof of the coal. Such objects had long been known to geologists under the name of *stigmariæ*,[1] but though it was clear they represented some part of a plant, their precise nature long remained an enigma. At length a

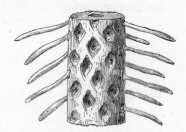

Fig. 66.—*Stigmaria ficoides ;* a coal measure fossil.

railway cutting through the Lancashire coal-field exposed half a dozen trees resting upon a seam of coal, but sending their strong roots downwards into the under-clay, where they ramified in all directions and gave off rootlets. It was found by Mr. Binney that these roots were nothing but the well-known *stigmariæ*, and that the characteristic stigmata, or pits, were not leaf-scars, as had been suggested, but points from which rootlets had been given off. The stigmariæ passed upwards into fluted tree-stems, which are not un-

---

[1] *Stigmaria*, from στίγμα, *stigma*, "a mark ;" in allusion to the scars left by the rootlets.

commonly found in the coal and the shales, and are known
as *sigillariæ* (Fig. 67).[1] There is consequently no doubt
that the stigmaria is nothing but the root of the sigillaria,
and that the under-clay represents the soil of an ancient
forest in which these and other trees flourished.

In examining one of these sigillaria-stems, it will probably be found that the bulk of the trunk consists of
stony matter, but that this is coated by a thin layer of

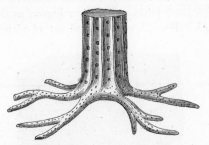

Fig. 67.—*Sigillaria* attached to stigmarian roots.

coal which represents the original bark of the tree. Hence, it
may be assumed that the old trunk rotted away, leaving
a hollow tube of bark which has become transformed into
coal. But, although coal may have been produced in this
way to a limited extent, it would be rash to conclude
that the whole of our coal was formed by such a trans-
formation. What kinds of vegetable matter have been
concerned in the production of coal cannot be determined
without the aid of the microscope.

On attempting to break a mass of coal, it will generally
be found that it splits much more readily in certain

[1] *Sigillaria*, from Lat. *sigillum*, a seal ; the leaf scars resembling the
impressions of a seal

directions than in others. Thus, it breaks easily along the
planes of bedding, which of course run parallel to the
general stratification of the coal-measures. The top and
bottom layers thus broken, commonly present dull black
almost sooty surfaces, and easily soil the fingers when
handled. But the mass of coal also splits with ease in
certain directions which run vertically across the stratification, and the broken surfaces thus produced are generally
bright and smooth, and do not soil the fingers : the direction
along which these joints run is often known as the "face"
of the coal. Then there is a third set of planes at right

Fig. 68.—Cuboidal block of coal split along natural planes.

angles to both the other sets, and less perfect, so that the
fracture here is more irregular; this direction is sometimes
called the "end" of the coal. On the whole, then, there
are three directions, perpendicular to one another, in which
the coal may be divided ; and it thus yields blocks more or
less regular in shape, and roughly resembling cubes or dies,
such as that shown in Fig. 68.

The dull black substance running along the planes of
stratification or bedding of a piece of coal is sometimes
called, from its resemblance to charcoal, *mineral charcoal*,
and it is likewise known as *mother of coal*. This substance

is often fibrous, and is made up to a large extent of the remains of stems and leaves.   But the constitution of the mass of the coal is very different from that of the mineral charcoal, which indeed forms only thin layers spread out between the laminæ of the coal.   If a slice of coal, cut so thin as to be partially transparent, is examined under the microscope by light passing through its substance, it will usually present some such appearance as that shown in Fig. 69.[1]   This section, which has been taken parallel to the

FIG. 69.—Microscopic section of Better Bed coal, Yorkshire.   Magnified 25 diameters.

face of the coal, shows a blackish or dark-brown mass forming the ground, in which are embedded numerous granules and streaks of yellowish colour.   These streaks represent the edges of tiny bags which have been cut through, and which, in certain coals, may be seen entire even with the naked eye.   Thus, there is a valuable seam of coal near Bradford, in Yorkshire, known as the " Better Bed," which contains vast numbers of these little discs, each

[1] From a paper by Mr. E. T. Newton in the *Geological Magazine*, Dec. 2, Vol. ii., No. 8, August, 1875.

about $\frac{1}{20}$th of an inch in diameter, and therefore readily visible. These discs are the larger bodies cut through in the section, and appear to be sacs which sometimes inclose granules similar to those scattered through the dark ground-mass, and which are not more perhaps than $\frac{1}{700}$ of an inch in diameter. Botanists conclude that these minute bodies are the *spores*,[1] or reproductive bodies of a flowerless plant; while Prof. Morris suggested, many years ago, that the larger bodies are the cases which inclosed the spores and are themselves known as *sporangia*. Similar bodies are well seen in microscopic sections of the curious combustible substance known as "white coal" which is in course of formation in Australia.

There can be no doubt that these spores and spore-cases were shed by trees closely related to those extinct forms which are well-known under the name of *Lepidodendron*.[2] Remains of the lepidodendron have been found, with cones still pendant from the branches of the tree; and similar cones, called *Lepidostrobi*, are scattered in abundance through the coal-bearing rocks. The cones are made up of scales, and in some specimens it is possible to detect spore-cases, containing spores, still preserved between the scales. Mr. Carruthers has given the name of *Flemingites* to a lepi-dodendroid plant which has been found to have spores, closely resembling those which occur in the mass of the coal. There seems therefore scarcely any room for doubt that the little bodies so plentifully scattered through most coals were derived from plants more or less resembling the lepidodendron.

[1] *Spores* are one of the kinds of bodies by which flowerless plants are reproduced.

[2] *Lepidodendron*, from λέπις, *lepis*, a scale; δένδρον, *dendron*, a tree; in allusion to the scale-like leaf-scars on the stems.

But what kind of trees were these ancient inhabitants of the coal-forests, and to what existing plants could they claim kinship ? To answer this question it is necessary to turn not to our forest trees, but to such lowly plants as the club-moss or *Lycopodium.* It may seem almost absurd to compare such different objects as these ; for the club-moss is a weak herb, and even in the most favourable conditions does not rise to a height of more than two or three feet, while the lepidodendron must have been a gigantic tree, certainly reaching, in some cases, to a height of a hundred feet. Yet, in the form of their stems, and in the character of their fructification, the resemblance between the two is so striking, that the student is forced to admit that the club-moss is but a miniature edition of the old lepidodendron. But, though the ancient and the modern plants thus differ so much in size, it is curious to note that their spores are of nearly the same dimensions.[1]

At first sight, it no doubt seems surprising that objects so minute as the spores and spore-cases of extinct plants allied to the club-moss should form any considerable proportion of those vast masses of coal which occur in beds several feet in thickness, and extend over areas measured in miles. Yet in this case, as in that of the diatoms, the enormous numbers compensate for want of size in the individuals. Clouds of yellow dust, consisting of spores, may be shaken from a branch of club-moss ; and the spores of the diminutive species still living are so abundant that they form an article of commerce. The druggist rolls his pills

---

[1] In some of the living club-mosses there are two kinds of spores, one being much larger than the other. The larger are known as *macro-spores,* whilst the smaller are called *microspores.* Prof. Williamson, of Manchester, who has paid great attention to the structure of coal-plants, has made the important suggestion that the large bodies, termed "sporangia" in the text, are really macrospores.

R

in lycopodium spores; and, by thus coating them with a resinous powder, enables them to roll over the tongue without direct contact with its moist surface. And, before the days of the electric light, the stage-manager was in the habit of using this highly combustible resinous material, under the name of "vegetable brimstone," to produce a blaze of mimic lightning.

From what has now been said, it appears probable that most coal has been formed in something like the following way. A forest of lepidodendrons, sigillarias, ferns, and other plants, grew up on an old land-surface, which is now represented by the under-clay, or its equivalent. Season after season, showers of spores fell from these flowerless plants, and, accumulating on the soil, became mixed with the fallen fronds, and with larger or smaller portions of the stems of the surrounding trees. While a large proportion of the soft vegetable matter slowly disappeared by decay, or left only a highly carbonized residue, of which the part that retains a recognizable structure is the "mother of coal," the resinous spores resisted decomposition, and remain distinguishable in all the less altered coals. The roots of the *Lepidodendra* were often preserved by the clay in which they grew, and became the fossil *stigmariæ*.

When a layer of vegetable soil had thus accumulated to a considerable thickness, the land slowly subsided, and the old forest was buried beneath deposits of mud and sand, which have since hardened into shales and sandstones. Compressed beneath these sediments, the vegetable matter underwent peculiar changes, which resulted in the formation of coal. Then a time came when the sedimentary deposits were upheaved, and another forest sprang up on the new land, forming a second bed of coal. Hence every seam of coal indicates fresh movement of the ground; and, when it is remembered that, in the South Wales coal-field, as many as eighty distinct beds of coal may be recognized, it will be seen that the coal-measures offer striking evidence of oscillations of the level of the land. Between each elevation and depression, there must have been time enough for the formation of a thick vegetable soil, and, in some cases, this must have taken vast periods of time; thus, in South Staffordshire, there is, or rather was, a famous bed of coal measuring as much as *thirty feet* in thickness. Remembering, then, the slow growth of a forest, the great thickness of some of our coal seams, and the number of separate beds in the coal-measures, it will be readily conceded that these strata represent a lapse of time which is probably to be counted by hundreds of thousands of years.

Before it was understood that each bed of coal grew where it now stands, it was supposed, by many geologists, that coal had been formed by the alteration of wood drifted out to sea. Great rafts of timber and other ac-cumulations of vegetable matter are unquestionably carried down by such a river as the Mississippi; and this matter, becoming buried in the silt of the estuary, might undergo changes resulting in the formation of coal. But, though small deposits of coal may have been formed in this way, no accumulation of drift-wood would be competent to pro-duce beds of pure coal of uniform thickness and great extension, such as those in any of our coal-fields. More-over, there are the *stigmariæ* to show that the plants grew where their remains are found.

There is, however, a kind of imperfect coal which shows by its texture that it has been formed from wood. So ligneous indeed is its texture that the coal is commonly called *lignite*. In this country, such coal is found only in

insignificant quantity at Bovey Tracey in Devonshire, but
in many countries, which are poor in true coal, the lignite
occurs in large deposits and is an important fuel. A few
years ago, some old timbering in a mine in the Hartz,
known to date back about four hundred years, was found to
be converted into this lignite or "brown coal." Hence,
there can be no doubt that, under certain conditions of
decay, wood may be transformed into a coal-like material.

Lignite may be regarded as vegetable matter not completely mineralized. Even the ordinary coal of our own
country is subject to further alteration, and may become
still more removed in characters from its original condition.
Thus, in the coal-field of South Wales, a curious change may
be traced in passing from one end of the field to the other.
In the eastern part, the coal is of the ordinary kind, such as
is seen in our scuttles, and is called *bituminous coal;* towards
the middle of the field this passes into *semi-bituminous coal,*
which is a kind of fuel that does not burn with a bright
gassy flame, but is valued for feeding the engines of steamers,
since it emits but little smoke ; finally, in the western part of
the coal-field, this steam-coal passes into a substance called
anthracite,[1] which is still less inflammable and still more
removed from the original form of vegetable matter.   Such
changes in the character of the coal appear to be closely connected with the disturbance and fracture of the coal seams.
Most deposits of coal have been thrown into basin-like
shapes, and the beds are often broken up and otherwise
disturbed by, the injection of igneous rocks and by lateral
pressure.   In these disturbed regions, the coal has been
altered into an anthracitic material.   The alteration which
has been effected appears to be much like that which
takes place when coal is artificially distilled, for the

[1] *Anthracite,* from ἄνθραξ, *anthrax,* coal or charcoal.

manufacture of ordinary illuminating gas. That part of the coal which contributes to the blaze of a fire is removed, while the coke-like portion is left behind.

The chemical changes which have taken place during the conversion of vegetable matter into the several varieties of coal may be seen by a comparison of their analyses, as given in the following table :—

	Carbon.	Hydrogen.	Oxygen and Nitrogen.[1]
Wood (Oak)	48·94	5·94	45·12
Peat (Irish)	55·62	6·88	37·50
Lignite (Bovey Tracey) . . .	69·94	5·95	24·11[2]
Bituminous Coal (Newcastle) . .	88·42	5·61	5·97
Steam Coal (South Wales) . . .	92·10	5·28	2·62
Anthracite (South Wales) . . .	94·05	3·38	2·57

Changes of the kind indicated by these analyses have been carried on, during the past history of the earth, on an enormous scale ; and the great extent and thickness of the deposits of coal, which have thus been produced, show that vegetable life has played no insignificant part in the formation of the rock-masses which build up the earth's crust.

[1] The quantity of nitrogen being small is added to the oxygen. The analyses are calculated exclusively of the ash, or mineral matter contained in the coals.

[2] Exclusive of nitrogen.

CHAPTER XV.

It has already been pointed out that when an aquatic
animal dies, its hard parts, such as a shell, or bones, if it
happen to possess any, will stand a fair chance of constituting a permanent contribution to the solid materials of
the earth, by becoming embedded in mud, and in this way
preserved from destruction.

Such names as "Shell-haven," near Tilbury, on the Essex
coast, and "Shell-ness," in the Isle of Sheppey, sufficiently
indicate the abundance of shells, which accumulate in certain
regions of the estuary of the Thames; and, on many other
parts of the English coast, enormous multitudes of shells are
scattered upon the sea-beach and embedded in its sands
and mud.

Vast quantities of dead shells accumulate on oyster-beds,
and the dredge brings up similar objects, wherever it is
allowed to scrape along the bottom of the sea, around our
coasts. Moreover, in some parts of the Channel, small
reefs are built up of nothing but the sandy habitations which
are fabricated by certain marine worms.

This operation of the formation of new land by animal agents is manifested in the most conspicuous

manner and on a gigantic scale, by the coral reefs and islands of which we hear so much in accounts of voyages in tropical seas.

It is extremely common to hear, or read, that these masses of land are constructed by coral "insects." As a matter of fact, however, the animals mainly concerned in the formation of these deposits are widely different from insects; while they are very similar to certain marine organisms, of much simpler structure than any insects, which abound on our own coasts.

Scarcely any visitor to the sea-side can fail to be familiar with the peculiar flower-like creatures which are popularly called *sea anemones*.[1] They are commonly to be found attached to the rocks in little pools of salt water left between tides. The body of the sea anemone is a fleshy sac, more or less cylindrical in shape, and closed at one end, which forms the base, by means of which the creature fixes itself to any solid object. Upon occasion, it can quit its hold and, by movement of this fleshy base, is able to crawl over the sea-bottom. In marine aquaria, sea anemones may sometimes be seen creeping up the glass sides of the tank, in this fashion. At the opposite end of the cylindrical body, there is a mouth, surrounded by a great number of feelers or *tentacles*, disposed in a circle, or more commonly in several circles one within another. So sensitive are these feelers that, if one be lightly touched, they are all quickly drawn in, and the creature shrinks to a small conical mass, looking like a mere knob of jelly stuck to a stone. But, when the feelers are freely spread out, they form a graceful crown, variously coloured and giving the animal a very flower-like appearance, not altogether

---

[1] *Anemone*, from the flower so called ; from ἄνεμος (*anemos*) wind, in allusion to the flower being easily blown about by the breeze.

unlike that of a China-aster, or some other member of that great group of plants represented by our daisies and dandelions.

If any little animal, such as a shrimp, chance to come within reach of the outspread feelers, it is at once carried to the mouth and thrust into a sac, which occupies the centre of the body. Between the walls of this sac and those of the body, there is a wide space, so that the arrangement may be compared to that of a common inkstand; the inner sack representing the glass vessel which holds the ink, and the rest of the body the body of the inkstand, into which the ink-holder drops. And, just as there are holes round the top of the inkstand for holding pens, which holes open into the interspace between the inkholder and the body of the inkstand; so, round the top of the body of the sea-anemone, there are openings, by which the cavities contained within the feelers communicate with the interspace between the inner and the outer sacs. Beyond this point, however, there are two important differences between the sea-anemone and the inkstand. For the inner sac is open at the bottom; and, consequently, the interspace between the inner and the outer sacs, and the cavities of the feelers, are in free communication with the cavity of the inner sac; and, therefore, by means of the mouth, with the exterior. Hence, all the cavities are full of sea-water. In the second place, in the sea-anemone, a number of vertical partitions stretch from the inner sac to the outer wall of the body, whereby the interspace between the two is divided into numerous chambers.

The food which is taken into the inner sac undergoes digestion; its nutritive parts are dissolved and are diffused through the fluid which fills the body, and which thus serves the purpose of blood; while the indigestible hard parts are cast out again by the mouth. The body of

a true insect is divided into segments; it has a digestive canal
which does not open into the cavity of the body; it has
distinct organs of circulation and respiration, and a peculiarly
formed nervous system.   None of these features are to be
met with in the sea-anemone; which, therefore, is an animal
of much lower grade than an insect.   Indeed, it is much
more nearly allied to the jelly-fishes, which float in the sea,
and to the fresh-water polypes of our ponds.   The general
name of "polype"[1] is, in fact, applied to the sea-anemones
no less than to the latter.

The substance of the body of the common sea-
anemones is quite soft, and none of them acquire a greater
consistency than that of a piece of leather.   But there are a
few animals, which live at considerable depths in our own
seas, and very many in other parts of the ocean, the
structure of which is, in all essential respects, similar to
that of the sea-anemones, but which nevertheless possess a
very hard skeleton (Fig. 70).   This skeleton, inasmuch as
it is formed by the solidification of the base and side-walls
of the body of the polype, necessarily has the form of a cup,
and it is termed a *cup coral*, to distinguish it from other
kinds of coral such as the *red coral*, which, though produced
by similar animals, are formed in a different manner.   Not
only are the walls of the body thus hardened, but vertical
partitions of the same character extend from the walls of
the cup to its centre, in correspondence with the partitions
which divide the cavity between the inner sac and the body-
wall.   The hardening of the lower part of the body of the
coral polype, and that of the partitions, is effected by the
deposition, within their substance, of carbonate of lime

---

[1] *Polype*, from πολὺς, *polus*, "many," and ποὺς, *pous*, "foot;" an
animal with several feet or several tentacles; thus the octopus derives
its name from having eight of these organs.

extracted from the sea-water in which the animal lives; just as the calcareous salts of the bones are extracted from the milk, and deposited in those parts of the body which are becoming bone, in a growing infant. The deposit converts the base of the polype into a solid cement, which fixes the animal to the surface to which it is attached; and, if the polype goes on growing not merely in height, but in breadth, while the process of calcification extends as it

FIG. 70.—*Caryophyllia Smithii*, a coral-polype from the coast of Devonshire.[1]

grows, the coral will necessarily assume the conical form exhibited in Fig. 71. It will be understood that the deposit of calcareous matter does not extend into the region of the feelers, or into the inner sac, so that the formation of the coral skeleton no more interferes with the performance of the functions of the body in the polype, than

[1] From Mr. Gosse's *Naturalist's Rambles on the Devonshire Coast.* 1853.

the development of the bones of a man does with his
eating and drinking.

Sooner or later, the coral polype dies ; then, the feelers,
inner sac, and all the soft upper parts of the body, and
those which cover the skeleton, decay, and are washed away,
while the skeleton, or *corallum*, as it is called, is left as a
contribution to the solid floor of the sea (Fig. 72).

Such solitary coral polypes as have been described give

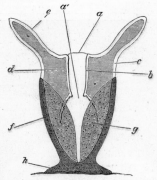

Fig. 71.—Diagrammatic section of a single cup-coral, to show the general structure
of the polype, and the relation of the skeleton to the soft parts.

a, mouth ; *b*, inner sac or stomach; *a'*, its inner opening ; *c*, the soft outer wall of
the body ; *d*, the interspace between the inner sac and the body-wall, with its
partitions ; *e*, the tentacles ; *f*, the calcified body-wall or cup of the coral; *g*, the
hard partition of the coral ; *h*, the base by which the coral is fixed.

rise to numerous eggs, the young developed from which
float away, and sooner or later, fixing themselves, take on
the form of the parent. Very often they have other modes
of multiplication. A coral polype may give off small
buds, each of which grows into a perfect animal with its
own stomach, mouth, and feelers, but remains closely connected with the parent. In other cases, the coral animal
spontaneously splits into two halves ; and these, in turn, may

divide and subdivide, the product of each division growing
into a perfect polype. By frequent repetition of these
processes of budding and splitting, the corals may form
masses of great size; in some cases, branching like a tree,
with separate polypes budding out in all directions; and, in
other cases, spreading into a confused mass, like the well
known "brain-stone coral," which is to be seen in every
museum. Since the multiplication of the polypes may go
on to an almost unlimited extent, it is evident that the

Fig. 72.—*Thecopsammia socialis*, Pourtales.

aggregated mass of coral may be of enormous size, although
the separate polypes are but small. In fact, it is the growth
of coral, in this manner, that forms those masses of land
which are known as "coral-reefs" and "coral-islands."

Such land is popularly said to be "built" by the coral-
animals, but it should be understood that it is not a constructive work, like the nest of a bird, or the comb of the bee.
The land is simply an accumulation of the calcareous remains, or skeletons, of the coral-polypes. The formation of
this land is, indeed, very much like the formation of the

peat-bog, described in the last chapter. It was there shown that the bog-moss dies below, while it continues to grow above ; and, in like manner, the coral-polypes die below, leaving their calcareous skeletons, while they continue budding and growing above : hence, a coral-island can be said to be " built " by the polypes only in the same sense that a peat moss can be said to be "built" by the plants of the remains of which it consists.

Many islands in tropical seas are skirted by low banks of coral-formed rock. At high tide, the surface of the rock is, for the most part, submerged, and its position is then marked only by a white line of heavy breakers. But, at low water, the surface is more or less exposed, forming a broad and bare platform, which rises slightly above sea-level. Some islands are completely bordered by a margin of this coral-rock, while others are fringed only at certain points. Where a stream runs down from the land, and carries sediment to sea, the reef is generally absent, for the coral-polypes do not thrive in muddy water. Rocky ridges, which fringe a shore in the manner just described, are known as *fringing-reefs*.

In other cases, the coral-rock is not directly attached to the coast, but stands off at some distance, so as to form a barrier, perhaps many miles from land. Such reefs are consequently called *barrier-reefs*. Between the coast and the reef there is a channel of comparatively shallow water, forming a harbour, to which entrance is gained by a breach here and there in the reef, the reef itself constituting a natural breakwater. Patches of coral-rock, forming small isolated reefs, may be scattered about the quiet channel, and the barrier itself may be broken up into a chain of detached reefs. Along the north-eastern coast of Australia there is a chain of these barrier-reefs stretching for a length of about 1,200 miles, and standing at an average distance of twenty or thirty miles from the coast. The channel between this barrier-reef and the land is termed "the inner passage," and has a depth of about twenty or five-and-twenty fathoms ; while, outside the barrier-reef, the depth of the sea suddenly increases to many hundred fathoms.

In addition to the fringing and barrier-reefs, there is yet another kind, differing from those principally in being quite isolated from other land. The coral-rock thus forms a true island, rising from the sea usually as a low strip of land, more or less ring-shaped, but generally of irregular outline. In places, the strip of coral-land may bear a rich growth of cocoa-nut palms and other tropical forms of vegetation ; while, inside the rim of land, there is a shallow lake, or *lagoon*, of clear green water, which strikingly contrasts with the dazzling white coral-rock of the beach. Access to the lagoon is gained by a gap in the shore, and thus the island generally presents a horse-shoe shape. Several openings may occur in the belt of land, and the island consequently becomes broken up into a chain of islets. These coral islands are plentifully scattered through the Pacific and Indian Oceans, and are often known under the Maldive name of *atolls*.

In explaining the formation of coral-land, it should be remembered that the corals themselves are powerless to raise the land above low-water mark, for the polypes perish when exposed above water. Dry land is, however, formed mechanically ; blocks of dead coral being broken off by waves from one part of the rock, and piled up upon another. The loose blocks are cemented into compact masses by means of coral-sand and coral-mud, produced by the tear and wear of the coral-rock. In the case of fringing reefs, the seaward, and, in that of atolls, the windward, side

of the mass of coral is usually the highest, for it is here that
the coral-polypes flourish most luxuriantly ; while the dash
of the breakers, during storms, tears off fragments of the
coral rock, and heaps them up on this side. It should be
borne in mind that the land is not entirely formed of corals,
since other creatures living in the lagoon, and on the banks
of the reef, contribute their remains to swell the mass.
Vegetable life too is not without its effect on the formation
of the new land ; and, indeed, the outer edge of a reef is
often formed, in large measure, of *nullipores*, a kind of sea-
weed, the tissues of which are strongly impregnated with
carbonate of lime.

Although corals of some kinds may be found in almost all
seas, those particular species which grow together in masses,
and thus form reefs and islands, are limited to the warmer
parts of the world. Prof. Dana, who has had ample
opportunity of observation, believes that the reef-forming
coral-animals are restricted to waters in which the mean temperature for the month, even in the coldest season, never
falls below 68° F.[1] If, then, a line be drawn through all
parts of the ocean north of the equator, where the coldest
month has this average temperature, and a similar line south
of the equator, they will include a zone within which all the
coral-reefs of the world are situated. It need hardly be said
that these lines will not be straight lines running in circles,
round the world, like parallels of latitude, but will be irregular lines, rising in one part and falling in another, according as the temperature is locally affected by the presence of
ocean-currents or by the proximity of land. This belt of
warm water, congenial to the coral-makers, never extends
beyond about 30 degrees from the equator.

Though the reef-building corals abound in many parts of

[1] *Corals and Coral Islands.* By James D. Dana, LL.D. 1875.

this zone, they are not found in all parts of it. They are absent, for example, on the western coasts of Africa and America; and, where great rivers debouch, the sediment and the fresh water, which they pour into the sea, interfere with the growth of the coral polypes. Moreover, reef-forming corals are restricted, not only in their superficial distribution, so as to be limited to certain *latitudes*, but also in their vertical distribution, so as to be limited to certain *depths*. Indeed, the needful conditions for the growth of the polypes are found only in comparatively shallow water. From the observations of Mr. Darwin, it appears that these corals do not flourish at greater depths than between 20 and 30 fathoms, and are, for the most part, restricted to about 15 fathoms of water. Knowing this, it might not unnaturally be assumed that coral-reefs and coral-islands would always be confined to shallow seas. As a matter of fact, however, soundings outside a barrier-reef, or an atoll, often show an enormous depth of water, the outer edge sinking down abruptly like a coral-wall. The early navigators knew that coral-islands were not unfrequently surrounded by very deep water; but this fact presented no difficulty, until naturalists became aware of the small vertical range to which the living corals are limited. Various attempts were then made to reconcile the two apparently opposed facts; but no satisfactory explanation was given until Mr. Darwin, about forty years ago (in 1837) advanced a most ingenious hypothesis, which not only perfectly solved the puzzle, but brought the several classes of coral-reefs into close relation with each other.

According to Mr. Darwin's view, the coral-rock has, in all cases, been originally formed in water not deeper than about 20 fathoms; and, when found at greater depths, it must have been carried down by subsidence of the rocky foundation

on which the polypes lived and died. The details of
so simple, yet complete an explanation, deserve closer
examination.

It has already been shown that coral-polypes can multiply
by processes of budding and splitting; but it should be
added, that they can also multiply by means of germs, which
are thrown off from the parent as free-swimming bodies.
Suppose that some of these embryonic corals settle upon a
sloping shore, in shallow water, where the conditions of life
are favourable ; there they may go on multiplying, until they
form masses of considerable extent, skirting the land, but
never extending seawards to a depth of more than 20 or 30
fathoms. Let the land, with its little fringing-reef, now
slowly sink ; that part which is carried down lower than
about 30 fathoms will consist of nothing but dead coral; but
the upper part of the reef will continue to grow, and, if the
subsidence be not more rapid than the upward growth, the
level of the reef will appear to remain stationary, at about the
sea-level. It has been said that the coral-polype flourishes
best at the outer margin of the reef, where it is bathed
by the surf. For this and other reasons, the reef is
highest at this edge ; while, between the outer margin of the
reef and the shore, there is a channel formed by the entry
of sea-water during subsidence. In fact, the fringing-reef,
as it has been slowly carried down, has become converted
into a barrier-reef. This will be easily understood by reference to the sections in Figs. 73 and 74. In Fig. 73 an
island, A, is skirted by a fringing-reef, B B : on the sinking
of the land to a lower level, as in Fig. 74, the bank of
coral, B B, becomes thicker by upward growth, and a
channel, C C, comes to be formed between the barrier
and the shore.

Outside the barrier, on its seaward edge, there may be a

S

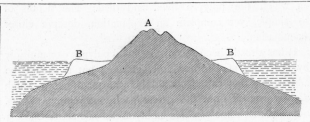

FIG. 73.—Diagrammatic section of an island surrounded by a fringing-reef.

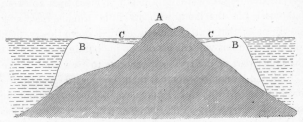

FIG. 74.—Diagrammatic section of an island surrounded by a barrier-reef, with intervening lagoon.

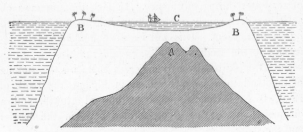

FIG. 75.—Diagrammatic section of a coral island, or atoll, with central lagoon.

great depth of water, varying according to the extent to which subsidence has gone on. By continued subsidence of an island encircled by a barrier, the lagoon, C C, becomes wider and wider. At length, only a few rocks may stand up in the centre of the lake; even these may at last disappear, leaving nothing but a sheet of water surrounded by the reef, and the barrier in this way becomes converted into an atoll, as shown in Fig. 75. Here the original land, A, has entirely disappeared beneath the growth of coral, B B, which surrounds the lagoon, C.

Assuming then that, where barrier-reefs and coral-islands occur, they indicate areas of subsidence, Mr. Darwin has been able to map out the Pacific and Indian oceans into zones in which the land is, or has been, slowly sinking.[1] These zones alternate with areas in which elevation is probably going on, as indicated by the occurrence of active volcanoes. Fringing-reefs tell less about movements of the sea-bottom, for they may occur where the land is either stationary or rising. In some cases, an old fringing-reef is found standing high and dry above water, like a raised beach, and thus showing clearly that the land has been subject to elevation.

[1] *The Structure and Distribution of Coral Reefs.* By Charles Darwin, M.A., F.R.S. Second Edition. 1874.

CHAPTER XVI.

THE FORMATION OF LAND BY ANIMAL AGENCIES.—
FORAMINIFERAL LAND.

THE operations of the reef-building coral polypes, described in the last chapter, are carried out on a gigantic scale. The Australian barrier-reef, alone, spreads a constantly increasing deposit of coral limestone over an area larger than that of Scotland ; [1] while the totality of the surface, over which coral reefs are spread in the Pacific ocean, exceeds that of Asia. Moreover, reefs and atolls are conspicuous objects, forcing themselves on the attention of the traveller by their beauty and their singularity, and awakening that of the navigator by the dangers which they create. But the conversion of the contents of the ocean into solid rock is constantly taking place, over a still greater area, and probably as rapidly, by agents which are inconspicuous, and, indeed, for the most part, invisible ; not only by reason of their minuteness, but because the results of their work accumulate, not in shallow waters, but at the bottom of the deep sea. Out of sight, they would be also out of mind, if various circumstances had not, of late years, led to the careful exploration of the depths of the ocean.

[1] The area of the barrier-reef is estimated to be 33,000 square miles ; that of Scotland is 31,324 square miles.

Almost everything that is known about the deep-sea bottom and its inhabitants has been learnt within the last quarter of a century. When it was first proposed to bring the Old World into relation with the New, by means of a telegraph-cable, it became necessary to make a careful survey of that portion of the sea-bed on which the cable was to rest. The bed of the North Atlantic was first examined, in detail, in 1853, by Lieutenant Berryman, in the United States brig *Dolphin;* and, in 1857, it was thoroughly surveyed, between Ireland and Newfoundland, by Captain Dayman in H.M.S. *Cyclops.* During these surveys, numerous samples of the sea-bottom were procured; and those which were brought up by the American survey were submitted to Ehrenberg and Bailey, while those from the English survey were examined by myself. In subsequent years, the exploration of the sea-bottom has been actively carried on in various parts of the world; and the valuable series of observations made during the expedition of H.M.S. *Challenger* has given us exact information of its nature, at a series of stations, in all the great oceans.

In the ordinary method of sounding, or ascertaining the depth of the sea, a leaden weight is attached to the end of a graduated line, and rapidly run out until the weight strikes the bottom. To procure a sample of this bottom, the lead is " armed ; " that is to say, the bottom of the weight, which should be slightly hollow, is covered with tallow, and a small quantity of the mud or other material at the bottom sticks to this grease, and may thus be brought up for examination. Such rude means are sufficient for sounding in shallow water, but more complicated instruments are required for deep-sea soundings. Most of these instruments act upon a principle first suggested by Lieutenant Brooke, of the U.S. Navy—that of causing the weight to detach itself from the line on reaching the bottom. The sounding-line thus runs down carrying a weight, but comes up free, bringing only a sample of the bottom, which is collected on the floor of the sea in a cup, or a tube, or a scoop.

Without referring to the various modifications of sounding apparatus which have been employed by successive deep-sea expeditions,[1] it will be sufficient to describe the sounding machine which was very largely used, during the recent voyage of the *Challenger*. This is represented in Fig. 76, and a section is given in Fig. 77. The apparatus is a modification of one which had been used by Captain Shortland in H.M.S. *Hydra*, whence it is sometimes called the "Hydra Machine;" its present form, however, is due to Lieutenant Baillie.

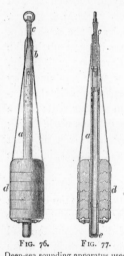

Fig. 76.   Fig. 77.

Deep-sea sounding apparatus used by the *Challenger*.

This apparatus consists of a metal tube *a*, mostly of iron, five and-a-half feet in length, and two and-a-half inches in diameter. Its upper end is furnished with a brass cylinder, *b*, in which a heavy piece of iron works up and down, like a piston in a cylinder. At *c*, this iron is furnished with a shoulder, which carries the iron-wire sling to which the sinking-weights are attached. These sinkers, *d*, are made of iron, cast in the form of cylinders, each with a central hole; they are provided with teeth and notches, so as to fit one

[1] Descriptions and figures of these instruments will be found in *The Depths of the Sea*, by Sir C. Wyville Thomson. The sounding apparatus itself may be seen in the Museum at South Kensington.

into another; and thus several may be fitted together, forming a compact mass perforated by a central canal, through which the tube passes. As the instrument runs down, water enters the tube *a*, at its open end *e*, and passes out through holes in the upper part. On striking the bottom, the tube sinks into the mud or other material, and a small quantity enters; and this is prevented from escaping by means of a pair of butterfly-valves, opening inwards, which are attached to the bottom, *e*. When the floor of the sea is touched, the brass cylinder, *b*, is pushed up, and striking the shoulder, *c*, of the iron piston, throws off the sling, and thus releases the weight. Thus, when the line to which the instrument is attached is hauled in, it comes to the surface, carrying nothing but the tube full of the sea-bottom. It is by means of such instruments that the deep sea has been sounded, and samples of the bottom brought to the surface for scientific examination.

The careful soundings made during these surveys revealed the remarkable configuration of the Atlantic sea-bed. This is shown in Fig. 78, which shows the contour of the floor of the sea between Valentia Island off Ireland, and St. John's in Newfoundland. It will be seen that there is a gradual downward slope from the Irish coast, for a distance of about 200 miles; then there is a more rapid descent[1] leading to a vast undulating plain which stretches across the ocean, until it reaches a distance of about 300 miles from Newfoundland, and from thence it gradually ascends towards the American coast. This great submarine plain, which has been called the

---

[1] In the diagram this descent looks like a steep cliff. But this is a deception arising from the exaggeration of the vertical height. Drawn to a true scale as in D, Fig. 78, the inclination of the slope is seen to be not more than 1 in 25, or that of a hill of moderate steepness. If it were a mere question of gradients, a waggon could be driven along the sea-bottom from Ireland to Newfoundland without any difficulty.

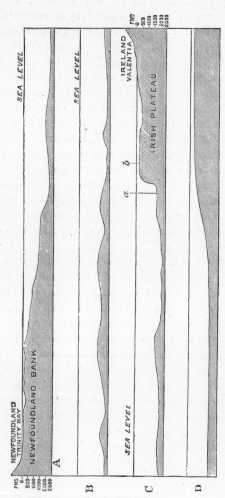

Fig. 78.—ABC. Section of the Atlantic sea-bed between Newfoundland and Ireland; from Captain Dayman's soundings. Vertical scale 15 times the horizontal scale.
D.—Section of the slope between *a* and *b*, in fig. C, drawn to natural scale.

" telegraph plateau," has a width of more than 1000 miles, and
an average depth of more than 1000 fathoms. It is almost
uniformly covered with a wide-spread deposit of fine creamy
or greyish mud, generally called " ooze." When this mud
is dried, it hardens into a grey friable substance, which may
be used for writing on a board, as chalk is used. Moreover,
when any acid is poured upon the mud, the greater part of it

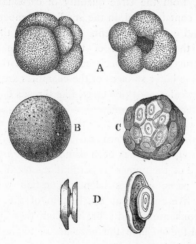

FIG. 79.—A *Globigerina bulloides*, D'Orb. ; B. *Orbulina universa*, D'Orb. ; C.
A coccosphere ; D. A coccolith, profile and three-quarters view (after Haeckel).

dissolves with effervescence, just as a piece of chalk would
do ; and it can readily be ascertained that the ooze, like
chalk, consists mainly of carbonate of lime.

This calcareous ooze, however, is not mere mineral
matter ; for, when a little is placed under the microscope,
the greater part of it is seen to consist of such bodies as
those represented in Fig. 79 A. Each of these consists of
several globular chambers, one of which is smallest and one

largest, while the others are of intermediate dimensions, disposed around a common centre, and adherent together. Each chamber has an opening in the face which is turned towards the centre; and, in the living state, all the chambers are filled with a protoplasmic substance, which spreads over the surfaces of the chambers, and sends out long radiating contractile threads. The walls of the chambers are hard and brittle, from the large quantity of carbonate of lime which they contain; and, in the smaller chambers, they are very thin and quite transparent. In the larger, they become thick, and the outer part of their substance acquires a prismatic structure. In specimens taken from the sea with great care, the outer surfaces of the chambers are beset with long slender calcareous processes, like threads of glass; but these very readily break off.

The bodies thus described are the skeletons of animals of a very simple character, known as *Globigerina bulloides*, belonging to the group which has been named the *Foraminifera*,[1] in consequence of the numerous perforations usually visible in their hard parts. It has been a question whether the *Globigerinæ* live and die at the bottom of the sea, where their skeletons are found; or, whether they live at the surface, and the shells in the ooze are therefore merely the skeletons of those which have died at the surface, and have thence fallen to the bottom. The investigations of the *Challenger* have now placed it beyond doubt that, whether any of them live at the bottom or not, they certainly swarm in prodigious numbers at, and a few fathoms below, the surface. They were taken by the tow-net, in all latitudes, over an area extending for between 50° and 60° on both sides of the equator; and though they abounded most in warm and temperate climates, they were not entirely

[1] *Foraminifera*, Lat. *foramen*, an aperture; and *fero*, I carry.

absent towards the northern or the southern limits of this range.

Over the whole of this enormous extent of the ocean, therefore, we must imagine an incessant rain of *Globigerina* shells; which, after falling from the surface, through perhaps two or three miles of sea-water, at length rest in, and add to, the ooze at the bottom. It is probably an over-estimate if we assume that the average bulk of the calcareous matter contained in each full grown *Globigerina* amounts to $\frac{1}{1,000,000}$th of a cubic inch. Nevertheless, the example of the effect of pluvial denudation, however slow and insignificant the wear and tear of rain and rivers on dry land may appear to be, when continued through long ages, in destroying the solids of the globe, prepares the mind to view, in this incessant downpour of lime-drizzle, a no less potent agent of reconstruction. If we suppose that the total thickness of the deposit of solid matter on the sea-bottom, arising from the foraminiferal shower, is as much as one-tenth of an inch a year; then, if the present state of the Atlantic and Pacific oceans has existed for only 100,000 years, this apparently unimportant operation will have sufficed to cover their floors with a bed of limestone no less than eight hundred feet thick.

Although the *Globigerina* shells constitute the greater part of the substance of the ooze, the remains of other organisms are found with them. Among these, other *Foraminifera* are very common; and especially one form, the *Orbulina*, Fig. 79 B, which is very closely allied to, if not a condition of, the *Globigerina* itself.

Besides these, there are innumerable multitudes of very minute saucer-shaped disks, termed *coccoliths*, which are frequently met with associated together into spheroidal aggregations, the *coccospheres* of Wallich, Fig. 79 C, D.

The exact nature of these very curious bodies is not at present known.

In addition to the calcareous organic remains which constitute the greater part of the ooze, it contains multitudes of siliceous skeletons, some of which belong to simple animal forms, such as *Radiolaria* and sponges, while others are vegetable organisms, belonging to the group of *Diatoms* described in the last chapter. The *Diatoms* and the *Radiolaria* inhabit the surface of the ocean, along with the *Globigerinæ* and *Orbulinæ*, but the sponges live at the bottom. Here and there, the remains of other animals which inhabit the depths of the sea, such as starfishes, sea-urchins, and various shell-fish, are also imbedded in the ooze, and contribute to the solid submarine deposit.

It is very interesting to remark that, just as the process of pluvial denudation is only, in part, a conversion of solid into fluid matter, and, for the rest, effects a mere transference of solids; so, the process of reconstruction of solids, which takes place in the superficial parts of the ocean, by the agency of the *Globigerinæ*, is not permanent. In other words, there is reason to believe that the *Globigerina* shells in the ooze, at the bottom of the sea, do not represent all the work in the way of withdrawing calcareous matter from solution in sea-water, which has been done by the *Globigerinæ* at its surface.

It has been seen that living *Globigerinæ* are found in the uppermost stratum of the sea, all over the warm and temperate parts of the world. Hence, it would seem to follow, that Globigerina-ooze should be found covering the bottom of the sea over the whole of these regions; and, in fact, it is met with, at all depths, between 250 and 2,900 fathoms, over an immense extent of both the Atlantic and the Pacific oceans.

But there are some areas of these oceans, occupying many thousand square miles, in which the sea-bottom is covered, not with Globigerina-ooze, but with a red mud, which appears to be nothing but clay in a very finely divided state. These areas are usually met with only at a very great depth, over 2,500 fathoms in fact; and the naturalists of the *Challenger* observed that, in passing from the adjacent region covered with the ordinary Globigerina-ooze, into one of these red-clay areas, a region, covered with a sort of grey mud ("grey ooze"), intermediate in its character between the Globigerina-ooze and the red clay, was traversed. Where the grey ooze began, the *Globigerina* shells appeared to be corroded, as if they had been attacked by an acid; and, as the red clay was approached, they became more and more fragmentary, and at length altogether disappeared.

There can be no doubt that the foraminiferal shower falls over the area, occupied by the grey ooze and the red clay, just as persistently as elsewhere. What then becomes of the shells? There seems to be no escape from the conclusion that the calcareous matter of which they are composed is dissolved away. The *Globigerinæ* are so minute, that their skeletons must take a great length of time to subside through the three or four miles of water, which overlie the deeper sea-bottoms. But sea-water contains much carbonic acid; and, it has already been seen, that carbonate of lime, especially if finely divided, is soluble in such water. Hence, it is highly probable, that the foraminiferal shower is, in part, redissolved before it reaches the bottom; and that, other things being equal, the greater the depth, the greater will be the loss suffered in this manner.

The difficulty is to understand, not why the *Globigerinæ* should disappear from the bottom of the very deep parts of the ocean, but why the process of solution should be so much hastened, at depths between 2,500 and 3,000 fathoms, that an abundant residuum of undissolved shells is left, at the former depth, and none at all, at the latter. Here is a problem the solution of which cannot as yet be given.

Again, what is the "red clay" which takes the place of the Globerigina-ooze? It has been suggested that it is the residuum left after the *Globigerinæ* have been dissolved; but there is no sufficient evidence that pure and clean *Globigerina* shells contain any appreciable proportion of such mineral matter.

An alternative supposition is, that the red clay is simply the finest of the washings of the land, which have gradually drifted into the greatest depths of the ocean; while another explanation which has been offered is, that it is the result of the decomposition of the volcanic ejections which are borne about by the winds, and finally scattered over the surface of the ocean; and which, as a matter of fact, are found floating, far and wide, in the shape of pumice. Fragments of volcanic minerals are everywhere found in the Globigerina-ooze; and, it is highly probable, that a "volcanic shower" is intermixed with the foraminiferal shower all over the ocean. If this be the case, then, in those localities in which the *Foraminifera* are dissolved before they reach the bottom, the volcanic minerals would remain as the sole constituent of the ooze; and, by their decomposition, they might give rise to the red clay.

From what has been said it follows, that if, in consequence of one of these movements of upheaval to which reference has been made, the present bed of the Atlantic were raised to the surface and became dry land, the many thousand square miles of new dry land thus produced, would be found to be covered, for an unknown thickness (amounting possibly, and indeed probably, to hundreds of feet) with a

bed of softish limestone. The great bulk of this calcareous
rock would be made up of entire, or fragmentary, *Globigerina* and *Orbulina* shells ; but it would contain, in addition, other *Foraminifera*, shells of shellfish, remains of
starfishes, and sea-urchins, and of such other animals provided with hard skeletons, as are now living in the Atlantic.

It would, in fact, be a highly "fossiliferous" limestone
with more or less silex, in the shape of *Radiolaria*
skeletons and sponge spicules, scattered through its mass,
and would constitute an element of no small magnitude
and importance in the composition of the earth's crust.

CHAPTER XVII.

THE GEOLOGICAL STRUCTURE OF THE BASIN OF THE THAMES ;
AND THE INTERPRETATION OF THAT STRUCTURE.

In the preceding chapters, the general character of the River Thames and the form of the surface which it drains, have been considered ; its waters have been followed to the sea, and, thence, by way of the atmosphere, back to that surface ; while the atmosphere, and the waters of the land and sea, have been traced back to the elementary bodies of which they are composed. The river, and the rains which feed it, were next considered as a grinding and dissolving machinery, by which the surface of the Thames basin is being insensibly worn away and its materials carried down to the ocean ; while the sea, so far as it washes the banks and shallows of the estuary and of the adjacent coasts, was shown to be a no less persistent destroyer of the dry land. And then, seeing that all rivers and all oceans are engaged in the business of denudation and dissolution, it became a matter of interest to discover what natural operations, if any, tend to compensate this constant wear and tear of the dry land. Such compensating agents were found in the forces which tend to raise submerged land ; in volcanoes, which transfer fluid matter to the surface, where they solidify; and lastly in living matter; which, on the whole, tends constantly to increase the solids of the globe, at the expense of its fluid and gaseous components.

With these conceptions of the general nature of the agents which are now at work in modifying the crust of the earth, it will be possible to start with profit upon a new series of considerations.

The Thames basin presents, as has been seen, a surface diversified with hills and valleys; this surface is everywhere covered with a comparatively thin layer of soil, which, in many places has been more or less altered in character by the builder, the road-maker, or the farmer, and is then known as "made ground." But beneath this lies the subsoil, which forms the uppermost part of the solid floor of the basin. It has been seen that this subsoil varies very much at different places, being here gravel or sand, there clay, in another place chalk, in another a different kind of calcareous rock. Moreover, it has been incidentally mentioned, that these materials are arranged in layers or strata; so that, if the floor of the Thames basin could be cut down vertically, the faces of the section would present a succession of layers, one above the other. It has been mentioned that quarries and railway cuttings, here and there, afford the opportunity of examining the strata in their natural relations and order of superposition. Sections of this kind afford direct evidence of the structure of the earth for only a very little way below the surface; but more is to be learned from the deep borings for wells, artesian and other, which have been referred to in Chapter II.

Such borings have been carried to a depth of 1,300 feet,[1] and they show that the subsoil of the Thames basin, in and

[1] A famous boring for water at Kentish Town, in 1854, was carried down to a depth of 1,302 feet. The boring passed through 236 feet of London clay; 88½ feet of Lower London Tertiaries; 645 feet of chalk;

about London, is everywhere made up of beds of gravel, sand, and clay of varying thickness ; these rest upon a thick bed of chalk ; and, beneath this, follow strata of sandstone, hardened clay, and calcareous rocks of a totally different character from the chalk. Whether we travel to the north, the south, and the west, or the east of London, we find the bed of chalk, which underlies London at a depth of upwards of 300 feet, coming up to the surface.   In other words, the layer of chalk, beneath the Thames basin, is bent up, on all sides, in such a manner as to have the form of a very shallow dish,[1] the bottom of which is covered with horizontal layers of sand and clay, while its eastern end is notched by the estuary of the Thames. Passing over the upturned edges of the layer of chalk on the north, the west, and the south, other rocks, as we have seen, lie at the surface; and, some of these, such as the greensand and the gault, are of the same nature as those which follow on the chalk in the vertical borings. It is obvious, therefore, that the stratum of chalk lies on the greensand and gault strata, just as a basin fits inside one a size larger. In the western part of the Thames basin, it has been seen that the subsoil rocks consist of limestones, sandstones, and clays. These beds are found beneath the chalk, greensand, and gault, some distance to the eastward. Underneath London, however, they are absent; for the borings which have been carried deep enough to traverse the chalk, greensand, and gault, enter rocks which are unlike any found at

13½ feet of upper greensand; 130½ feet of gault; and 188½ feet of clays, sandstones, and conglomerates, which were of doubtful age.

[1] The form into which the layer of chalk is bent is altogether independent of that of the Thames basin itself, although the two happen, to a certain extent, to correspond. Every area drained by a river has a more or less dish-like form, whatever may be the arrangement of the strata which constitute its floor.

the surface of the Thames basin ; though strata of a similar
character appear at the surface, further to the west.   All the
different strata which thus make up the floor of the Thames
basin contain fossil remains of animals or of plants, or of
both, sometimes in great abundance.

Such is a broad and general statement of the facts which
have been ascertained respecting the structure of the floor of
the basin of the Thames.   How are they to be interpreted ?
Some light may be thrown upon this question by considering
the method which is pursued by antiquaries and archæo-
logists, in order to extract trustworthy history from the works
of men.

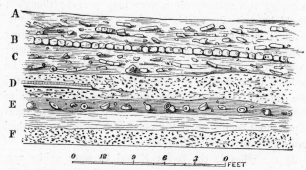

Fig. 80.—Section exposed in Cannon Street, London, 1851.

In 1851, during some improvements which were being
made in Cannon Street, in the city of London, a deep
digging exposed a section such as is represented in Fig. 80.[1]
At some distance below the level of the street, A, an old
pavement, B, was found; while, deeper than this, and
separated from it by a considerable quantity of soil, C,

[1] This section was recorded at the time by Mr. Chaffers.   See his
Marks and Monograms on Pottery.

was another pavement, D, of the kind which is termed
tessellated; and underlying this was another bed of soil, E.

There can be no reasonable doubt that the modern roadway, A, was laid down after the old pavement, B, and
that this pavement again is of later date than the tessellated
pavement. The three layers of soil, those between the
pavements and that above the pavement, B, contained
fragments of pottery, coins, and other articles, such as are
apt to accumulate in the rubbish of great cities.

Taking all the circumstances of the case into consideration, this Cannon-Street section affords to the archæologist
sufficient grounds for the conclusion, that human beings
occupied this locality for a very long period; though it
would be quite impossible to say how long, without independent evidence. Moreover, as the pottery and other
relics in the layer E, are of a totally different character
from those in the layer C, the archæologist would be
justified in supposing, either that the people who inhabited
the locality during the time represented by E, were of
different race from those who inhabited it during the time
represented by C; or, if the same, that their posterity had
undergone some great change.

If the relics in the layers E and C, were unlike anything known, the conclusions of the archæologist thus far
would be quite justifiable, but he could get very little further.
As a matter of fact, however, when the relics in the bed E
are compared with what are known, on independent grounds,
to be the coinage and pottery-work of the ancient Romans,
they can be identified with the latter; while the tessellated
pavement is no less characteristically Roman. On the other
hand, the coins and other objects in the stratum C, have all
the characters of those which are known, from independent
evidence, to have been produced in England, in the period

which ranges from the Norman conquest to the sixteenth century. Hence it might be concluded that the pavement B, was put down, at least as late as the sixteenth century; and this inference is confirmed by the fact, that such a pavement was known to exist in the locality, before the great fire of 1666.

Thus it will be observed, that the general conclusions deduced from the character and contents of the successive beds of made ground in Cannon Street, are fully borne out by independent evidence; and, if nothing were known of the ancient history of England, beyond such archæological facts as these, they would leave no doubt as to the fact, and the relative age, of the Roman occupation.

The principles, on which the interpretation of the Cannon Street section rests, are two : 1st. In such cases as that under consideration, the uppermost stratum is the latest formed, and the lowest, the oldest. 2nd. The similarity of bodies having a definite form and structure is presumptive evidence of the similarity of their origin. It is the former principle which justifies the conclusion that the pavement B is older than the pavement D ; it is the latter, which leads us to say that a piece of pottery is Roman rather than English. All the conclusions as to the history of the earth, deduced from the structure of its crust, are based upon analogous principles. If certain strata can be shown to have been deposited by aqueous agencies, then the uppermost of these strata is the newest, and the undermost is the oldest. If the fossils which are embedded in these strata can be proved to be similar, in all essential respects, to the hard parts of living animals and plants, then they are evidence of the existence of such animals and plants, antecedent to, or during the deposition of, these strata.

On referring again to the Cannon-Street section, it is seen

that below those deposits of soil, which show, by the character of their embedded remains, that they are of Roman date,
there is first a thin layer of clay, and then a deposit of gravel,
F. These lower beds did not yield, at this locality, any
relics of human workmanship; and, indeed, the explorer
who examines them, soon finds that he is dealing with
deposits in which neither Englishman, Roman, nor Briton
has left any mark.

The gravel exposed in this section forms part of a wide-
spread sheet, which covers a large portion of the valley of
the lower Thames. Its range in the neighbourhood of the
metropolis is shown on Fig. 81 ; which is a map, giving the
area of the superficial deposits, or "drifts," as they are
sometimes called,[1] in the Thames valley between Kingston
and Woolwich. The dotted part shows the gravel as
exposed at the surface. This gravel consists, principally, of
rounded and subangular pieces of flint, derived from the
chalk, the spaces between the stones being mostly filled with
sand. The origin of so vast a deposit of gravel is by no
means clear; but there is reason to believe, that much of it
is an old river-gravel, formed by the Thames when the river
flowed at a greater height ; and, probably, with much larger
volume, than at the present day.

Along the banks of the Thames, and of most other rivers,
it is not uncommon to find successive terraces of gravel,
which mark the height at which the river flowed at different
periods. Thus in Fig. 82 (which is a section from Wimbledon to Wandsworth Common across the river Wandle,
similar to that given on p. 139) it is believed that the river
(R) ran at one period, over the higher terrace, No. 1, and

---

[1] So called because it was formerly believed that such deposits had
been driven over the surface by great floods. The word is conveniently retained without any reference to the origin of such deposits.

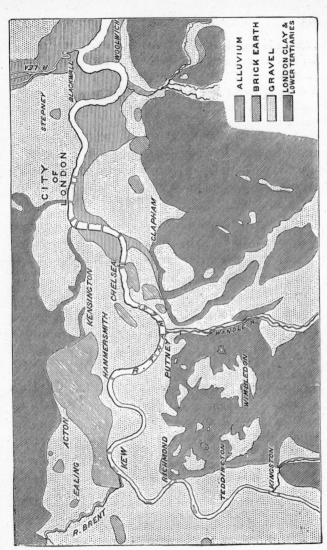

Fig. 81.—Map of the Valley of the Thames between Kingston and Woolwich.   Scale three miles to one inch.

then cut its way down to the lower level, No. 2. The higher
deposit is consequently the older, and is distinguished sometimes as the *high-level gravel;* while the lower deposit, which
is of more recent age, is known as the *low-level* or *valley
gravel.* In a section of strata, such as that in Cannon
Street, the uppermost beds are the most recent; but, on
the banks of a river, the higher deposits are presumably
the oldest, and will contain the remains of animals that
inhabited the valley before the river reached its lower level.[1]

In many places around London, the sheet of gravel is
overlaid by a thin deposit of brownish *loam,*[2] represented on

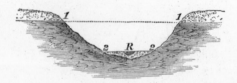

FIG. 82.—Section across the Valley of the Wandle, showing high-level gravels and
valley-gravel.

the map as *brick-earth,* since it is largely worked by brick-
makers. This earth forms an excellent soil for vegetables,
and many of the market-gardens at Fulham and elsewhere
are situated upon it. It is probable that this brick-earth
has been thrown down by the river in flood. When the
Thames has overflowed its banks, it has deposited silt upon
the neighbouring land ; or, possibly, there may have been a

---

[1] There is no real contradiction here. The higher gravels of the
river valley do not lie upon, but only at a higher level than, the lower
gravels. There are no exceptions to the rule, that of two strata, one
superimposed on the other, deposited by water action, the upper is the
more recent, if the beds have not been disturbed since their deposition.

[2] *Loam* is a sandy clay ; *marl* a calcareous clay.

time when the river spread out, at certain parts of its course, into wide lake-like areas, and quietly deposited mud and sand at the bottom of these sheets of water.   The strips of *alluvium* (p. 142) deposited by the river along its margins, in comparatively modern times, are also indicated on the map, Fig. 81.   This marshy land, bordering the Thames and its tributaries, spreads out below London into wide flats; and it occasionally contains shells, bones and other organic remains.   Of the vegetable relics, which are found in some of the marshes, and indicate the site of an ancient forest, no mention need be made here, since they have already been noticed at p. 212.

Fossils are not confined, however, to the comparatively

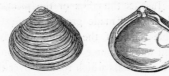

Fig. 83.—*Cyrena (Corbicula) fluminalis.*

modern mud which forms the alluvium of the Thames ; but they are also found, more or less abundantly, in the older superficial deposits, such as the gravels and brick-earths. Thus, they are especially abundant in the brick-earth which is worked at Erith and Crayford in Kent, and at Ilford and Grays in Essex; while, above London, they have been found in the sands and loam of Brentford.   Many of these fossils are land and fresh-water shells, which once lived in the river and on its banks ; and are, for the most part, not different from those living in the locality at the present day. Some few of the shell-fish, however, have long ceased to dwell in the rivers of this country, though still found in

other parts of the world. Such, for example, is the little
shell represented in Fig. 83, and known as *Cyrena*, or
Corbicula, *fluminalis*. This is not uncommon in the old
deposits of the Thames, but is not living at the present time
in any English, or indeed in any European river, though
it is still found in the Nile and in Kashmir.

While the shells of the old Thames deposits represent
species, most of which are still living in Britain, it is far
otherwise with the bones which are found in the same beds.
Many of these bones, indeed, are those of animals extremely
different from any which now inhabit this country, or are
known to have inhabited it within historical times. And,
yet, there can be no doubt that the animals which have left
these remains, once lived and died within the area of the
Thames basin. Just as the coins or the pieces of pottery
which are found in old "made ground" beneath London,
are unquestionable relics of the people who dwelt in the
city, when the soil was in course of accumulation ; so, these
bones represent the animals which roamed over the Thames
valley during the period when the deposits in which they
occur were in course of formation.

When the brick-earths of Kent and Essex were being
deposited, the *fauna*, or animal population, of the Thames
basin, included, in addition to many animals still living
here, a number of extinct mammals,[1] such as the mammoth
(*Elephas primigenius*) ; this was a kind of elephant adapted
to live in a cold climate by having a thick woolly coat.
Fig. 84 represents a restoration of this extinct elephant.[2]
Another species of elephant (*E. antiquus*) also lived in the

---

[1] *Mammals*, from Lat. *mamma*, breast ; a great group of back-boned
animals which suckle their young.

[2] This is reduced from Brandt's figure in his *Mittheilungen über die
Naturgeschichte des Mammuth oder Mamont*. St. Petersburg. 1866.

Thames valley; and along with the elephants were three distinct kinds of rhinoceros (*R. tichorhinus, R. megarhinus,* and *R. hemitœchus*). All these animals are extinct; but the hippopotamus which lived in the ancient Thames is not to be distinguished from that now dwelling in Africa. The brick-earths also contain the remains of a species of lion (*Felis spelœa*), no longer living, but which is likewise found in some of the bone-caves of this country. Among other animals which lived here, at the same period, may be

FIG. 84.—The Mammoth (*Elephas primigenius*).

mentioned the brown bear, the grizzly bear, the spotted hyæna, and two kinds of large wild oxen,—the bison and the urus. The gigantic Irish " elk " (*Cervus megaceros*), which is now extinct, has also left its bones in the brick-earth; and Professor Boyd Dawkins found, at Crayford, a skull of the musk-sheep (*Ovibos moschatus*), which is a creature living at the present day only in Arctic America. Most of these are represented, not by a mere bone or two, indicating an occasional straggler, but by remains so abundant as to show that the animals which they represent were important

members of the old fauna. Thus, the collection of Sir
Antonio Brady contains portions of no fewer than a hundred
elephants, all collected from the brick-earth of Ilford.

Such, then, is the curious assemblage of animals which
fed at one time in the valley of the Thames, and have left
their bones and teeth in the ancient deposits of the river.
Some of these mammals have since died out, and are no
longer to be found in any part of the world; others have
wandered to the south; while others, again, have retreated
northwards, a few, however, still remaining in the present
fauna of the country. The strange association, in the same
deposit, of both northern and southern forms—these indicating a warmer, and those a colder climate—offers per-
plexing evidence as to the climatic condition of the country
at the time in which they lived. It is certain, however, that
at one time, the climate of the Thames basin must have
been extremely severe, since some of the deposits in the
northern districts present unmistakable evidence of the
prevalence of glacial conditions (p. 165). Evidence of the
kind given in Chapter X. shows that there must have been a
time when Britain, north of the Thames, was covered either
with land-ice, or with an icy sea, from which the boulder clay
and glacial gravels were deposited. Possibly, some of the
gravel in the Thames basin may be glacial drift, which has
been disturbed and re-deposited by the river. And, it should
be mentioned, that the remains of the reindeer are abundant
in many of the superficial deposits of the Thames valley,
though not in the brick-earth, which has yielded so many of
the fossils previously noticed. Indeed, the relation of this
brick-earth to the glacial period is by no means clear; some
geologists believing it to be more, and others less, recent
than the true glacial drifts.

It becomes an extremely interesting question to determine

whether man shared possession of the Thames valley with
the group of animals, the remains of which are found in the
old fluviatile deposits of gravel and brick-earth. In the British
Museum, there has been, for many years, a rude spear-shaped
weapon in black flint, represented in Fig. 85. This was
found, associated with an elephant's tooth, in an excavation
near Gray's Inn Lane, London; and a description of it was
published as far back as 1715. It is indeed the earliest
recorded relic of human workmanship which has been found

FIG. 85.—A palæolithic implement,
from Gray's Inn Lane.

FIG. 86.—A neolithic implement
from the Thames at London.

in association with the ancient fauna of the Thames Valley.
Of late years, however, considerable attention has been
given to the subject, and many other flint implements have
been discovered in the high-level gravels of the Thames
basin. Acton, Ealing, Hackney and Highbury are localities
near London which have yielded such implements; and
they have also been found in numbers, between Herne Bay
and the Reculvers, where they have fallen out of the gravel
which caps the chalk cliffs of the North-Kent coast. Even

the brick-earths of Crayford and Erith have yielded a worked flint or two; though no implements of the type noticed above. So many of these flints have been found in the old gravels, not only in the Thames Valley but in various other parts of England, and also in the valleys of northern France, that there is no reason to doubt the existence of man, in this part of the world, during the period at which the older river-drifts were deposited. Moreover, some of these implements have been found in such close association with the bones of extinct animals, that there is equally little doubt as to the co-existence of man with the old fauna of this period. It is probable, indeed, that the early flint-using man came hither from the continent with some of the extinct mammalia; at a time when Britain was connected with the European mainland by an isthmus occupying the position of what is now the Straits of Dover.

Flint implements, such as that represented in Fig. 85, are the oldest known relics of man. They indicate a time, before the commencement of history in Western Europe, when man was ignorant of the use of metal, and fashioned his weapons and implements out of stone. The more ancient of these prehistoric implements, such as that in Fig. 85, are simply chipped into shape; but other stone implements occur, which are neatly ground, and even polished. Fig. 86 represents a stone *celt*[1] which was dredged up from the Thames, at London, and is now in Mr. Evans's collection.[2] These more highly finished stone implements are never found in the old high-level gravels,

[1] *Celts*, from Lat. *celtis*, a chisel; not, as often supposed, because they were used by the people called Celts.

[2] Figs. 85 and 86 are reduced from figures in *The Ancient Stone Implements, Weapons, and Ornaments of Great Britain*. By John Evans, F.R.S., &c. 1872.

or along with the extinct mammalia ; but are confined to the most superficial deposits, and to the present level of the river. That period in which man was in the habit of using implements exclusively of stone is known to antiquaries as the *stone age;* and Sir John Lubbock has distinguished the early part of this period, in which unpolished stone was in use, as the *palæolithic*[1] age, and the later period, when man had advanced to the stage of grinding and polishing his weapons, as the *neolithic*[2] age.   Fig. 85 represents therefore a palæolithic, and Fig. 86 a neolithic implement.

All the deposits hitherto described in this chapter—such as the gravels and brick-earths—consist of loose materials distributed in patches, more or less extensive, over the surface of the solid rock.   Hence, they are classed together by the geologist as "superficial deposits ;" and are not represented on a geological map, unless the map be constructed for the special purpose of exhibiting the surface-geology, as in the case of the little sketch-map, Fig. 81. An ordinary geological map shows, in fact, the kind of rock which would be exposed on the surface of the ground, if the superficial deposits were removed.   In some cases, there are no deposits of this kind, and then, of course, the actual rock of the country is exposed.   The map of the basin of the Thames given in Plate V., is coloured, in such a manner, as to show what rocks would be seen on the face of the country, if it were not obscured by gravels, loams, and other superficial accumulations.

The small areas of light brown tint in Surrey and Berks represent the highest, and therefore the newest, beds within the Thames basin.   They are well seen in the sandy tracts of Bagshot and Ascot Heaths ; and, from the former of these

---

[1] *Palæolithic*, from παλαιός, *palaios*, old ; λίθος, *lithos*, stone.

[2] *Neolithic*, from νέος, *neos*, new.

localities, the deposits in question have received their name of *Bagshot beds*. It has been already explained (p. 25) that the hills of Hampstead, Highgate, and Harrow are capped by Bagshot sand; but these areas are too small to be represented on the map. Very few fossils occur in these sands, but those which have occasionally been found are fragments of marine shells, thus showing that the area in which they occur has been, at some time, under the sea. There is little doubt that the Bagshot sands were once spread over a wide surface in the lower part of the Thames basin, and that a great portion of them has since been removed by deundation.

Reference to Fig. 7 (p. 26) will show how the Bagshot sand usually rests upon the *London Clay*. This clay, which is the next rock in passing downwards from the Bagshot beds, is represented in Plate V. by a dark-brown colour, and is seen to cover a very wide area. It is, for the most part, a stiff brown clay, which has evidently been deposited, as fine mud, upon the bottom of the sea, not far from land. In fact, in the Isle of Sheppey, the clay has yielded a great variety of vegetable remains, some of which indicate a very warm, not to say tropical, climate. Thus the fruit of the *Nipadites* represented in Fig. 63 (p. 230) has its modern representatives in Bengal and the Asiatic Archipelago. Such relics of terrestrial vegetation indicate that land could not have been far from the water in which the clay was deposited; and the occurrence of the bones of crocodiles also tends to the conclusion that the Sheppey clay represents the delta of some ancient river. On passing from Sheppey towards London, and farther to the west, the vegetable fossils of the London clay disappear, while marine shells are to be found locally, as at Highgate. Many of these shells, though they belong to extinct animals, resemble those which are

CIRCENCESTER — Lechlade
THAMES OR 1819

Oxford

CHILTERN HILLS

Windsor
Reading   Teddington

R. KENNET

SALISBURY
PLAIN

GEOLOGICAL MAP OF THE BA

Chiltern Hills

N

PROBABLE

GEOLOGICAL SECTIO

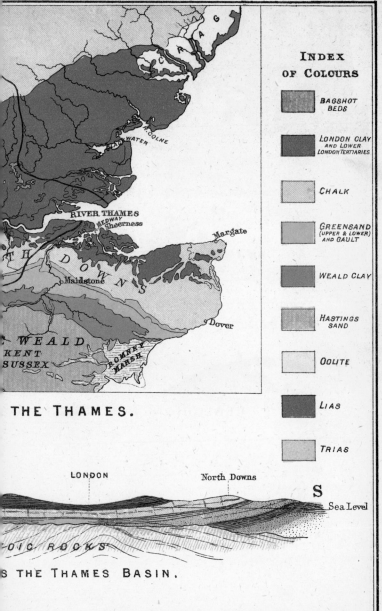

Plate V.

INDEX
OF COLOURS

BAGSHOT
BEDS

LONDON CLAY
AND LOWER
LONDON TERTIARIES

CHALK

GREENSAND
(UPPER & LOWER)
AND GAULT

WEALD CLAY

HASTINGS
SAND

OOLITE

LIAS

TRIAS

THE THAMES.

LONDON   North Downs   S

                                Sea Level

OIC ROCKS

S THE THAMES BASIN.

confined at the present day to warmer seas; Fig. 87, for example, is a fossil *Nautilus*, a genus which is represented by several species in the London clay. When it is re-membered that, beneath London, this clay is about 400 feet thick, it will be readily admitted that such a deposit of fine muddy matter must have required an enormous period of time for its deposition. Moreover, it must be borne in mind, that, in the case of this clay, as of so many other sedimentary deposits, the present thickness does not necessarily indicate its original thick-ness, for much may have been re-moved by denudation.

Beneath the London clay of the Thames basin, there is a series of comparatively thin beds, known as the *Lower London Tertiaries*. These come to the surface along the edge of the clay, as it rises from the margin of the basin, but their

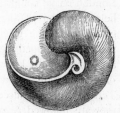

FIG. 87.—*Nautilus centralis,* from the London clay.

width is too small to admit of representation on the map in Plate V. Their position, however, is indicated in Fig. 11, (p. 31). The uppermost members of the group consist of rolled flint pebbles, which evidently represent an old beach of shingle, associated with sands, which often contain marine shells. These beds are known, from the localities in which they are best exposed, as the *Blackheath* or *Oldhaven beds*. They are succeeded, below, by clays, some of which are rich in shells similar to those now living in brackish water; whence it is concluded, that the beds must have been deposited in an estuary. From the two localities in which these strata are typically developed, they are known as the *Woolwich and Reading beds*. Below these, come the *Thanet beds*, of which good exposures may be seen between Herne Bay and

U

the Reculvers, and in Pegwell Bay, in the Isle of Thanet, where they consist of sands containing marine shells.

All the strata noticed above are classed together in one great group known as the *Tertiary or Cainozoic*[1] *series*. The former name refers to the fact that geologists have been led, in their study of the earth's crust, to recognize three great groups of rocks, of which, those hitherto described in this chapter, represent the uppermost or third, reckoning from below upwards. The Tertiary series, as developed in the London basin, comprises all rocks, from the Thanet sands below, to the Bagshot beds above. Over this Tertiary group, come the glacial-drifts, and river-gravels, which are sometimes grouped together as a fourth set of deposits, and are consequently known as the *Quaternary series*, while by others they are called *Post-tertiary* formations. While the Tertiary beds are succeeded *above* by the quaternary series, they are followed *below* by another great group, known as the *Secondary* or *Mesozoic*[2] *series*, of which the uppermost member is the well-known chalk.

The pale-green tint on the map (Plate V.) covers a large area occupied superficially by the *Chalk;* while the relation of this rock to the overlying Tertiaries may be seen in the coloured section in the same plate,[3] and has already been shown diagrammatically in Fig. 11 (p. 31). The ground formed by the chalk usually consists, when not covered with drift, of gently undulating downs, carpeted with soft turf. Good examples of chalk scenery may be seen in the North Downs of Surrey and Kent, and in

---

[1] *Cainozoic*, from καινὸς, *kainos*, recent ; ζῶον, *zoon*, an organism.

[2] *Mesozoic*, from μέσος, *mesos*, middle.

[3] This section, drawn by Mr. Whitaker, of the Geological Survey, is supposed to be taken along the line, A B, on the map. The vertical scale of the section is about twelve times greater than the horizontal scale, and the latter is evidently larger than that of the map.

Salisbury Plain; while, along the south-eastern coast, it forms those dazzling white cliffs which gained for this island the old name of Albion. The chalk, which, beneath London, is 600 or 700 feet thick, is chiefly composed of carbonate of lime, in some parts interspersed with beds of flints, which are nearly pure silex. There cannot be the least doubt that the chalk represents the mud of an ancient sea-bottom, for multitudes of remains of animals have been obtained from it, most of which belong to such groups as are exclusively marine at the present day. The area once occupied by the chalk was therefore, at one time, covered by sea. And it may be further concluded that it was at some distance from any extensive land, inasmuch as the chalk contains no such mixture of clay and sand, as would be derived from denudation. But there is another reason for believing that the chalk ocean was pretty deep; that is to say, over 100 fathoms. If a slice of chalk is cut, ground thin, and mounted in Canada balsam, so as to become transparent, shells of *Foraminifera* may almost always be detected in it; and, sometimes, they abound. The commonest form is a *Globigerina*, indistinguishable from that which constitutes the bulk of the Atlantic ooze. Moreover, coccoliths and coccospheres are plentiful in the chalk: which thus differs from the ooze, chiefly, in the greater proportion of granular particles, without any definite shape, to recognizable organic remains; and, in the entire absence of those siliceous shells and skeletons, which are so constant in the ooze (Figs. 88 and 89).[1]

The former difference presents no difficulty. The chalk

---

[1] Fig. 88 represents a section of chalk from Little Hampton, on the coast of Sussex, while Fig. 89, which is placed by its side for comparison, represents a sample of Atlantic ooze, taken by Captain Dayman from a depth of 2,250 fathoms. Both figures are magnified to the same extent.

may have been formed in just the same way as the *Globigerina* ooze, which is now being deposited; and the proportion of shells which have been broken down into mere dust, may have been increased by the pressure to which it has been subjected; while, in some parts, the original structure may have been often more or less completely obliterated by the percolation of water; just as in coral-rock, the shapes of the component corals become lost, and in diatomaceous deposits (Chap. XIV.) the individual diatoms run into a sort of opal, from the same cause.

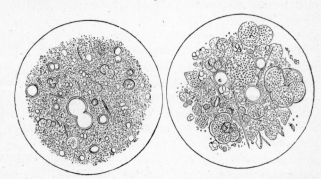

FIG. 88.—Microscopic section of chalk   FIG. 89.—Atlantic ooze from a depth
from Sussex.   Magnified about   of 2,250 fathoms.   Magnified
220 diameters.   about 220 diameters.

With regard to the second difference, it may be remarked, that there is no reason for doubting that the ocean, under which the chalk was deposited, contained as great an abundance of organisms with siliceous coats and skeletons, as the present Atlantic. The conclusion is, therefore, that such siliceous remains have once existed in the chalk, but have been dissolved; and it is supported by the fact, that, even the sponges, the remains of which are found in the chalk in great abundance, have lost the siliceous spicula which existing sponges of similar kinds always contain. On the other hand, the chalk contains flints, of which no trace is found in the ooze. On the whole, it is probable, that these flints represent the siliceous organisms which were contained in the Cretaceous ooze, when it was de posited, but which have been dissolved up by percolating water, and re-deposited in the shape of amorphous silex; just as the diatoms in the Bilin beds have been dissolved and re-deposited as opal.

The lowermost beds of the chalk rest upon sandy de-posits, which are termed the *Upper Greensand.* Some of these sandy beds are not the mere mechanical detritus of siliceous rocks, but contain numerous greenish grains of definite and well-marked forms. They are, in fact, the casts of the internal cavities of foraminiferal shells in a compound of silica, iron, and clay, which is known as silicate of iron and aluminium. This substance has been deposited in the cavities of the shells, the calcareous matter of which has been subsequently dissolved away, and has left the hard cast behind. A similar sandy deposit is taking place off the eastern coast of the United States, upon the Agulhas bank, near the Cape of Good Hope, and elsewhere, at the present time, in depths varying from 100 to 700 fathoms. A tolerably deep sea, therefore, covered the area now occupied by the chalk, not only during the time which was occupied by the deposition of the chalk, but ante-cedently to that period.

But we can carry the evidence of the existence of a sea covering the western part of the Thames basin, to a still more remote period. The organic remains which are found in the lower cretaceous strata and in the oolitic and liassic beds, which underlie the chalk, and are exposed in this region, are chiefly those of marine animals. In the neighbourhood of Oxford, beds of the oolitic series are exposed, which are so rich in fossil corals that they go by the name of the *Coral-rag*. These corals resemble those which are now forming reefs, and the coral-rag itself is altogether similar to modern coral-limestone; so that there can be no reasonable doubt that the coral-rag is the product of the reefs of a sea, which covered this region long before the chalk began to be deposited.

Putting all these facts together, it becomes clear that the present condition of the basin of the Thames was preceded by one in which the river flowed at a higher level and the climate was much more extreme, if not much colder, than it is at present, during which the quaternary deposits were formed. Antecedent to this, was a period in which the region, at present covered by the London clay, was a great estuary, and the climate was much warmer than at present. This was preceded by the period during which the chalk was deposited, when the greater part, if not the whole, of the Thames basin was far beneath the surface of the sea; and a similar condition appears to have obtained as far back as positive evidence carries us.

It further becomes certain, that the whole thickness of the floor of the Thames basin, from the Bagshot sands to the furthest point reached by the borer, is nothing but mud which has been accumulated, by various agencies, at the bottom of the sea, and which has subsequently been up-heaved. Much of this mud represents the denudation of the land surfaces, which were contemporaneous with these deposits; but still more is the work of animal life. Upheaved into dry land, the rain has worn and excavated its surface, and accumulated into streams, which, gradually cutting their way deeper and deeper, have at length, produced the

varied contours of the present Thames basin. Thus, para-
doxical as it may sound, the river is older than the hills
and dales amongst which it flows, and which appear to
determine its course.

If the question be asked, how long a time has been
occupied in the formation of the floor of the Thames basin;
the only reply which can be given is, that most certainly it
was of enormous duration, but that there are no means of
estimating it with accuracy. The whole mass has been
constructed, as has been seen, of the products of denudation or of those of vital processes. There is not the
least reason for supposing that either of these products were,
on the average, formed more rapidly in those ancient times
than they are now; and there is independent evidence, that
some of these rocks, such as the chalk, were deposited very
slowly. It may be taken to be certain that the thickness
of chalk which represents a year's accumulation in the
Cretaceous ocean, is but a small fraction of an inch. But
suppose it were an inch; then, as the chalk beneath
London is 600 feet thick, it follows that this bed alone
represents 7,200 years.

In point of fact, however, not only is it almost certain
that we should be much nearer the truth, in assuming that
the chalk beneath London took ten times as long as this to
accumulate; but, it can be proved, that the strata which
overlie the chalk, in the London basin, represent but a mere
fraction of those which have been deposited elsewhere,
since the time at which the chalk was formed. The most
niggardly computation which lies within the bounds of
probability, presents us with a sum total of several hundreds
of thousands of years, for the time which has elapsed since
the sea, of which the chalk is the bottom-mud, flowed over
the site of London.

The study of the fossils contained in the strata of the
Thames basin is not only of essential importance in proving
the changes which have occurred in its physical geography,
but it brings to light other remarkable facts in the history of
the region. It has been seen that animals, which now live in
both colder and warmer climates than those of the Thames
basin, are found associated together in the drifts ; and that,
in the older rocks, the remains are such as resemble the
present inhabitants of warmer climates. But, while the great
majority of the animals and plants of the drifts are identical
with, or very similar to, those which now live somewhere or
other; the inhabitants of the world in former ages become less
and less like those which now exist, as we go back in time.
Thus, although in their general character, the animal
remains of the London clay resemble those of animals now
living in hot climates, it is only a small percentage which are
identical with living forms; while the rest have altogether
vanished and become extinct. In the chalk, this feature is
still more marked. Of the many thousand beautifully-pre-
served kinds of animal remains which have been obtained
from that formation, only a very few of the lower forms are
identical with species now living. Hence, notwithstanding
the similarity of the chalk to the *Globigerina*-ooze, the
remains imbedded in the former at once distinguish it from
the modern deposit.

The common-sense reasoning which deduced from the
facts of the Cannon Street section, the conclusion that a
people, having the language and customs of the ancient
Romans, preceded the English inhabitants of that locality,
applied to the subjacent strata, has permitted no doubt that,
at some period before the Roman occupation, the Thames
valley was the haunt of savages armed with flint weapons ;

that elephants and rhinoceroses, bears and hyænas, roamed through its forests; and that the hippopotamus wallowed in the streams of what was, in all probability, a river of much larger dimensions than the present Thames.   Arguments of similar cogency have led to the conclusion, that the solid floor of the Thames basin, throughout the thirteen hundred feet of thickness which have been directly explored, owes its origin to agents of denudation and reconstruction, such as are at work at the present day; and testifies to the general uniformity of nature, throughout a period which must be counted by hundreds of thousands of years.

Looking at the record of the past history of the Thames basin, as it now lies before us, it would appear to indicate an uninterrupted progress from marine to terrestrial conditions —as if the bottom of the ancient sea had been gradually upheaved and converted into dry land, after the deposit of the Tertiary strata.   But, it must be recollected, that the ordinary stratified deposits accumulate only under water. A dry land surface leaves no indication of its existence, except so far as it may support fluviatile, or lacustrine, deposits; or be overgrown by a vegetation, thick and strong enough not to be swept away in the next period of sub-mergence.   Thus it is possible, and indeed probable, that the ancient rocks which lie beneath the chalk and gault, were upheaved and remained as dry land, for an immense period after their formation, and were submerged, and became part of the floor of the ocean, only at the end of the Secondary period.   The chalk may have been a dry land surface for ages before the formation of the London clay estuary; and the greater part of the London clay itself, with its superjacent Bagshot beds, has probably been dry land, ever since the latter were formed.

There is no reason to believe that any one of this vast

succession of changes in the physical geography of the Thames basin, has been brought about otherwise than gradually. In all probability, no human inhabitant of the region which has been the seat of these changes, would have been more inclined to doubt that things always had been as he saw them, that we are at present. And, although it is demonstrated that the living population of the region has undergone so thorough a change, that hardly a species which inhabited sea, or land, in the Cretaceous period, is to be found in, or near, the Thames basin of the present time; it is probable that, at any given epoch, the most observant and accurate naturalists might have continued their observations for centuries together, without being able to discover that the forms of animals and plants were other than fixed and permanent. Twenty generations of day-flies, however sharp their eyes, would fail to make out that the planet Uranus changes its place in the heavens.

CHAPTER XVIII.

DISTRIBUTION OF LAND AND WATER.

THE disquisitions contained in the preceding chapters have been devoted to the description and the elucidation of the phenomena offered to common observation by a single river-basin—that of the Thames. But, it has been incidentally remarked, that this is only one of the many river-basins of Great Britain; and it is now needful to see what lies beyond its boundaries. If we cross its northern water-parting we enter the basin of the Ouse; if we proceed westwards, we pass into that of the Severn; while, to the south, lie the basins of the Medway, which is almost an affluent of the Thames, and of several smaller rivers. Each of these basins, or any which lie beyond them, might have served as our text; though few are so well adapted for the purpose as that of the Thames.

Passing from river-basin to river-basin, the observer would find bolder reliefs than he has met with in the Thames valley, in the almost mountainous hills of Wales, Cumberland, and Scotland; the strata would often possess a different composition, and would contain organic remains of other kinds; and the rainfall and other climatal conditions would, sometimes, differ widely from those of the

[1] Prof. Ramsay's *Physical Geology and Geography of Great Britain* should be studied by those who desire further information on these subjects.

Thames basin; but there would be nothing new in the general truths exemplified by the study of these additional facts.

Whatever direction the journey of the traveller from London might take, he would, sooner or later, reach sea-water, which, whatever its local name, is really a dependence of the Atlantic Ocean; and he would, thereby, convince himself that the land of Great Britain constitutes what geographers term an *island*. Indeed, it is an island of no great magnitude; for there is no point of its surface from which the sea coast may not be reached, by three days' good walking.

Of a roughly triangular form, it measures about 600 miles from south to north, by about 320 miles from east to west, at its broadest part; and its superficial area amounts to 89,644 miles. In other words, its superficial area is nearly equal to that of a square, 300 miles in the side ($300 \times 300 = 90,000$). There is no subject respecting which people have more vague ideas, than in regard to the relative areas of the different parts of the earth's surface; and it will be useful, in considering other parts of the world, to take the area of Great Britain as a unit of superficial measurement, represented by the Roman numeral I. Thus I. will represent 90,000 square miles; II. 180,000; $\frac{1}{2}$ 45,000, and so on.

Separated from Britain on the west, by a sea which is not more than thirteen miles wide, where it is narrowest (between Fair-head and the Mull of Cantire) is another island of considerable size, that of Ireland. This island measures 300 miles from north to south, by 180 miles, from east to west, and has an area of 32,513 square miles ($\frac{1}{3}$). Moreover, fringing the west coast of Britain, especially in its northern part, and extending beyond its northern end, there are numerous smaller islands, such as the Hebrides, the Orkneys, and the Shetlands. There are a few small islands off the eastern and the southern coasts; but only one, the Isle of Wight, is of sufficient magnitude to make it worth mention. Soundings, taken in the seas which surround the group of British islands, show that they all rise from a sort of submarine plain, which slopes gradually downwards, from the eastward, to the westward. In the German Ocean and the British Channel, as the seas in the east and south are termed, the depth of water rarely exceeds fifty fathoms (300 feet); and, to reach a general depth of as much as 100 fathoms, we must sail many miles to the north of the Shetlands; or to the west of the Hebrides and Ireland; or still further to the south and west of Cornwall. (Fig. 90, p. 302.) [1]

This shelving plateau is a westward continuation of the shores of Norway, Denmark, Holland, Belgium, and France, which form a continuous coast line to the eastward of Britain. They are separated from it by an extent of sea, which is very narrow (twenty-one miles) at the straits of Dover, but gradually widens to the north-east and south-west of that point.

On crossing this narrow strait, the traveller sets foot upon the largest continuous mass of land in the world. Starting thence towards the east, and bearing a little to the north, he might travel for more than 7,000 miles, through northern Europe and Siberia, without seeing the sea, until he struck upon its shores in Behring's Straits; at the narrowest part of which, he would be separated, by only thirty-six miles, from the opposite shore of North America. A more circuitous route, through Eastern Russia, and then, by way of Armenia and Syria, to Egypt, would enable the pedestrian to travel

[1] From De la Beche's *Researches in Theoretical Geology*.

almost due south, until he again met the sea at the Cape of
Good Hope, nearly 6,000 miles, in a straight line, from
his starting-point. China, Burmah, India, Persia, Arabia,
Algeria, Morocco and the Gold Coast, might all be reached

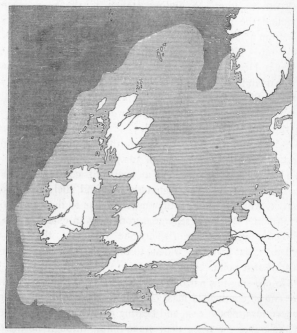

FIG. 90.—Map showing the effect of an upheaval of the sea-bottom around the
British Isles, to the extent of 100 fathoms. The half-shade represents the area
which would then become dry land ; the extent of this area is indicated by the
fact that 1,000 square miles on the same scale is represented by this square ☐

by a foot passenger from any point of this expanse of dry
land ; the longest dimension of which, from the west coast
of Africa to Behring's Straits is somewhere about 15,000
miles.

The total area of this great surface of dry land, which, with its islands, constitutes the *Old World* of geographers, is 22,392,430 square miles (CCXLIX. nearly). Although it is surrounded by water on all sides, it no longer receives the name of an island, but is termed a *continent;* or is more usually regarded as composed of the three continents of Europe, Asia, and Africa. Between the two former, there is no natural demarcation, and they would be, for most purposes, better spoken of as one region, under the name of *Eurasia.* But Africa is obviously marked off from the rest, in consequence of its connection with Eurasia only by a very narrow neck of land, the Isthmus of Suez, now cut through by the Suez Canal.

The surface of Eurasia and of Africa is divided into river-basins by water-partings, and is diversified by elevations and depressions, like those which have been met with in the British Islands, but on a scale proportioned to its relative magnitude. It would be beside the purpose of this work to study their features in detail; but the broad aspects of the great system, of which the Thames basin forms an insignificant part, may be sketched.

The mountains of England, as we have seen, stand apart from its main water-partings; but those of the Eurasian continent coincide with the lines of separation of the great water-sheds. A sinuous band of highlands, which often rise a mile above the sea-level, and the highest peaks of which some-times attain between five and six times that height, stretches almost continuously from the waters of the Atlantic in the west, to those of the Pacific on the east of the Eurasian continent. (See map, Fig. 91.)

At the western end, this highland zone is narrow and not very high, and, as the mountain range of the Pyrenees, separates France from Spain; this is followed by the

FIG. 91.—Map of the World, showing the direction of the principal chains of mountains.

broader and higher mass of the Alps, which splits to inclose
the plain of Hungary; and is then continued, to the eastward, by the Balkans, the mountains of Asia Minor, and
those of Armenia and the Caucasus. The highlands of
Persia and of Beloochistan connect these last with the
Hindu Kush; beyond which the elevated land spreads out
into an immense half-moon-shaped mass, the southern and
eastern escarpment of which is formed by the Himálayas
and the ranges continued from them into China; while the
northern and western escarpment is constituted by the Thian-
Shian and Altai mountains. The interval between these is
occupied by lower, but still much elevated, table lands;
and the area of these eastern Asiatic highlands is probably not less than five-and-twenty times as great as that of
Britain.

To the north of this great mountain system, there is an
enormous plain, which stretches through northern Eurasia
to the Arctic Ocean. It commences in Europe, in what
are called the Netherlands, or the Low Countries; or rather,
its beginning may be traced in the flat districts of our
eastern counties, for Britain, as already explained, is but
an extension of north-western Europe. Thence it is continued by the great North-German plain, which stretches
across Europe to Russia, where its continuity is broken
by the low range of the Ural mountains; but only to be
renewed, on their eastern side, by the vast plains of
Siberia. To the south of the east-and-west mountain-system
of Eurasia, there is no similar plain; and the mountains come
down much nearer to the sea on the south, than on the
north, side. In fact, the great line of elevation does not
traverse the middle of the continent, so as to divide it into
two equal halves, one lying on the north and the other on
the south; but it runs very much nearer to the southern

than to the northern shores, of the continent. As a consequence of this arrangement, a section taken across Eurasia from south to north would show—first a short slope rising rather abruptly from the sea to the top of the mountains; and then, on the other side of the ridge, a very long slope, running gradually down to the sea-level in the north. This kind of relief is illustrated, though exaggerated, in the contour given in Fig. 92, where *a* represents a section across India culminating in the Himálayas, *b;* at *d,* the section runs across another range called the Kuenlún, which has a general direction parallel to the Himálayas. Between these two mountain-chains is the elevated plateau or table-land of Tibet, *c;* at *e* the Altai mountains are crossed, the land between the two ridges *d, e,* representing the plains of

FIG. 92.—Diagrammatic section across Eurasia.

Mongolia and the desert of Gobi; and then, from the Altai range, the section is continued across the vast Siberian plains to the northern sea.

It is in Eurasia that the highest land in the world is to be found. The loftiest known peak is that of Mount Everest, in the Himálayas, which rises to a height of 29,000 feet, or about 5½ miles above sea-level. And several other mountains in the same range attain to nearly as great altitudes; thus Kanchinjanga reaches the height of 28,178 feet, and Doulagiri that of about 27,000 feet.

It is also in Eurasia that the greatest depressions are to be found. The most remarkable of these is that in which the Caspian sea lies. This inland sea is a body of salt-

water which covers an area as large as Spain, and has the
level of its surface about eighty-three feet below that of the
Black Sea; while the bottom of the hollow in which the
water rests falls to about 3,000 feet, or nearly three-quarters
of a mile, below the level of the ocean. The Caspian itself
occupies the deepest part of an enormous depression, which
appears to have been connected, at a late geological period,
with the Mediterranean Sea. This great basin, which also
includes the inland sea of Aral, covers an area at least as
large as Central Europe. The Caspian sea alone occupies
an area of 126,646 square miles (I.$\frac{1}{3}$ nearly). The Dead
sea is another salt-lake much below the sea-level, its surface
being about 1,300 feet below that of the Mediterranean.

Since water naturally flows towards the lowest accessible
level, it is only to be expected that these depressed areas
should receive the drainage of the surrounding country. A
large number of rivers do, indeed, discharge themselves into
these great lakes; and hence such rivers differ essentially
from ordinary rivers, like the Thames, in that they never
reach the open sea. Such streams are often called *continental rivers*, since they are confined to continental areas,
and their basins are contained within the land. Thus
the Dead sea receives the river Jordan; the Caspian
receives the Ural and the Volga—the latter, by the way,
being the longest river in Europe—while the sea of Aral
receives the Amu Daria (Oxus) and Sir Daria (Jaxartes)
which come down from the high plateau of Pamir in Central
Asia. As none of these salt lakes, or inland seas, are in
communication with the ocean, the water which is brought
down to them by these rivers must be got rid of by evaporation; while the soluble matters, which the rivers dissolve
from their drainage-areas, must go on accumulating in the
lake.

Africa (11,290,030 square miles, CXXV.), as already re-marked, may be regarded as an appendage to Eurasia. In historic times, the only connection has been with Asia by means of the Isthmus of Suez ; but there are good reasons for believing that, even in post-tertiary times, Africa must have been also united with Europe ; the connection having been effected across what is now the Strait of Gibraltar ; and, also, by means of land which stretched over to Italy, and of which Malta and Sicily are points still above water. In the northern part, Africa has rather an east-and-west extension, like that of Eurasia. And, though it has no general axis of elevation ; yet, suoh mountains as it does possess, have a tendency to stretch in the same direction. This is seen, for example, in the Atlas mountains in north-western Africa, and in the Kong mountains parallel with the northern shores of the Gulf of Guinea. The southern part of the continent extends, on the contrary, in a north-and-south direction ; and the elevated lands of Abyssinia and Zan-guebar follow the same course.

One of the most striking physical features of Africa is the great northern plain which forms the desert of Sahara. This has an area fifty times as large as that of Britain, depressed in some places below the sea-level, but rising, in others, to 2,000 feet above it. From the occurrence of marine shells in the superficial deposits, and for other reasons, it is believed that much of the Sahara is an old sea-bottom, which must have been below water at a comparatively recent geological period. The proposal to admit the waters of the Mediterranean artificially into the depressed portions of the desert has been seriously entertained.

Regions of inland drainage may be found in some of the table-lands in the heart of Africa. Lake Tchad, for example, is a shallow sheet of water which receives the drainage of the surrounding area. This lake has long been known. But, within the last twenty years, some very large bodies of fresh water have been discovered in the eastern part of Central Africa. These include Lakes Tanganyika and Nyassa; the Victoria Nyanza, the Albert Nyanza, and the Alexandra Nyanza. The noble sheet of water which is called the Victoria Nyanza is about 3,800 feet above sea-level, and is probably the largest known body of fresh-water at this altitude; it is believed to have an area of about 30,000 square miles ($\frac{1}{3}$). In this great region of lakes are the head-waters of two of the most remarkable rivers of Africa—the Nile which flows to the north, and the Congo which runs to the west. The Nile, which takes its course through Abyssinia, Nubia, and Egypt, is especially notable for the fact that it runs for more than a thousand miles without receiving a single tributary.

The eastern coast of Eurasia, as we have seen, is washed by the Pacific ocean. Lying off its whole length, in somewhat the same fashion as Iceland and the British islands lie off its west coast, and as the Canaries and the Cape de Verd islands lie off the west coast of Africa, is a long series of outlying isolated masses of land of various sizes, termed the Kuriles, the Japanese islands, Formosa, and the Philippine Islands; and these are continued, southwards and eastwards, by the islands of Celebes and New Guinea. On the other hand, the general direction of the southernmost prolongation of the eastern end of Eurasia, the Malay Peninsula, is continued to the south and to the east, by Sumatra and Borneo, and by other smaller islands. They rise from an Asiatic submarine plain, just as Britain rises from the European submarine plain (Fig. 90, p. 302). Borneo has twice the area of Britain, while Sumatra is also very large. These Asiatic islands, which constitute the

Malay archipelago, are separated, between Bali and Lombok, by a narrow, but deep, channel from the Papuan Islands, of which New Guinea is the largest.   Separated from it only by the narrow straits of Torres, is the sub-continental land of Australia, which has an area of 4,700,000 square miles (LII.), and therefore is considerably larger than Europe (3,775,400 square miles, XLII.); and this, again, is divided only by a narrow strait, that of Bass, from Tasmania. Nearly parallel with the east coast of Australia, but more than a thousand miles distant from it, is a great chain of islands, beginning near New Guinea, with New Britain and the Solomon islands; and, with a great break to the south of New Caledonia, ending in the islands of New Zealand.

These islands stand in the same sort of relation to the great dry-land area of Australia, as the Japanese and Philippine islands, of which they are, in a sense, the continuation, do to that of Asia.   Beyond them, to the eastward, a broad zone of the Pacific ocean is dotted over with the small islands of Polynesia.

On looking at a map of the land area which has now been described Fig. 91), it is obvious, that the chief part of it lies in the north, and that it tends to thin out into pointed, or broken, masses towards the south.   The Malay and Papuan islands, with Australia on the east, as it were, balance Africa on the west; and if we regard them, for the moment, as south-eastern continuations of Eurasia, answering to its south-western continuation in Africa; it will be seen, that the eastern coast-line is broadly parallel to the western.   In the northern parts, the western coast is convex to the west, and the eastern concave to the east; while, in the southern parts, the western coast is concave, and the eastern, convex.

Seventeen hundred miles of sea separate the westernmost part of the British Islands from another, considerably smaller, but still great, continental land which stretches for 10,000 miles from north to south, and has an area of 15,800,000 square miles (CLXXV.). This is the *New World*, formed of the two almost distinct masses of North and South America, joined by the narrow isthmus of Panama.

It will be observed that the eastern coast of the American continent presents the same sort of rough parallelism with the western coast of the old world, as the latter does with its eastern coast. Where the one is convex, the other is concave, and *vice versâ ;* and the Atlantic ocean lies, like a great winding canal, from 800 to nearly 4,000 miles broad, between the two. The western coast of the American continent would repeat the curvature of the western coast of the old world, were it not that, in its northern portion, it trends far away to the west, to approach Asia in Behring's Straits. Again, in the new world, as in the old, the larger mass of land lies to the north; the area of North America standing to that of South America, in the proportion of about 17 to 14 ; while there is a remarkable similarity of form between South America and Africa. But, instead of being much longer, from east to west, than it is from north to south, the American continent is much longer, from north to south, than it is from east to west.

In accordance with this north-and-south elongation, an elevated tract runs from south to north, through nearly the whole length of the two continents. Narrow in the south, it attains a considerable breadth, and a great elevation in the Andes of Bolivia, Peru, and Chile ; in which last country, Aconcagua rises to 24,000 feet. After sinking to a mere range of hills in the isthmus, it rises and widens out into a great table land, which occupies more than a third of the width of North America. Several ranges of mountains, known under the general name of the Rocky Mountains,

which have a more or less north-and-south direction, take
their rise in Mexico and in the western territories of the
United States, from this table-land, or from its escarpments.

Just as the east-and-west line of mountains in Eurasia, is
nearer to the south than to the north coast; so the north and
south axis of America is nearer to the west than to the east
coast. Hence, the western slope of the American conti-

FIG. 93.—Diagrammatic section across North America.

nent is very abrupt, while the eastern side is carried
gradually down to great plains, which are drained by some
of the noblest streams in the world; such as the Mississippi
in North, and the Amazon, in South, America. If then, a
section were made across North America, from west to east,
it would present an appearance something like that represented diagrammatically in Fig. 93. Here, it is seen that

FIG. 94.—Diagrammatic section across South America.

there is a sharp rise, from the Pacific coast on the west, to
the Washington range, *a*; and, thence, to the summit of the
parallel chain of the Rocky mountains, *b*. From the
eastern slope of the Rocky mountains, the section runs
across the basin of the Mississippi, but rises again before
reaching the eastern coast. This rise, *d*, represents the
Appalachians, which form a range of mountains running

parallel to the eastern side of the continent; and thus
reproducing, on a smaller scale, the physical features of the
opposite shore. South America presents a similar section
(Fig. 94). A very sharp rise leads from the Pacific to the
range of the Andes, *a*, whence a broad plain stretches to
the Atlantic coast, relieved only by the highlands of
Brazil, *b*.

It has been pointed out by Professor Dana [1] that, in all
parts of the world, the highest mountains border the largest
oceanic basins. This rule is strikingly illustrated by the
relief of the American continent. Thus, the Rocky
mountains, which face the vast Pacific ocean, are considerably higher than the Appalachians, or Alleghanies,
which are opposite to the much narrower Atlantic.

America presents the grandest illustrations of fresh-water
phenomena to be found in any part of the world. Its river-
systems are framed on a gigantic scale; the basin of the
Amazon, for instance, embracing an area of 1,500,000
square miles, (XV.) and that of the Mississippi about
980,000 (XI.) miles. The drainage of the north-western
part of America is remarkable for its connection with a
chain of lakes which present a total area of 90,000 square
miles (I.) of fresh-water. These are known as lakes
Superior, Michigan, Huron, Erie and Ontario; and their
waters are ultimately discharged into the Atlantic Ocean by
the River St. Lawrence. It is in passing from Lake Erie to
Lake Ontario, that the stream is suddenly precipitated to a
depth of 162 feet, to form the falls of Niagara. The
peculiar chasms through which some of the North American
rivers run, are illustrated by the Colorado cañon figured on
p. 137.

----

[1] From whose *Manual of Geology* the contours of the sections in Figs.
92 to 94 are taken.

The preceding sketch of the disposition of the form and size of the dry land takes no account of many considerable islands; and especially leaves out of consideration those which, like Greenland, are covered with ice and snow, and are rendered almost inaccessible by the accumulation of ice in the sea which surrounds them. (See Fig. 95.)

Fig. 95.—Map of Arctic regions.

The total area of dry land has been estimated at about 52,500,000 square miles (DLXXXIII.). Whether the voyager travels south, or north, from the coasts of this dry land, his progress is, sooner or later, stopped by the ice, which accumulates in the seas of the cold northern and southern regions; but, without taking the frozen seas into account, the area of the ocean is twice as great as that of the land. Moreover, though it is doubtful if the sea anywhere attains a depth greater than the height of the highest mountains, the average depth of the sea is greater than the average height of the land above the sea; so that, in all ways, there is much more sea than dry land.

It has been calculated that of the entire surface of the earth, 144,500,000 square miles are covered by water; and

Fig. 96.—Continental or land hemisphere.

Fig. 97 —Oceanic or water hemisphere.

as there are 52,500,000 square miles of dry land, the quantity of water exceeds the quantity of land, nearly in the pro portion that 8 exceeds 3. In other words, for every square mile on the earth's surface, there are nearly three square miles of water.

Again, it may be observed that the land and water are not uniformly distributed, so as to preserve the same proportions in all parts of the world. The northern parts evidently contain much more land than water, while the southern parts contain much more water than land. There is, in fact, about three times as much land in the northern half of the world as in the southern half. Fig. 96 represents that half of the world which contains the greatest amount of land, and Fig. 97 the other half, which contains the greatest proportion of water.

CHAPTER XIX.

FIGURE OF THE EARTH.—CONSTRUCTION OF MAPS

In considering the form, size, and other characters of the Thames basin, we found no occasion to trouble ourselves about the shape and size of the earth as a whole ; and, as what is true, in this respect, of the area of the Thames basin, is true of all areas of the earth's surface, it is obvious that all the facts stated in the last chapter might have been ascertained by the ordinary processes of land-surveying, and that they do not necessarily presuppose a knowledge of the configuration of the world.

One's earliest and most natural impression is that the surfaces of the land and sea are everywhere flat, if local elevations are left out of consideration ; and, for many ages, it was the accepted belief of mankind that the land was a huge flat cake surrounded on all sides by an illimitable ocean. But when, in 1520, Magellan, sailing westward from Europe, passed round the southern end of South America ; and, his ships keeping their bows continually in the same direction, eventually reached the coasts of Asia, and thence returned to the place from whence they set out, it was demonstrated that, at any rate along the track he followed, the surface of the earth was round.

But without having recourse to a voyage of circumnaviga-
tion, very simple reasons afford proof that the surface of the
earth is curved, not only in one direction but in all directions;
or, in other words, that it has the shape of a ball.

One of the most commonly cited, but at the same time
one of the most convincing proofs of this rotundity, is based

FIG. 98.—Disappearance of a ship at sea.

upon a simple observation which any one can make for himself at the sea-side. If a ship be watched, as she leaves
port, it will of course be seen that she gets smaller in size
and fainter in outline the farther she stands out to sea. But,
in addition to this change of size and of distinctness, the
figure of the ship suffers a change. In fact, the hull of the
vessel seems gradually to sink into the sea, and at length disappears altogether. Yet it might fairly be supposed that the
hull, being the largest part, would remain longest in view.

After the hull has passed out of sight, the lower sails, in like manner, are lost to view; then, the upper sails appear to dip beneath the water; and, at last, only the tops of the masts are to be seen peeping above sea-level (Fig. 98 [1]). A telescope may make so much as is to be seen of the ship more distinct; but, it will not bring the lower part again into view, after it has once been lost.   There seems to be no way of explaining this gradual disappearance of a vessel beneath the surface of the sea, on the supposition that the earth is a flat plane; but the explanation becomes easy enough, if it be admitted that the surface is slightly convex. Fig. 99 may be taken to represent a section of the sea, show-ing the successive positions of a ship as she rides over the

FIG. 99.—Ship approaching shore.   Curvature of sea.

curved surface.   If the observer is stationed on the tower, on the left of the figure, his line of vision might be represented by the straight line which runs across the diagram.   When a ship is at a distant point on the right hand of this figure, the observer sees only the top of the masts; because the surface of the water rises, like a flat dome, which comes in the way of his seeing the lower parts of the vessel.   But, as the ship approaches the shore, the upper sails come into view; then the lower sails are seen; and, last of all, the hull itself.

To the sailor who is approaching land, similar appearances

[1] Figs. 98 to 100 are taken, by Mr. Bentley's permission, from M. Guillemin's work entitled *The Heavens*.

are presented; the first points which are visible to him are the peaks of hills, or the tops of buildings. He is prevented from seeing the bases of these objects by the bulge of water, which rises between him and the shore. Now, as these appearances are not confined to any one locality, but are seen in every part of the world, it follows that the earth must have a general curvature. In fact, it can be shown that the convexity is everywhere very nearly the same; and it is, therefore, clear that the earth is a globe-shaped body.

It is possible to obtain similar proof of the earth's roundness by observing a vessel which is stationary. Suppose that a person who is about to bathe in a calm sea, sees a small boat a mile or two from shore. Let him then get into the water, and, with his eye only a few inches above sea-level, look along the surface of the water in the direction of the boat. He will now find that the boat is more or less hidden, or perhaps altogether lost from sight. In fact the curved surface of the sea obstructs the view; and the obstruction is greater, the lower the position of the bather's eye. When a man is standing on shore, his eyes are raised something like five feet above ground; but, when his head is in the water, they are only a few inches above the sea level, and his view is accordingly obstructed. When the observer is in an elevated position, he is able to look over the low hill of water which interferes with the prospect at lower levels: hence, more of a distant ship can be seen from the top of a tower than from its base.

If a person standing on a wide plain, with nothing to obstruct his view, looks round about him, he finds that the boundary of his vision extends equally in all directions, and thus forms a circle. This boundary is called the *horizon*.[1] The term horizon, at least as used in this sense, therefore

---

[1] *Horizon*, from ὁρίζω, *horizo*, to bound.

denotes the circle of vision which seems to separate the
sky from the earth on land, or the sky from the water on
sea.   But, if the observer mounts a hill, or ascends a
tower, or climbs to the mast-head of a ship, he finds that
his circle of vision becomes extended, and he can see
objects which were before beyond his range; in other
words, his horizon increases, or becomes a larger circle.
This is illustrated by Fig. 100.   A person standing at the

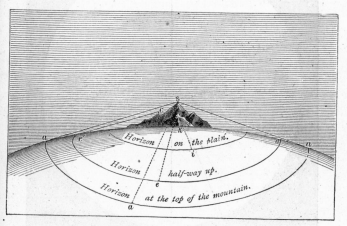

FIG. 100.—Enlargement of horizon by ascending a hill.

foot of the mountain at *k*, has his view limited by the
circle *i*; if he goes half-way up the mountain to *c*, his
horizon expands to the circle marked *e;* and, if he goes
quite to the top, *s*, it enlarges to the circle *a*.   If a man's
eyes are five feet above ground, as they might be if he
stood at the base of the hill, the radius of his horizon will
be less than two miles and three-quarters; but, if he went to

Y

the top of St. Paul's, his horizon would then have a radius of more than twenty-four miles.

Since it is found that the horizon is invariably circular in every part of the world, it is proved that the earth must be

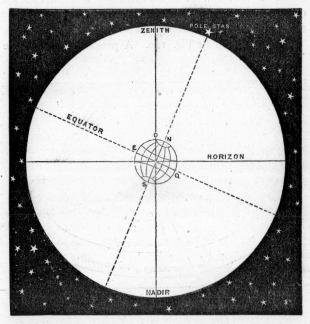

Fig. 101.—The earth within the star-sphere.

spherical. For a sphere is the only kind of solid which presents a circular contour from whatever point it is viewed.

Other means of demonstrating that the surface of the earth is rounded, and not flat, may be obtained from observations on some of the heavenly bodies. One interesting mode of proof may be explained by the help of Fig. 101.

Here the earth is represented as hanging in the centre of a great space, which is bounded on all sides by a starry vault. Let a person be standing on the earth at the point O. That point in the heavens which he sees directly over-head, when he looks up, is called the *zenith;* and the opposite point, which is immediately beneath his feet, and which it is therefore impossible for him to see, since the solid earth stands in his way, is called the *nadir.*[1] The direction of the straight line joining these two points is the direction in which a plumb-line hangs when the plummet is free. An imaginary plane passing exactly midway between the zenith and the nadir constitutes the *horizon.*[2]

It was explained on p. 9, that very near to the north pole of the heavens there is a star called the pole star. That point on the horizon which is immediately beneath the north celestial pole is the true north, and the other cardinal points on the earth's surface are also referred to the horizon. Now, suppose a person at O in Fig. 101, observes how high the pole star is above the northern horizon ; and that two persons travel from this point,— one going due north, and the other due south—and that they observe, at different times, the apparent altitude of

[1] *Nadir* and *zenith* are words of Arabic origin.

[2] There are, in fact, two kinds of horizon. It was said above (p. 320) that the horizon is the circle which limits a person's vision, wherever he may happen to be. This circular boundary, so far as it is formed by the surface of the earth, is distinguished as the *apparent*, or *sensible*, *horizon*. The great plane which is shown in Fig. 101 passing through the centre of the earth, and extended to the celestial sphere, is distinguished as the plane of the *true* or *rational horizon*, which is an imaginary circle, dividing that sphere into two equal halves, one above and one below the true horizon. Practically these two horizons coincide, for the distances of the stars from us are so great, that, if the apparent horizon were extended until it met the celestial sphere, it might be regarded as coincident with the rational horizon, to which it would be sensibly parallel, though separated from it by half the earth's diameter.

the same star, or its height above their horizon. To the man who travels northwards, the pole star will appear to mount higher and higher in the heavens; and, if the ice in the arctic regions did not bar him from getting so far, he would eventually find this star over his head. In fact, it will be seen from Fig. 101 that the pole star is in the zenith of an observer at N. But, to the person who travelled south-wards, the pole star would appear to be steadily sinking lower and lower in the sky; and, when he got midway between the north and south poles of the earth, at the line called the *equator*, he would find that the star actually seemed to touch the horizon ; while, if he continued his course to the south, it would disappear altogether. But the person who stayed at home, at O, would not have observed any movement in the position of the star. In fact, it may be assumed for our present purpose, that this star is fixed ; and its regular movement apparent to the travellers, has been due to their own change of position on the earth's rounded surface, as shown in the figure. This, therefore, proves that the earth is convex, at least in a north-and-south direction.

If the travellers, instead of going northwards and south-wards, had taken their journey due east and due west, they would not have observed any alteration in the altitude of the pole-star. But, the traveller to the east would have found that the sun rose earlier and set earlier than it did when he was at O ; while the traveller to the west would have found that it rose later and set later. It can be shown that this is a proof of curvature in an east-and-west direc-tion ; and, therefore, by combining the two sets of observa-tions the rounded shape of the earth's surface may be fully established.

Engineers and surveyors are in the habit of taking the earth's sphericity into account in their calculations. If, for

example, a canal has to be cut, an allowance must be made
for curvature in order that the depth of water in the canal
may be the same throughout.   A convincing experiment to
prove the rotundity of the earth was made by Mr. Wallace,
in 1870, in the Bedford Level.   Three signals, each thirteen
feet four inches above water-level, were erected at distances
of three miles apart.   On looking through a telescope,
adjusted, in such a manner, that the line of sight touched
the tops of the first and last poles, it was found that the
middle signal was upwards of five feet above the line.
This rise was of course due to the convexity of the earth's
surface.

Such evidence as that which has been adduced in this
chapter, proves conclusively that the earth has a curved
surface, and that the curvature is that of a globular
body.   Very delicate operations have enabled men to determine the figure of the earth with the greatest accuracy, and
have shown that this figure is not exactly that of a true
sphere. The sphere is, in fact, a little flattened in the neighbourhood of the poles, so that, using a popular comparison,
it may be likened to the shape of an orange : only it must
be remembered that the earth's flattening is *very* much less
proportionally than that of the orange.   In consequence of
this flattening, a line running round the globe through the
north and south poles is not exactly a circle, but is an
ellipse, or something like a circle which has been slightly
squeezed at opposite points. Fig. 102 is such an ellipse,
but the extent of flattening is exaggerated prodigiously.
The *polar* diameter, or the line which passes through the
earth's centre, from pole to pole, is found to measure 7899·5
miles There is some reason to believe that the *equatorial*
diameter, or the line which passes through the earth's centre,
from point to point on the equator, is not the same in all

directions, and that the equatorial circumference is not exactly a circle, but is slightly elliptical; its longer diameter measuring about two miles more than its shorter diameter. The average equatorial diameter is about 7926·5 miles : in other words the equatorial exceeds the polar diameter by about twenty-seven miles. The proportion of twenty-seven miles to 7,926 miles is very nearly that of 1 to 294, and hence the earth is said to have an *ellipticity* of $\frac{1}{294}$.

These variations from the shape of a true sphere are so extremely slight, in comparison with the great magnitude of

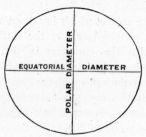

FIG. 102.—Difference between polar and equatorial diameters of the earth.

the earth, that, speaking roughly, the earth may for practical purposes be called sphere ; and it may be regarded as having the shape represented by our ordinary globes. In fact, the departure from the spherical shape is too slight to affect a model of this kind, unless it is of unusual magnitude.[1]

In order to represent any country by drawing its outline upon a globe, or upon a map, it is necessary, in the first place, to have some means of fixing the position of places upon the surface of the earth. The means by which this is accomplished may be easily understood. Suppose that it

[1] In a globe of 2 ft. 6in. diameter, for example, the difference of the polar and equatorial diameters would be very little more than $\frac{1}{10}$th of an inch.

is desired to fix the position of the point P, in Fig. 103 ; let any two straight lines be drawn at right angles to each other, such as OA and OB, and then measure how far the point P is from one of them, say OB. Let P be three inches from OB, then it is known that the point must be some-where in the course of the dotted line CD, which is supposed to be three inches from OB. Some clue has thus been obtained to the position of the point, but it is not yet definitely determined. To fix the point, it is necessary to measure its distance also from the other line OA ; let this distance be two inches : it is clear that the position of the point must be somewhere in the line EF, which is everywhere two inches from OA. But as it has also been shown to be in the line CD, it is evident that its position is fixed at P, for this is the only point at which the two lines cross. The distances three and two, re-ferred to these lines OB, OA respectively, will accurately mark

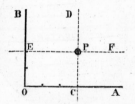

Fig. 103.—Co-ordinates of a point.

the position of P, and they are called by mathematicians the *co-ordinates* of the point.

Geographers use co-ordinates in this way to indicate the position of places upon the surface of the earth. When they wish to mark the place of any point, they refer it to certain fixed lines which they imagine to be drawn upon the surface of the globe. They proceed on the convenient fiction that a line is traced entirely round the earth, midway between the two poles ; and this line, which is practically a circle, they call the *equator*[1] (Fig. 104). The equator consequently divides the world into two equal halves—a

---

[1] *Equator,* from Lat. *æquo,* to make equal.

northern hemisphere and a southern hemisphere. It is
further supposed that each of these halves is banded round
by a number of circles, which run parallel to the equator,
but get smaller and smaller on approaching the poles. These
circles are called *small circles*, while the equator is called a
great circle. The centre of a great circle must be the centre
of the sphere on which the circle is drawn ; and, it is plain,
that if the earth were to be cut through at the equator by a
flat plane, this plane must pass through the earth's centre :

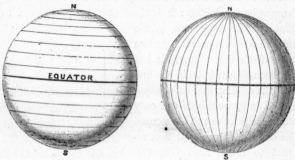

Fig. 104.—Parallels of latitude.   Fig. 105.—Lines of longitude.

but planes passing through any of the small circles, parallel
to the equator, would not pass through this central point.

The equator serves the place of the line OA in Fig. 103 ;
it is, in fact, a standard line from which distances may be
measured. Every circle is divided, for convenience of
calculation, into 360 equal parts, called *degrees;* and it is
supposed that the circumference of the earth is divided in
this way. The distance of any place from the equator,
measured along a circle which passes through the poles, and
expressed in degrees, is called the *latitude* [1] of that place.

---

[1] *Latitude,* from Lat. *latitudo,* breadth.

The distance from the equator to the north pole is one-fourth of the earth's circumference, and therefore the latitude of the pole is said to be 90°, or one-fourth of 360° measured from the equator northwards. In like manner, the south pole is in 90° south latitude. London is described as being in " 51° 30′ N. lat. " ;[1] a description which tells us at once that London is situated in the northern hemisphere, at a distance of 51½°, or about 3,560 statute miles from the equator. The latitude of so large a place as London will of course vary in different parts : the middle of London Bridge is in 51° 30′ 24″ N. lat.

Latitude alone could never fix the position of a place. Any number of places, for example, might be situated, like London, on the circle which runs round the northern hemisphere at 51½° from the equator. Two sets of standard lines are therefore needed, just as two lines were required in Fig. 103. Geographers have consequently been led to draw a number of imaginary circles round the globe, all running through the north and south poles, as in Fig. 105. These are called lines of *longitude*, and they differ in several respects, beside that of direction, from lines of latitude. All lines of longitude form circles which have the earth's centre as their centre ; in other words, they are all great circles. But all the lines of latitude, except the equator, are small circles. Again, the lines of latitude form equidistant circles, and are hence commonly called *parallels* of latitude. But no one can speak of " parallels of longitude," because these

---

[1] Each *degree* of latitude is divided into 60 equal parts called *minutes*, and each minute into 60 equal parts called *seconds*. Degrees are represented by the symbol °, minutes by ′, and seconds by ″. Minutes and seconds of *time* are distinguished by the initials *m* and *s* respectively. A minute of latitude is a geographical mile, called by nautical men a *knot*. The geographical mile contains 2028 yards, while our statute mile contains only 1760 yards.

lines are not parallel, inasmuch as they all meet together and
cross at each of the poles.   It is common, however, to refer
to these imaginary north-and-south circles as *meridians*, for
the reason pointed out on p. 7.

While latitude is always measured from the equator,
longitude has no natural starting-line.   The reckoning may
begin indeed from any meridian, and different countries
actually use different lines for this purpose.   The meridian
from which the reckoning begins is called the *first*, or *prime
meridian;* and, in this country, it is the meridian which passes
through the observatory at Greenwich.   Greenwich, therefore, has no longitude ; and, in like manner, all places due
north and south of Greenwich have no longitude, since they
are on the same meridian.   But all places to the east, or to
the west, of this first meridian have their longitude, which
is expressed in so many degrees or minutes or seconds, and
is designated as east or as west, according to its position
with reference to Greenwich.   Thus London Bridge has a
longitude of 5′ 10″ W.   As the equator is divided into 360
degrees, it may be supposed that a meridian passes through
each of the 360 divisions.   Hence a degree of longitude
measured at the equator, is the $\frac{1}{360}$th part of the circumference of the earth.   But in going to the north, or to the
south, of the equator, the meridians draw closer and closer
together until they meet at the poles, as shown in Fig. 105.
Each parallel of latitude, whether large or small, is divided,
like the equator, into 360° ; and, therefore, the length of
a degree of longitude gets less and less in passing from the
equator, where it measures 60 geographical miles, to either
of the poles, where it vanishes altogether.   The reckoning of
longitude proceeds from the first meridian to the east and
to the west, until the figures reach 180° ; the reckoning of
latitude proceeds from the equator to the north and to the

south, until the figures reach 90°. Hence no place can have a greater latitude than 90°, or a greater longitude than 180°.

It would be too long a story to explain how latitude and longitude are practically determined. Unless people happen to be mariners, or surveyors, or travellers, they never have occasion to fix their position by these means. But, still, every one is concerned more or less with latitude and longitude, for it is by means of these co-ordinates that we can find out any given place upon a map or a globe. The cross-lines of latitude and longitude form, indeed, a frame-work on which the geographer traces the outlines, which show the distribution of land and water upon the surface of the earth.

On a terrestrial globe, it is easy enough to lay down the lines of latitude and longitude, and then to draw the outline of any country. But when a map, instead of a globe, is to be made, it is not so easy to see how these lines should be drawn. If the peel were taken off half an orange, it would be found impossible to spread this rounded peel upon a flat table, without the skin giving way at certain points. A map of the world, for this reason, can never give a true repre-sentation of the surface of the earth.

It was said in the first chapter (p. 5) that a map of the Thames is an outline-sketch of the river, as it might be drawn by a person in a balloon, at a great height, immediately above the place which is mapped. This statement is perfectly true as far as it goes. As long as the man in the balloon looks at the country directly beneath him, he sees it in its true aspect ; but, if he looks a long way off, the curvature of the earth produces distortion in the distant outlines. In one kind of map, however, the person who makes it is supposed to be standing at an immeasurable

distance, and to depict what he sees upon a flat plane
which is placed between his eye and the earth[1] (Fig. 106).
But his representation will be distorted much in the same
way as the shadows of objects are distorted when the
light does not fall square upon their surfaces. Hold a
plate in the sunshine, in front of a flat surface, and, when
the light comes down perpendicularly upon it, the shadow is
a true circle; but, incline the plate, and the circle passes
into an ellipse; and, as the plate is inclined more and more,
so the ellipse gets narrower and narrower, until at last, when

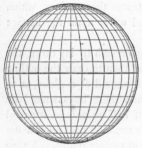   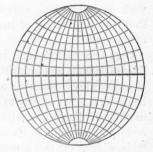

FIG. 106.—Orthographic projection.   FIG. 107.—Globular projection.

the sunlight is passing along the edge of the plate, the
shadow is reduced to a straight line. The shadow is said
to be *projected* on to the flat surface; and the method of
throwing a representation of the rounded surface of the
earth on to a flat sheet of paper is also called projection.

In the method of projection which has been just explained—that in which the eye of the map-maker is supposed
to be infinitely distant—the central parts of the hemisphere

[1] This is the method of *orthographic projection.* The parallels of
latitude become straight lines, as seen in the figure.

are accurately represented, but the countries towards the
circumference are crowded together and diminished in size.
This defect has led to another method of projection, in
which the map-maker is supposed to have his eye on the
very surface of the globe, and to look through the solid
sphere as though it were a globe of glass, so as to see the
countries which are on the opposite side; the outlines are
then drawn as they would be projected on a transparent
screen stretched across the middle of the sphere, and in
front of the observer's eye.[1]

In this method, it is found that the countries towards the
centre are contracted, while those near the circumference
are enlarged.   The map is therefore distorted in exactly
the opposite direction to that of the previous projection.
Hence it seems natural that if the map-maker took up his
position at some intermediate point, having his eye neither
on the surface of the sphere, nor at an unlimited distance
from it, an accurate representation might be obtained.
The most favourable point of sight has been calculated,
and although the view obtained in this way is still distorted,
the distortion is less than in the other projections.   This
method is consequently the usual way in which the pair of
hemispheres are drawn (Fig. 107).

If instead of attempting to represent half the world at
once, the map-maker is required to represent only one
country—say Europe—he usually resorts to a different
device.   Imagine a roll of paper screwed up like a sugar-
bag, and then placed over a model of the globe, like a
paper extinguisher : this cap will not fit the globe completely, but can be made to touch the central parallel of
latitude of the country which is to be mapped.   Let the

---

[1] This is the method of *stereographic projection:* the lines of latitude
are represented as arcs of circles.   Fig. 107 may be taken to represent
this projection, as it does not differ much from the *globular projection.*

outline of the country be projected on this cone; then, on unfolding the paper, it may be spread out on a flat surface: hence this method is known as that of *conical development* (Fig. 108). Most maps of Europe furnish examples of this construction.

Any of these maps will serve tolerably well for the use of landsmen, but they are not what the mariner wants. He requires a chart which will give him the true bearing of places, so that he may steer direct from one point to another, and this he gets by the use of *Mercator's projection.*[1]

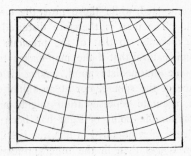

Fig. 108.—Conical development.

Suppose the outlines of the various countries of the world, and the system of lines of latitude and longitude, were depicted on a globular bladder placed inside a glass cylinder; on blowing more air into the bladder it will stretch in all directions, and it may be supposed to be sufficiently elastic to press on all sides against the inner surface of the cylinder. The parallels of latitude then touch the glass, and form circles round the cylinder, while the meridians stretch out, and

---

[1] Mercator was a native of Flanders, born in 1512. His real name was Gerard Kauffman, but, according to the custom of the times, his surname, which means a *merchant*, was translated into Latin as *Mercator*.

form lines which run up and down the length of the cylinder. If, when the bladder touches the inside, it could be ripped up, and spread out flat, it would form Mercator's projection. (Fig. 109.) All the lines of longitude are straight lines at equal distances apart; and all the lines of latitude are also straight lines, but not at equal distances. On a globe, the meridians run together near the poles, but on this projection

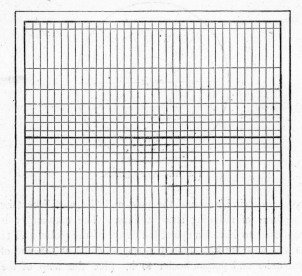

FIG. 109.—Mercator's projection.

they are equidistant; hence the high latitudes are evidently too much spread out to the east and west, and to counteract this distortion, the parallels of latitude are also stretched north and south. By thus increasing the distances between the parallels of latitude, as they advance from the equator, the shape of the land is preserved, but its size is grossly exaggerated. The polar regions are not brought within

Mercator's projection, for the poles are supposed, by the cylindrical development, to be indefinitely distant. Such a map is therefore not used in the navigation of arctic seas, but is otherwise universally employed by mariners.

For arctic charts the *polar projection* represented in Fig. 110, is commonly used. Here the parallels of latitude are

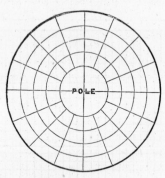

FIG. 110.—Polar projection.

concentric circles around the pole, and the meridians take the form of radiating straight lines. The map-maker is supposed to have his eye at the centre of the globe, and to depict what he sees upon a plane which is at the end of the axis, and perpendicular to it. (See the map of the Arctic regions, p. 314.)

CHAPTER XX.

THE MOVEMENTS OF THE EARTH.

IT has been shown in the preceding pages that the waters of the earth are in a state of constant circulation ; that the atmosphere is never in repose; that the solid materials of the earth's crust are slowly but incessantly changing their position ; and that the matter of the organic world is subject, in a yet more marked degree, to cyclical changes. Absolute repose is, indeed, a state utterly unknown upon the earth's surface. Nor is the globe itself exempt from movements which are of a still grander kind. The huge ball which was described in the last chapter is constantly in motion. Part of this motion is a movement of rotation, whereby the earth is perpetually spinning round like a top ; and part is a movement of revolution, whereby it progresses through space, and is carried round the sun.

If the earth were fixed in space, without either of these motions, it is plain that the half which happened to be turned towards the sun would enjoy uninterrupted sunshine, while the opposite half would be plunged in permanent shadow; in other words, perpetual day would reign in one half, and perpetual night in the other half. The illuminated hemisphere, on which the sun's rays were constantly shining, would, of course, become intensely hot ; while the darkened hemisphere would become intensely cold, by the unchecked radiation of its heat into space. Under such circumstances, the hottest part of the world would be the middle of the sun-facing hemisphere, because the solar rays would there fall square upon its surface ; while the heat would diminish, in all directions towards the circumference, because the rays would be received in a more slanting direction on those parts which were farther from the centre of the lit-up half.

If the earth had no atmosphere, the contrast of climate between the two halves of the globe would be most intense ; for the half turned towards the sun would monopolise all the heat sent to it, while the other half would constantly lose heat by radiation into space. But, if the earth were enveloped in an atmosphere, currents would be raised in this air, and these currents would tend to moderate the climate. From the highly-heated centre of the illuminated hemisphere, the warmed air would rise and spread, on all sides, through the higher regions of the atmosphere ; while the less-heated, and therefore denser, air from the surrounding parts, would rush in, through the lower regions of the atmosphere, to supply its place. Hence, any one on the surface of such an earth would find winds blowing from all points of the compass directly towards the middle of the sun-facing hemisphere.

If the earth now began to rotate, what would happen would depend upon the direction of the imaginary line, or axis, round which it turned. The axis coincides with the earth's polar diameter, and the points on the surface which were described in the last chapter as the earth's *poles* are the extremities of this imaginary line. Suppose, first, that the axis coincided with a prolonged radius of the sun, as in the first diagram in Fig. 111, where the axis is represented by a thick line, and the sun, which must be supposed to be at a very great distance, is represented by a small circle. Then, it is clear, that the same half of the earth would always be turned towards the sun ; and the only effect of the twirling round would be to modify the direction of the winds, in a manner which will be explained presently. But now suppose

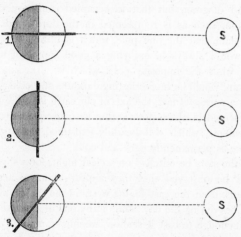

FIG. 111.—Diagram to illustrate effect of changing the position of the earth's axis in relation to the sun.

that the axis were *perpendicular* to a prolonged radius of the sun, as represented in the second diagram : then the rotation of the earth would bring different parts of the surface, in succession, towards the sun, and they would thus become, in turn, illuminated and warmed. In fact, the rotation would produce the alternation of day and night; and the days and nights would be equal all over the world, and at all times.

The poles would be the coldest parts ; and all points of the surface, at equal distances from the poles, would be equally warmed and equally illuminated; while the winds, arising from the lower currents, would be directed obliquely, from the poles towards the equator, and those formed by the upper currents would blow in the contrary direction.

Suppose, once more, that the axis were neither in the position indicated in the first, nor in that shown in the second diagram, but that it occupied some intermediate position, such as is represented in the third figure. Here it is plain, that the one pole, which is turned towards the sun, would always be enjoying a good supply of light and heat, while the opposite pole, which is turned away from the sun, would be in everlasting darkness and cold.

As a matter of fact, the axis of our earth is in the position represented in the last case ; but in consequence of other movements, which will be duly explained, no part of the surface is permanently dark and cold.

If the stars be watched on a clear night, for a short time, it will be observed that they appear to move across the heavens, from the east to the west, in the same way as the sun does during the day ; and, if any one of these stars were bright enough to cast a shadow, we might make a star-dial for the night, just as sun-dials are made for the day. If the star were one of those which never set in England, such, for example, as the star in the end of the tail of the Great Bear (Fig. 1), its shadow would, in the course of the night, sweep over a segment of a circle, just as the shadow cast by the sun sweeps over a segment of a circle during the day. Suppose the circle to be completed, and to be divided into 86,164 equal parts; then, observation would show that the shadow thrown by the star travels over these equal parts in equal periods of time, and each such period is what is termed a *second*. Consequently, the shadow would return to the same place night after night, in just 86,164 seconds.   If an accurate clock, beating seconds, had a dial, the circle of which was divided into 86,164 parts, and a single hand, which should cover one of these divisions, at every beat, the motion of the hand would exactly keep pace with that of the star-shadow. And, if any point of the dial were marked twelve, when the star-shadow was at any point of its course ; whenever the star-shadow returned to that place, the hand of the clock would again mark twelve.

Such a clock would keep what is called *sidereal*, or star-time, and the 86,164 seconds (or 23 hours 56 minutes and 4 seconds) would be a day by the "star-clock." As the apparent motion of the stars is due to the rotation of the earth on its axis, the hand of the star-clock would travel round the dial, in exactly the same time as the earth turns on its axis; which period of time (86,164 seconds) is termed a *sidereal day*.

For practical purposes, however, this clock would be of very little use.   Unless we happen to be astronomers, when we ask the time, it is not from any wish to learn how far the earth has turned on its axis, in reference to a particular star ; we want to know the time of day, or the time of night, whether it is forenoon or afternoon, or the like.   To apply to our sidereal clock for an answer to these questions, would be worse than useless.   For, supposing that on any particular day, twelve by the star-clock exactly corresponded with noon by the sun ; the day after, the star-clock would mark twelve nearly four minutes earlier ; and, the day after that, earlier still by a similar amount ; so that, in a quarter of a year, twelve by the star-clock would be six hours before noon and so on.   In short, twelve by the star-clock might mean any hour in the day or night. The reason of this is that day and night depend upon the sun, and the sun does not keep sidereal time. In the first place, the interval between the time when the shadow on a sun-dial marks noon on one day, and the time it marks noon on the next day, is always more than 86,164 seconds; and, in the second place, the difference is not always the same, but is sometimes more and sometimes less. If the sun-dial were a clock, in fact, we should say that it did not go very well; and the only way of making a good clock go, in such a manner as to show twelve at noon by the sun, or thereabouts, every day, is to strike an average of all the irregularities of the sun-dial, and add this average to the number of seconds, which would be marked by the revolution of the hand of a star-clock in the course of a day.

This average is 236 seconds, which, added to 86,164, gives the 86,400 seconds which compose the 24 hours, or *mean solar day*, of civil time. For convenience' sake these are counted, not by one revolution, but by two, of the hour-hand of an ordinary clock; and thus the XII. on our clocks shows, very nearly, the midday and midnight as determined by the sun's crossing the meridian. The coincidence of twelve by the clock with noon by the sun-dial, however, is exact only four times in the year; at the intervening periods, the dial is either faster or slower than the clock.

Since the earth's figure is nearly spherical, it follows, that different points on the earth's surface must move, during the daily rotation, with different velocities. Any point on the line of the equator will describe a circle equal to the circumference of the earth. The earth's circumference is about 24,000 miles; and, as the rotation is effected in nearly twenty-four hours, the velocity of its equatorial region must be something like 1,000 miles an hour. But, on going either north or south from the equator, the circle which is described by any point on the rotating sphere will be smaller, as is shown by the diminution in the diameter of the circles of latitude. Yet every point of the surface takes the same time to turn once round; and, therefore, the velocity, or rate of motion, must become less and less, as the circles get smaller and smaller. In fact, at the poles, the velocity is reduced to nothing. The pole represents simply the end of the imaginary line on which the earth turns, and is itself stationary.

Everything on the surface of the earth is necessarily carried round with the rotating globe. The atmosphere, as shown in Chapter VI. may be regarded as part and parcel of the earth; it forms, in fact, a gaseous shell, which completely encases the globe, and shares in all its movements. The atmosphere, therefore, moves round at the same rate as the surface on which it rests. But this surface rotates, as just explained, at different speeds, in different latitudes; and hence the atmosphere, while quiescent over the poles, moves with increasing rapidity in lower latitudes, until it attains 1000 miles an hour at the equator. Therefore, if a stream of air starts from one of the poles towards the equator, and moves in a direct north-and-south line; that is to say, along a meridian, it will constantly tend to lag behind the surface of the earth. At the starting point, the air is stationary, because the pole itself has no motion ; and, if we could suppose such a stream of air to flow due south without coming into contact with anything, the successive points of the earth's surface over which it passed, would turn under it with constantly-increasing swiftness ; until, at the equator, they would whirl by at the rate of 1,000 miles an hour to the east. Imagine the air thus

transported from the pole to the equator to come into contact with the surface of the earth in the latter region. The
immediate effect upon the bodies at that surface would be the
same as if they were transported, through still air, at the rate
of 1,000 miles an hour to the east. That is to say, they
would seem to be subjected to a frightful hurricane from
the east; just as the traveller in a railway carriage, passing
through perfectly still air, at the rate of sixty miles an hour,
feels a gale of wind blowing from the direction in which he
is travelling.

However, the polar air, in passing south, would soon
become influenced by the motion of the regions over which
it passes. It would thereby be deflected towards the east,
and this deflection would constantly increase, until it reached
the maximum at the equator. During its passage from high
to low latitudes, the velocity of the eastward movement im-
pressed upon the current would have been constantly increasing. But common experience shows that a body cannot
accommodate itself, in a moment, to any great change of
motion. If a carriage suddenly starts, or increases its velocity,
the passenger is likely to be thrown in an opposite direction
to that of the movement. The air, in like manner, lags
behind in passing from high to low latitudes ; and therefore while the earth rotates from west to east, the air, as it
passes south, acquires a relative motion from east to west.
Thus the current which started from the north pole would
acquire, during its course, a relative motion to the west ;
and, by combining the two motions—that from the north,
with that from the east—the wind thus produced would seem
to come from the north-east ; in other words, it would appear
as a north-easterly, and not as a due north, wind.[1]

[1] It may be well to remark that winds receive their names from the
quarters *from* which they blow.   Ocean currents, however, are generally

Such a case as this which has just been discussed is by no means imaginary. As a matter of fact, a stream of heated moist air constantly rises, by its relative lightness, from the neighbourhood of the equator, where the heat is greatest and the evaporation most rapid. To supply the place of the air which is thus raised, colder and denser air rushes in from the north and the south of the equatorial belt. Yet this inflowing air does not take the shape of a due north wind, in the one hemisphere, and of a due south wind, in the other hemisphere. The air comes from places where the velocity of rotation is less ; and, therefore, it lags behind the earth in its rapid rotation from west to east. Hence, the wind reaches the equatorial zone from the north-east on the north side, and from the south-east on the south side, of the equator. In this way it comes about, that winds, more or less constant in direction, blow across those parts of the Atlantic and Pacific oceans which lie for some distance on the two sides of the equator ; the direction being from N.E. in the northern tropics, and from S.E. in the southern tropics. Such steady winds were of so much importance to navigation, before the days of steam-ships, that much of the world's commerce depended upon them, and they were therefore called *trade winds*.

It has just been said that the trade-winds blow in a direction "more or less constant." This qualification is needed, because the character of the wind is greatly modified by local circumstances, such as the distribution of land and water, and the altitude of neighbouring land. The trade-winds are not equally well marked in the two great oceans ; nor are they equally strong at all seasons.

It may be inquired, what becomes of the air which

named after the point *towards* which they set. Hence a N.E. wind blows from the N.E. ; but a N.E. current flows to the N.E

rises from the heated equatorial belt? This air, on reaching
the higher regions of the atmosphere, flows over the currents which are sweeping across the surface below, and
thus produces currents which drift towards the north in the
northern, and towards the south in the southern hemisphere.
But these upper currents are blowing from regions of high
velocity, to regions of lower velocity, of rotation; they
therefore move more rapidly than the earth immediately
beneath them, and, as it were, outrun the earth in its rotation.
Hence they are deflected from a simple north-and-south
course, but in an opposite direction to that of the trades; so
that, in the northern hemisphere, they blow from the S.W.,
and, in the southern hemisphere, from the N.W. Such upper currents, moving directly counter to the surface winds,
may be recognised by their effects on high clouds. In the
higher regions of the atmosphere, they become chilled; and,
at about the thirty-fifth parallel of latitude, they are sufficiently dense to descend to the surface. Part of this air then
returns as an undercurrent to the equatorial belt, where it
becomes heated afresh, and once more rises, thus completing
the circulation in this part of the atmosphere; while another
part of the descending air continues its course as a south-
west wind, in the northern hemisphere; and, as a north-west
wind, in the southern hemisphere; but these winds are not
so constant as the trades. The prevalent S.W. winds of
this country may have, in part, such an origin. These winds
are the chief rain-bearers to the British Isles; and hence the
rotation of the earth is not without its effect upon the water-
supply of the Thames basin.

The diurnal rotation of the earth sufficiently explains a
good many of the apparent movements of the heavenly
bodies. Thus, every day, the sun appears to rise towards the

east, and, after marching across the sky in a curved path, to set towards the west. Every night, too, some of the stars appear, in like manner, to rise and set; and this is what they must certainly do, if, as we know to be the case, on independent grounds, the earth turns round upon its axis from west to east.

Every one must have noticed in travelling by railway, that if his own train is in a station, alongside of another, he constantly fancies the other train is moving, when it is his own which has gently started; and, on looking out of the window, when the train is at speed, it may be really difficult to persuade oneself that the telegraph posts, and the nearer trees and houses, are not whirling past the more distant objects, in a direction contrary to that in which the train is moving. And although, when one looks at the rising or the setting sun, it seems contrary to the evidence of one's senses that the sun is not moving and the earth is; yet this is one of the many cases, in which what is called the direct evidence of the senses is nothing but a hypothetical interpretation of the facts of which sensation tells us. That this apparently obvious and natural interpretation of the fact of the change of place of the sun and stars—an interpretation upon which the whole human race were agreed a few centuries ago—is wrong, and that it is the earth which rotates, has long been rendered highly probable; and the experiments of M. Foucault some years ago completed the proof.

The diurnal rotation of the earth does not explain all the apparent movements of the heavenly bodies. For example, it is observed that the sun does not rise, day after day, in exactly the same place. In mid-spring and in mid-autumn, it rises almost precisely due east; but, in midsummer, it rises to the north of the east point of our horizon, and, in mid-winter, it rises to the south of this point. The sun seems, in fact, to change his place in the heavens every day, but the circuit of changes is completed in the course of a year; so that, next midsummer, he will be again in just the same place as that which he occupied last midsummer. His apparent movement is, in fact, due to the movement of our earth around the sun, in a direction, like that of its rotation, from west to east. And, just as the time of one rotation of the earth on its axis constitutes a *day*, so the time of one revolution round the sun makes a *year*. This revolution is completed in about 365¼ days.[1]

It is in consequence of this annual motion of the earth that time, told by the stars, differs from time told by the sun. It was said above (p. 342), that the sidereal day is nearly four minutes shorter than the solar day. The sidereal day represents the period of the earth's rotation, but the solar day is due, not simply to the rotation; but to this movement, combined with that of the earth's progressive movement through space. The subject is worth examining, because it offers one of the best proofs of the earth's annual movement. Suppose that it were possible to see the sun and, at the same time, a certain star, on the meridian together, at noon to-day; then, it would be found to-morrow, that the star reached the same meridian nearly four minutes before the sun came there. But, it is clear, that if the earth simply rotated upon its axis, the star and the sun ought to reach the meridian at the same time. The delay in the sun's arrival is due to his apparent journey in the heavens, which is opposite to that of the diurnal rotation of the stars, so that

---

[1] More precisely 365 days, 6 hours, 9 minutes, 10·75 seconds of mean solar time. As the calendar year contains 365 days, the extra quarter of a day gives an additional day every fourth year, or *leap year ;* and, by this addition, the correction necessary to cause the seasons to fall in the same months of every year is nearly made.

the sun appears to move backwards among them. The stars are so extremely far off that their apparent position is not sensibly affected by our yearly march round the sun ; but the sun is so much nearer, that its apparent position is materially affected, and the sun, consequently, seems to lag behind every day. As a complete revolution is effected in the course of a year, $\frac{1}{365}$th part of the journey will be accomplished in a day. But a circle is divided into 360 degrees : therefore nearly one degree will be travelled over every day. Now the 360th part of 24 hours is 4 minutes ; hence the change of position, due to one day's apparent *annual* motion of the sun, is equal to the change of position due to about four minutes apparent *daily* motion.

The position which the earth occupies in relation to the sun, at different periods of its annual journey, will be understood by reference to Fig. 112. This shows the earth at four successive positions corresponding to the four seasons. The track which the sun appears to follow in the heavens, in consequence of our motion round him, is called the *ecliptic*";[1] and if it be supposed that a flat surface passes through this path, and through the centres of the earth and sun, that surface will form the *plane of the ecliptic*, and will coincide with the plane of the earth's orbit.

From what has been already said (p. 340), it might be concluded, that the earth's axis is neither in this plane nor perpendicular to it, but that it is inclined to the plane. It is in fact sloped, as represented in the figure, at an angle of 66° 32' ; and the extent of the slope remains the same in every part of the earth's path ; in other words, the axis may be said to remain parallel to itself, and to point to the same spot of the heavens.[2] Great as the diameter of the earth's

[1] *Ecliptic*, so called because *eclipses* only happen when the moon is either on or very near to this curved path.

[2] It should be mentioned, however, that the earth's pole undergoes

orbit is, it is insignificant when compared with the enormous distances of the so-called fixed stars. If, therefore, the north pole of the earth points towards the pole-star at one part of the earth's orbit, it continues to point towards it all through its journey, though that journey forms an enormous circuit in the heavens.[1]

Reference to Fig. 112 will now show plainly enough how the inclination of the earth's axis affects the amount of

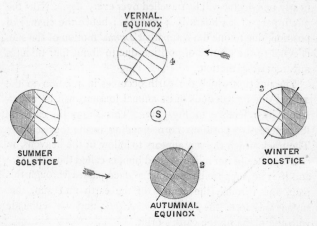

FIG. 112.—Diagram showing the earth's relation to the sun at different seasons.

light and heat which the globe receives from the sun at different seasons. Suppose that the earth is in the position

a slow change of position, so that it does not always point to exactly the same spot in the heavens. But this movement is so slow that it would take 25,868 years for the pole to make a complete revolution.

[1] If one walks in a circle ten yards in diameter, the apparent direction of objects fifty yards off will be obviously altered at every step; while the change of bearing of the spire of a distant church can only be detected by a theodolite; and that of a remote mountain top will appear to remain unchanged, even with such help.

which she occupies on June 21, represented at No. 1 in the figure. Here it is seen, that the inclination of the axis causes the north pole to be fully exposed to the sun; and the sun-lit half of the earth includes much more of the northern, than of the southern, hemisphere. As the earth turns round this sloping axis, the north pole and the surrounding parts will continue in sunshine, during the entire rotation. Within a circle measuring 23½° from the north pole, the sun will not set; and, within a similar circle around the south pole, the sun will not rise. Anywhere, outside the polar regions, there will be an alternation of day and night during the 24 hours; but the day, and night, will not be equal, except at the equator. Thus, a place in the northern hemisphere, like London, will have the day much longer than the night; for the figure shows that it will be kept, during rotation, longer in sunshine than in shade. In fact, when the earth is in this position, it is *midsummer* in the northern hemisphere; and, as the figure shows, it is *midwinter* in the southern hemisphere. These facts are more clearly indicated in Fig. 113, which is an enlarged figure of the earth in the same position as that of the small globe at No. 1 in Fig. 112.

As the earth travels round the sun, from June to September, it completes a quarter of its circuit. The days in the northern hemisphere have been getting shorter, and the nights longer; and when the earth has reached the position of No. 2 in Fig. 112, or on September 22, it is illuminated as represented in Fig. 114.[1] The boundary between the illuminated and the shaded halves runs directly along a meridian,

---

[1] From the point of view from which this figure is supposed to be taken, the inclination of the axis is not at first apparent. As the axis always points in one direction, it cannot now incline towards the sun as it did when in the position indicated in Fig. 113. In both figures, a

from pole to pole. Every place on the earth's surface will therefore be just as long in sunshine as in shade ; and there will be equal day and night throughout the world.

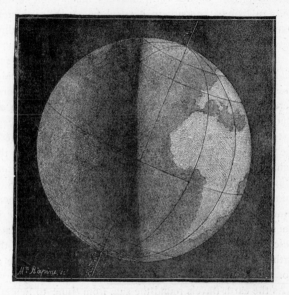

FIG. 113.—The Earth at the summer solstice.

In passing from No. 2 to No. 3 in Fig. 112, the nights in northern latitudes get longer, and the days shorter. When the earth is in the position of No. 3, which is about December

line drawn from the earth to the sun is supposed to lie in the plane of the paper. A plane drawn through both poles coincides with the plane of the paper in Fig. 113 ; while, as the earth has moved through a quarter of a circle in order to get into the position represented in Fig. 114, the plane of the poles is now at right angles to that of the paper ; and the north circumpolar region is seen, foreshortened, in the upper part of the figure.

21, it presents exactly opposite conditions of light and shade to those represented in Fig. 113. In fact, the north pole is now turned as far as possible from the sun, and the north-polar regions revolve in darkness, while the southern polar regions are enjoying uninterrupted day.

During the remaining half of its revolution, from No. 3

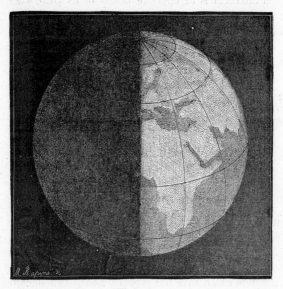

FIG. 114.—The Earth at an equinox.

back to No. 1, the earth passes through successive stages, similar to those just described, but in an inverse order. When she has reached the position indicated at No. 4, which she will do on March 22, there is again twelve hours sunshine in all parts of the world.

It will now be understood that, at two periods in the

A A

course of the year, when the earth is at opposite points in its orbit, the days and nights are everywhere equal. These periods are known as the *equinoxes*.[1] One occurs in March, and is therefore known as the *spring* or *vernal equinox*, and the other in September, and is consequently called the *autumnal equinox*. Again, there are two other periods, also, when the earth is at opposite points of its path, when the inequality between the days and nights is greatest. These periods are known as the *solstices*.[2]

In discussing the earth's revolution round the sun, it should be mentioned that the orbit is not strictly a circle,

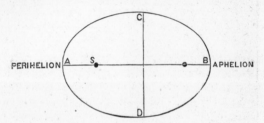

FIG. 115.—Diagram to illustrate perihelion and aphelion.

but is a curve of that kind which was described in the last chapter as an ellipse. In an ellipse (Fig. 115) the longest diameter, AB, is called the *major axis*, and the shortest diameter, CD, the *minor axis*. On the major axis, there are two points which have this property :—any two lines drawn from them to the same point of the curve, are always, when joined together, of equal length to the same straight line. These two points are known as the *foci* of the ellipse. In the great elliptical path of the earth, the sun occupies one of these foci, as at S. It is plain, there-

[1] *Equinox*, from Lat. *æquus*, equal ; *nox*, night.
[2] *Solstice*, from Lat. *sol*, sun ; *sisto*, I stand ; because the sun appears to stand still in the heavens at these points in its path.

fore, that, when the earth is at A, it must be nearer to the sun than when at B. The nearest distance is called the *perihelion*,[1] and the greatest distance the *aphelion*.[2]

It would, at first sight, seem a very fair assumption that when the earth is at perihelion it should be hottest, because it is then at its nearest point to the sun. As a matter of fact, however, the earth is at perihelion about Christmas, which is almost the coldest part of the year, in the northern hemisphere ; and it is at aphelion about the beginning of July. There are, indeed, several influences which tend to neutralize the effects of the sun's proximity. Thus, when the earth is at perihelion, the days with us are short, for the sun is not long above the horizon. Nor does he rise high in the sky, at this season ; and, hence, the rays fall very obliquely upon the earth ; so that they have less heating effect than if they fell more directly upon the surface. Again, it must be remembered that the earth moves more rapidly as it approaches the sun. These influences more than neutralise any augmentation of heat which may be due to increased nearness to the source of heat ; hence, the apparent paradox, that the earth is nearer to the sun during our winter than during our summer, becomes easily intelligible.

It is evident that the temperature of any locality depends chiefly on the duration of its supply of sunshine, and on the direction in which the sun's rays are received. In this country, for example, the temperature is highest when the sun has been shining during the long days, and when he rises highest in the sky. But the altitude, or height of the sun above the horizon, in England, never exceeds about two-thirds of the distance from the horizon towards the zenith.

[1] *Perihelion*, from περί, *peri*, near ; ἥλιος, *helios*, the sun.
[2] *Aphelion*, from ἀπο, *apo*, from ; and ἥλιος.

At the equator, the sun is directly overhead, or in the zenith, at noon in the spring and autumn, and is never more than $23\frac{1}{2}°$ from the zenith at either solstice; while the days and nights are of practically equal length all the year round. Within a circle of $23\frac{1}{2}°$ latitude, on each side of the equator, there is a belt called the *torrid* or *tropical* zone. At every place within these zones, the sun is in the zenith twice a year, and is never more than $47°$ from the zenith. Hence the intense heat of tropical regions. The boundaries of these zones are called *tropics;* and the countries just outside these circles form *sub-tropical* regions.

Around each pole, a circle of $23\frac{1}{2}°$ radius may be drawn, which will include the *polar* regions or *frigid* zone. The Northern circle is called the *Arctic*, and the southern is called the *Antarctic* circle. At the poles themselves, the sun is above the horizon for six months continuously, and below it for an equal period. But, though the polar day is so long, the extreme obliquity of the rays prevents the continued sunshine from having so great a heating power as it would have further south. In fact, at the poles, the sun never rises more than $23\frac{1}{2}°$ above the horizon.

Between the polar and the tropical zones, there is, in each hemisphere, a broad belt of the earth's surface, which is known as the *temperate* zone. The distribution of the surface of the globe into zones is shown in Fig. 116.

These zones are distinguished, as has just been explained, by their differences of climate. The principal factor in the formation of climate is, of course, solar heat; the climate of any place depending, primarily, on the lengths of the days and nights, and on the relative duration of the seasons. But climate is also greatly affected by the nature of the surface, whether it be land or water. Water parts with its heat much more slowly than the land does, and it thus retains a

store which serves to equalize the temperature. On land
again, the climate depends, to a very great extent, on the
altitude. In fact, on ascending a high mountain, from a
plain in a hot country, the traveller meets with changes in
the character of the animal and vegetable life, which are
similar to those changes which may be observed in passing
from low to high latitudes. Even within the tropical

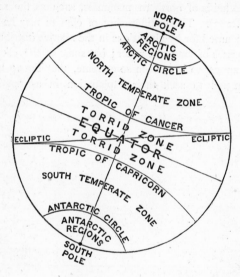

FIG. 116.—Zones of the earth's surface.

zone, the highest points of the existing high lands are
covered with perpetual snow. Climate is also modified
by winds, which transport heat and moisture from one place
to another; and by marine currents, such as the Gulf Stream,
the influence of which has already been described (p. 173).

Climate determines, to a very large extent, the character

of the animal and vegetable population of a country, or its fauna and its flora. In studying the past history of the basin of the Thames, as revealed by the organic remains described in Chapter XVII., it is evident that this area has at different times undergone great vicissitudes of climate; at one time supporting a tropical or sub-tropical vegetation, (p. 288), and at another time offering a congenial feeding-ground to herds of northern mammals, such as the musk-sheep (p. 283). These differences of climate may be partially accounted for by alterations in the relative distribution of the masses of land and water; but some of the climatic changes appear to have been so extreme, that the geologist has been led to seek their explanation in astronomical causes.[1]

[1] See, for example, Mr. Croll's *Climate and Time*, 1875.

CHAPTER XXI.

REFERENCE has frequently been made, in the course of the foregoing chapters, to the effects of solar heat upon the earth. Such references, however, have been incidental rather than direct; and little, or nothing, has been said, of set purpose, about the sun itself. It is proposed, therefore, in this concluding chapter, to give a simple sketch of what we know about the nature of the sun; and to show that the influence of this body may be regarded as the prime mover in the production of most of the phenomena which are exhibited within the basin of the Thames.

When the sun is shining in its full splendour, it is much too dazzling an object to be looked at with the unprotected eye. Viewed, however, through a misty atmosphere, or through a dark-coloured glass, it presents the appearance of a luminous disc, which is usually perfectly circular in shape and homogeneous over its entire surface.[1] The size of this bright disc does not, however, remain precisely the same throughout the year. It was explained in the last chapter

---

[1] "Usually," because the shape of the disc is sometimes distorted by atmospheric refraction, while its uniformity is occasionally, though rarely, broken by dark spots large enough to be seen by the unassisted eye.

(p. 354) that, in consequence of the shape of the earth's orbit, we are not always separated from the sun by the same distance; being, in fact, much nearer in December than in July. This difference of distance causes a corresponding difference of apparent magnitude in the solar disc. The apparent size of an object, as every one knows, varies according to the distance at which it is viewed, so that a halfpenny, held at arm's length, may actually seem larger than the entire sun.

Suppose that an object is situated at A B (Fig. 117); its apparent height will be measured by the inclination of the two lines, A O, B O, which are drawn from the opposite extremities of the object to the centre of the eye. A larger

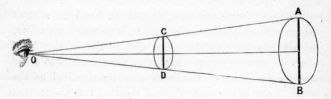

FIG. 117.—Figure to show that apparent magnitude depends upon the visual angle.

object will give a larger angle, and a smaller object a smaller angle. The apparent magnitude of an object will therefore depend upon the angle which it forms, or subtends, at the eye. If a small object, C D, be interposed in the line of sight, it may be so placed as to subtend precisely the same angle. Hence, a small object, near to the eye, may appear just as big as a large object which is a great way off.

It is easy to see from such a diagram as Fig. 117, how the actual size of the sun may be measured. Let a circular disc, say one inch in diameter, be cut out of cardboard; or take the halfpenny mentioned above, for this has exactly the diameter of one inch. Hold the disc, or the coin, at such a distance from the eye that it just covers the solar disc; keeping the object, of course, square to the line of sight. It will be found that the required distance is about nine feet. Now on reference to Fig. 117 it will be seen that the object A B has exactly twice the height of the object C D, and that it is also placed at exactly twice the distance; under these circumstances the two objects appear to the eye at O to have precisely the same height. To speak generally, the actual heights of two bodies which have the same apparent height, are directly proportional to their distances. Hence, the distance of the halfpenny bears to the distance of the sun just the same proportion that the actual diameter of the halfpenny bears to the actual diameter of the sun. The actual diameter of the sun is therefore found by a simple rule-of-three sum;[1] provided, of course, that the sun's distance be known. Astronomers have measured this distance, by methods too complicated to be described here, and have found it to be rather more than ninety-one million miles.[2] Hence, it follows, that the diameter of the sun—that is to say, the distance measured from side to side through the centre of the sun—is about 852,900 miles. The sun's diameter is therefore more than 107 times as great as the earth's diameter.

This comparison refers only to *diameters*. If sections of the sun and of the earth were made exactly through the centre of each, the *area* of the sun's section would be 107

---

[1] It will be understood that this rough method is simply introduced to illustrate the *principle* on which such measurements are made.

[2] As the earth is nearer to the sun at one season than at another (p. 354), the *mean*, or average distance, may be taken. The sun's greatest distance from the earth is 92,963,000 miles, and its least distance 89,897,000 miles; hence the mean is 91,430,000 miles, or about 107 diameters of the sun.

times 107 times as great as the earth's section. And if the *volumes*, or bulks, of the two bodies were compared, it would be found that the sun's bulk is 107 × 107 × 107 times greater than the earth's bulk. In other words, it would require more than a million and a quarter of bodies, having the same bulk as the earth, to be rolled together, in order to form a globe equal in size to the sun.

No adequate notion of the dimensions and of the distance of the sun is gained by casting the eye over the figures, which represent these magnitudes. But some conception of its enormous size may be formed by reference to Fig. 118, which shows a section of the sun, taken through its centre, compared with a similar section of the earth. It was shown in Chapter XIX. that the earth is a ball of vast dimensions; but it is, seen by Fig. 118, that this huge ball sinks into utter insignificance when compared with the mighty sphere around which it revolves.

As to the distance which separates the sun from the earth, that may be represented in a variety of ways; but, by none perhaps more strikingly than by that which Sir John Herschel has employed. He tells us that the ball of an Armstrong 100-pounder quits the gun with a speed of about 400 yards per second. Now if this velocity could be kept up it would require nearly thirteen years before the ball could reach the sun !

Soon after the discovery of the telescope, it was directed to the examination of the solar disc. It was thus found, in the beginning of the seventeenth century, that the sun's face, instead of being uniformly bright, is usually spotted with dark patches. Very little observation is needed to show that these spots are not constant, either in shape, or in position: sometimes indeed, though but rarely, they are altogether absent, and the face of the sun then seems per-

fectly pure. If the spots are watched day after day, they
may be seen to march slowly across the disc, all moving in
the same direction from the eastern edge or *limb*, towards
the western side, and completing the march in about fourteen

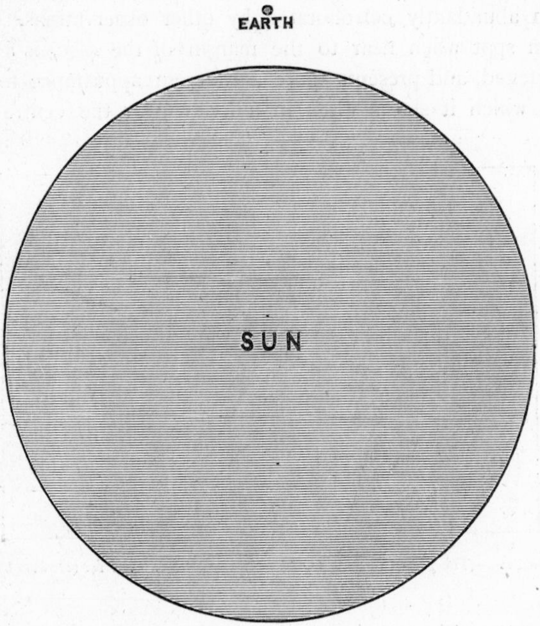

EARTH

S U N

FIG. 118.—Comparative sizes of the sun and the earth. In the course of engrav-
ing the circle representing the earth has become a little too large. In order
to represent the true distance of the earth from the sun, the two figures ought to
be about twenty-seven feet apart.

days. A fortnight afterwards, some of the very same spots
which were lost may possibly reappear on the eastern edge,
though altered in shape. This regular movement of the
spots teaches us that the sun rotates on its axis, and thus

resembles the earth. One rotation of the sun is accomplished in about twenty-six of our days.[1]

From the different forms which the same spot appears to assume, in passing across the disc, it may be inferred, that the shape of the sun is spherical; an inference which has been abundantly corroborated by other observations. A given spot when near to the margin of the disc, is foreshortened, and presents quite a different appearance from that which it shows when in full view near the centre of

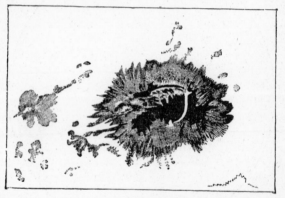

FIG. 119.—The great sun-spot of 1865 as it appeared on Oct. 14. (Howlett).

the disc. Fig. 119 is a central view of a great sun-spot which appeared in 1865.

If the spots always travelled across the disc in straight lines parallel to the sun's equator, it would obviously indicate that the sun revolved in an upright position; that is, with

[1] This time differs from the time given above as that at which a spot appears and reappears at the same edge of the disc (about 28 days). The difference is due to the earth's revolution.

its axis perpendicular to the plane of the earth's orbit. But, as a matter of fact, the spots travel in this direction only at certain seasons, and, at other times of the year, they may be seen moving in curved lines; the direction of the curve being sometimes towards the north, and sometimes towards the south. This change of direction is represented, though very much exaggerated, in Fig. 120; where the first figure indicates the apparent direction of movement in March, the second in June, the third in September, and the fourth in December. These varying directions of the paths of the spots at different periods are easily explained by supposing that the sun's axis is not perpendicular, but is oblique to the plane of the ecliptic; so that, sometimes, the sun's axis is inclined towards us, and, at other times, is directed from us. The rotation of the sun therefore takes place, like the rotation of the earth, around an inclined axis. The inclination of the sun's axis, however, is very much less than that of the earth's axis; being, in fact, only about $7\frac{1}{2}°$ from the vertical.

Observations on the motion of the sun-spots have also established the fact that the sun is not strictly a fixed body, around which the earth revolves, but that it has a motion of its own through space. The earth, indeed, not only revolves in a nearly circular path round the sun, but this path is being carried along with the sun at an enormous speed. Hence, the actual path which the earth describes in the heavens must be compounded of these two motions, and will probably be a spiral.

As so much of our knowledge of the sun has been derived from a study of its spots, it is worth while to inquire a little more closely into their nature. Reference to Fig. 119 will show that a spot is not equally dark throughout; the fringed margin, represented by a half-shade in the figure, is called the *penumbra*,[1] while the darker shade represents the *umbra;* and, within the umbra itself, there may sometimes be detected a yet darker part, which is called the *nucleus.* There is reason to believe that these spots are nothing but gigantic cavities, and that differences of shade correspond to differences of depth, the nucleus thus representing the most profound part of the hollow. The intensely luminous part of the sun, which is the seat of these spots, is called the *photosphere.*[2] It appears to consist of incandescent cloud-like matter, which is subject to violent disturbances, whereby depressions are produced, into which the solar atmosphere rushes from higher regions. The rapid changes in the shape

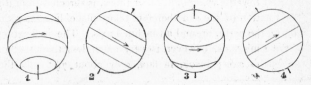

FIG. 120.—Apparent paths of sun-spots at different times of the year.

of certain sun-spots indicates the violence of this action. Some of the spots are so large as to occupy millions of square miles on the sun's surface.

Viewed through a powerful telescope, the whole surface of the sun seems to be coarsely mottled. This mottling is probably due to irregularities in the cloudy surface. Lower levels are indicated by the darkened spots, and, in these parts, light is lost by absorption through the overlying atmosphere; where, on the contrary, the light is unusually bright, there the sun-clouds are probably unusually

[1] *Penumbra,* from *pœne*, almost ; *umbra*, a shadow.
[2] *Photosphere*, from φῶς, *phos*, light ; the light-giving sphere.

high : such brilliant patches generally appear as streaks near the margin of the solar disc, and are termed *faculæ*.[1]

Above the luminous photosphere is another envelope, which is known as the *chromosphere*. During a total solar eclipse, when the sun is obscured by the moon's shadow, the dark disc is seen to be surrounded by a "glory," or fringe of radiant light, which is called the *corona* (Fig. 121). Within the corona, around the margin of the disc, variously

Fig. 121.—The corona and solar prominences as seen during a total eclipse in 1851 (Dawes).

coloured prominences may be detected ; and fantastically-shaped tongues of red flame may be seen to dart forth, sometimes to the extent of 70,000 miles or even to greater distances. Under ordinary circumstances, these effects are not visible, in consequence of the overpowering light of the photosphere. But a method has been devised by M.

[1] *Facula*, a little torch, diminutive of Lat. *fax*.

Janssen and Mr. Lockyer, whereby these prominences may be examined without waiting for an eclipse. Such examination has shown that the red flames consist, for the most part, of the gas hydrogen (p. 103). Above the region of incandescent hydrogen, there appears to be an enormous envelope of the same gas in a comparatively cool state. It is curious to find that the gas, which forms so large a proportion of the water of the earth, should be an important constituent of the sun. One of the chief chemical components of the river Thames is, in fact, one of the chief components of our central luminary.

It seems almost incredible that a person situated on the earth should be able to learn anything about the chemical constitution of the sun, which we know to be at least 91 millions of miles away. To attempt to subject the sun to any of the ordinary chemical processes of the laboratory is, of course, quite out of the question; but, within the last twenty years a new method of analysis has been introduced, whereby a great deal may often be learnt about the chemical composition and the physical constitution of an unknown body, by proper examination of the light which is emitted when the body has been heated until it becomes luminous.

Without entering into a close description of this method, which has been applied with such signal success to the examination of the sun, it is sufficient to remark that, when a beam of sunshine is allowed to pass through a small aperture in the wall of a dark chamber, and then to traverse a three-sided glass prism, like the drop of a lustre, it does not fall as a spot of white light, but is turned aside from its course, and spreads out into a broad band, which presents all the colours of the rainbow. This coloured band is called a *spectrum*. The course of such a beam of light is exhibited in Fig. 122; where A is the slit through which the light is admitted, and C is the cross-section of the prism : instead of falling as white light at B, the beam is deflected from its original path, and widens into a many-tinted band, DE, with red at one end and violet at the other extremity.

On closely examining the spectrum of the sun, which has thus been formed through a narrow slit, it is found to be crossed by a multitude of fine dark lines, which are indeed so many spaces in the bright band. A spectrum obtained from an ordinary gas-flame, or from the electric light, differs from the solar spectrum by being destitute of these dark

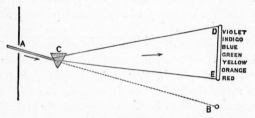

FIG. 122.—Formation of the solar spectrum.

lines ; the light of the flame being unbroken from end to end. But, if certain gases or vapours, such as hydrogen or sodium-vapour, be burnt in the path of the artificial light, lines are immediately produced in the spectrum. If the temperature of the substance which produces the lines be lower than that of the substance which gives the continuous spectrum, the lines will appear dark ; if the temperature be higher, the lines appear bright. Lines produced in this way have a definite position in the spectrum, so that the same chemical element, under the same circumstances, always gives the same set of lines. It is plain, therefore, that, by cbserving the position of the lines in the solar spectrum,

B B

and comparing them with the lines which are produced by the combustion of various terrestrial elements, the presence or absence of such elements in the sun may be inferred. For the examination of the spectrum, special instruments, called *spectroscopes*, are employed ; and the method of research itself, which was suggested and worked out by Profs. Bunsen and Kirchhoff, is known as *spectrum analysis*.

By means of spectrum analysis, it has been found that the sun contains a large number of elements, including hydrogen, sodium, lithium, calcium, barium, magnesium, zinc, iron, manganese, nickel, cobalt, chromium, titanium, aluminium, and copper. Quite recently Dr. Draper, of New York, has announced the discovery of oxygen, and probably also of nitrogen in the sun.[1]

From the surface of the sun, enormous quantities of light and heat are continually being radiated, or thrown out into space, in all directions. The earth, however, on account of its small size and its great distance, can receive but an extremely small proportion of the total amount which is thus shed. In fact, it is calculated, that our globe receives less than the two-thousand-millionth part of the total quantity of the sun's light and heat. All terrestrial phenomena, which depend upon solar light and heat, are therefore effected by means of this extremely minute fraction of the sun's stores of energy.

The sun is not only the principal source of heat and light to our earth, but it is the centre of attraction by which the revolving globe is maintained in its regular orbit. If a piece of iron be held in front of a powerful magnet, it will rush to the magnet, although there is no visible bond between them. If the same piece of iron be left unsup-

---

[1] For a detailed account of the constitution of the sun see *Contributions to Solar Physics*. By J. Norman Lockyer, F.R.S. 1874.

ported in the air, it does not remain suspended, but at once falls to the ground : in other words, it is attracted, or pulled, towards the earth, just as it was attracted or pulled towards the magnet ; though in neither case is there any visible means of attraction. The *force* by which the iron rushes to the magnet is called *magnetism ;* the force by which the iron rushes to the earth is called *gravitation.*[1]

It is by virtue of this force of gravitation that bodies upon the surface of the earth possess weight; and, the nearer bodies on the outside of the earth are to the earth's centre, the greater will be the pull, and the greater therefore will be their weight. In consequence of the earth's spheroidal shape, a body at the equator is more distant from the earth's centre than when at either of the poles. Hence, a given mass of matter, which causes the index of a spring weighing-machine to mark one pound in London, will cause it to mark rather more than a pound, in the Polar regions, and rather less than a pound, in the equatorial zone. If the same body could be carried into space, and placed aloof from the influence of all gravitation, its weight would entirely disappear, though the quantity of matter which it contained would remain unaltered.

The force of gravitation is by no means confined to the earth, but is an universal force, exerted, in greater or less degree, by every mass of matter in the universe. If two bodies, containing different quantities of matter, are allowed to act upon each other, each attracts and is, in turn, attracted, but not to the same extent. The greater the mass, the greater is the intensity of the attractive force. Now the sun is a gigantic mass of matter, and it tends to pull towards its centre all those bodies, including the earth, which circulate around it. At present (October, 1877) astronomers are acquainted with 182 bodies, called *planets*, which revolve

[1] *Gravitation*, from Lat. *gravitas*, weight.

in regular orbits around the sun. By far the greater number of these bodies are comparatively small and unimportant; but eight of them are large planets, of which the earth is one, though by no means the largest. All these planets are retained in their orbits by the force of gravitation exerted by the sun, which forms the great centre of the solar system.

Let a ball be tied to a piece of string, and whirled rapidly round; and while revolving in this way, let the string be suddenly cut. The ball does not continue to move in a circle, but darts off, in a straight course, until brought to the ground by terrestrial gravity. In like manner, the earth would rush into space in a straight path, if the bond of gravitation, the invisible string, were broken between the sun and the earth. The revolution of the earth in a nearly circular orbit is, therefore, maintained by means of gravitation. But gravitation is a force which varies in intensity according to the distance, in such wise that, if the distance be doubled, the intensity is diminished to one-fourth, if trebled, it is diminished to one-ninth, and so forth. It was shown at p. 354, that the earth is nearer to the sun at one time of year than at another; hence the attraction between the sun and the earth will vary at different seasons. In fact, when the earth is at perihelion, the attraction is greater, and the rate of revolution consequently greater also, than when she is at aphelion. This want of uniformity in the rate at which the earth travels is sufficient to explain the statement at p. 342, that a solar day is not always of the same length. Hence the introduction of the *mean solar day* of civil time.

Everything upon the earth's surface is subject to terrestrial gravity. Every particle of water tends to fall towards the centre of the earth, and thus the waters of the ocean are bound down so as to form an envelope around the globe. But while the water is thus held to the earth, it is also attracted by all the other components of the universe ; and, as the particles of water are free to move, the position of any given particle, and, hence, the form of the surface of the whole ocean, must be determined, other things being alike, by the balance of all these attractions. Most of the bodies which lie outside the earth are so distant, that their influence is inappreciable ; but it is otherwise with the sun and the moon. Each of these pulls the water, which lies on the face of the globe which is turned towards it, away from the solid earth ; while, at the same time, it pulls the solid earth away from the water which lies on the opposite face of the globe.

In any parallel of latitude, which traverses nothing but sea, the contour of the latter, if left to the attraction of the earth alone, will be, sensibly, a circle. Now suppose the sun or the moon to come to any meridian of that parallel, then the attraction of these bodies will convert the contour of the ocean into an ellipse, of which the long diameter will pass through the meridian in question, and that 180° from it ; while the short diameter will traverse meridians at 90° from these two.

If, before the intervention of the sun or moon, the water were everywhere of the same depth, it would now be deepest at the two meridians, 0° and 180° ; and shallowest at 90° and 270°. In other words, it would be *high water* at the former, and *low water* at the latter meridians.

Supposing the sun or the moon to be stationary, it is obvious that, in the course of the diurnal rotation of the earth, every point of the ocean under the parallel of latitude in question will have been twice raised to the height of high water, and twice lowered to the depth of low water ; which comes to the same thing, as if a wave, with a crest the height of high water and a trough the depth of low water, had passed twice round the parallel in the same space of time.

Thus, the rotation of the earth, combined with the attraction of the ocean by the sun and moon, gives rise to solar and lunar *tidal waves*. If the free motion of the waters of the ocean were not interfered with by the conformation of the land, and if there were no moon, high water would always take place a little after noon and midnight ; and low water would be a little after six o'clock in the morning and evening. Moreover, the rise and fall of these solar tides would be much less than our actual tides. For the great distance of the sun weakens his tide-producing value to such an extent that his effect, as compared with the moon's, is only as 4 to 9, or thereabouts.

The lunar tides, therefore, are much more important than those caused by the sun. If the moon always came to the meridian at the same time as the sun (as is the case at new moon) it is obvious that the lunar tide would strengthen the solar tide, and solar and lunar high waters and low waters would correspond.

Again, if the moon were always 180° from the sun (as is the case at full moon) the attractions of both would still conspire, though not so completely, to the same end, and the times of high and low water of both would still coincide.

On the other hand, if the moon always came to the meridian six hours sooner or later than the sun, it is obvious that the two tidal waves would tend to neutralize one another. It would be sun low-water when it was moon high-water, and *vice versâ*. In the former cases the high or low water would be the sum (or nearly so) of the solar and the lunar high or low waters, while, in the latter, it would be their difference.

As a matter of fact, the moon, revolving round the earth in a lunar month, comes to the meridian about fifty minutes later every day, and constantly changes its position in relation to the sun. Hence, in the course of every lunar month there are two periods (new and full moon) when the times of solar and lunar high water coincide, and the vertical movement of the water is greatest; and two periods (first and third quarters) when solar high water coincides with lunar low water, and the converse, and when therefore the vertical movement of the water is least. The former are called *spring tides*, and the latter *neap tides*.[1]

In the open sea, the water is raised by the attraction of the moon, or of the moon and sun combined, and then falls; so that the true tidal wave represents a mere oscillatory movement up and down. The lunar wave rises, in the open ocean, to a height of about $2\frac{1}{2}$ feet, and the solar wave, to about one foot. But, in narrow channels, the tidal wave becomes converted into a wave of translation, and the water actually moves backwards and forwards (p. 180). This was seen to be the case in the tidal part of the Thames, which was referred to in the opening sentences of the first chapter.

The movement of the water of the Thames at London Bridge, in fact, formed the starting-point of the studies which have gradually expanded into these one-and-twenty chapters. "What is the source of the Thames?" was the question first proposed for discussion; but, simple as this question seemed, it could not be answered, even in outline, until this last chapter had been reached; and something had

---

[1] It will be understood that only a very general notion of the origin of the tides is attempted to be given here. So complicated a subject is beyond the scope of this work.

been said about that vast body, more than ninety millions of miles away, around which the earth is constantly circling.

The Thames is fed, directly or indirectly, by rain; and the rain is condensed from vapour, which has been raised into the atmosphere by means of solar heat. Without the sun, therefore, there could neither be rain nor rivers; and hence it is not too much to say that the origin of the Thames is ultimately to be traced to the sun. Rain is dependent for its distribution upon currents in the atmosphere, but these currents are due to disturbances of equilibrium which are brought about by means of solar heat. Without the sun, then, there could be no winds. The currents of the sea engaged attention in another part of our work; but here again the sun is the prime mover. Whatever view be taken of the origin of such currents,—whether they are due to the immediate action of winds, or to variations of temperature in the water, or to the excess of evaporation in one place, over that of another—it is clear that the sun is the real agent in the formation of ocean-currents.

In another chapter, attention was directed to the phenomena which are presented by cold, and especially to the formation of glaciers; here, if anywhere, it might have been supposed that the sun certainly had no part to play. Yet, it must be remembered, that the ice of a glacier is water which has been distilled by the sun's heat, and that the descent of snow in one place connotes the evaporation of water in another locality. Without the sun, therefore, there could be no glaciers.

Considerable attention was given, in several chapters, to the phenomena of life, so far as they bore upon the subject under discussion. But every one knows that heat and light are such necessary conditions for the manifestation of life, that the earth would become lifeless, if sunshine were withheld. Without the heat which is derived from the sun, the temperature of the earth would fall far below the limit at which life can be sustained. Green plants decompose carbonic acid, and obtain their supply of carbon, only under the influence of sunshine; and, it has often been remarked, that our stores of coal represent so much sunshine of the Carboniferous period. Nor is this a mere wild fancy; for without the sun there would certainly have been no coal.

In studying the geological structure of the Thames basin, it was shown that the country had experienced great changes of climate at different periods of its history; and such changes depend entirely upon our varying relations with the sun. In fact, without the sun, the Thames could have had no geological history; for the upper beds, out of which its basin is shaped, are almost exclusively made up of fragments which have been worn from pre-existing land by means of running water; and the flow of water must be connected, directly or indirectly, with the action of the sun.

And thus we reach, at last, the goal of our inquiry. At the furthest point to which we have pushed our analysis of the causes of the phenomena presented to us, the sun is revealed as the grand prime mover in all that circulation of matter which goes on, and has gone on for untold ages, within the basin of the Thames; and the spectacle of the ebb and flow of the tide, under London Bridge, from which we started, proves to be a symbol of the working of forces which extend from planet to planet, and from star to star, throughout the universe.

INDEX.

THE END.

LONDON : R. CLAY, SONS, AND TAYLOR, BREAD STREET HILL.

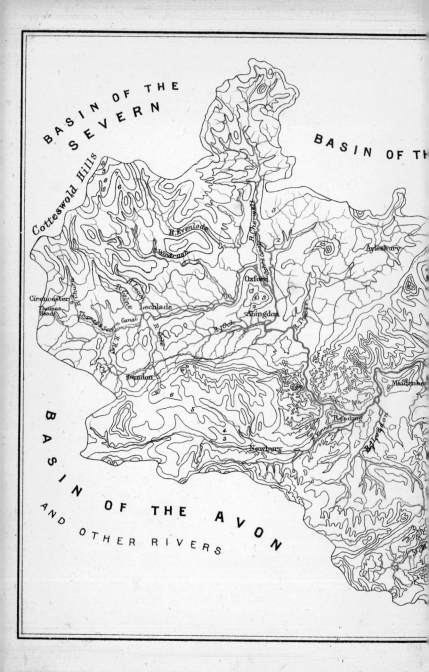

BASIN OF THE SEVERN

BASIN OF TH

Cotteswold Hills

R. Evenlode

R. Windrush

R. Churn

R. Coln

R. Leach

Cirencester
Thames Head
Thames & Severn Canal

Lechlade

R. Ray

Swindon

Oxford

R. Cherwell or Charwell

Abingdon

R. Ock

R. Thame

Aylesbury

Maidenhead

Reading

R. Kennet

R. Loddon

Newbury

BASIN OF THE AVON

AND OTHER RIVERS